D1588669

LYLE PRICE GUIDE
DOULTON

First Published in Great Britain in 1998

1 3 5 7 9 10 8 6 4 2

Copyright © Lyle Publications 1998

Ebury Press
Random House, 20 Vauxhall Bridge Road, London SW1V 2SA

Random House Australia Pty Limited
20 Alfred Street, Milsons Point, Sydney, New South Wales 2061, Australia

Random House New Zealand Limited
18 Poland Road, Glenfield, Auckland 10, New Zealand

Random House South Africa (Pty) Limited
Endulini, 5A Jubilee Road, Parktown 2193, South Africa

Random House UK Limited Reg. No. 954009

Papers used by Ebury Press are natural, recyclable products made from wood grown in sustainable forests.
A CIP catalogue record for this book is available from the British Library.

ISBN 0 09 186409 7

Printed and bound in Great Britain by Butler & Tanner Ltd., Frome

The photographs on pages 3, 7, 8, 12, 13, 103, 104, 105, 106, 107, 108, 109, 110 are reproduced with the kind assistance and permission of Royal Doulton Plc as are most of the character jugs and figures which are still in production, indicated by R.R.P. (Recommended Retail Price) after the value. We are also indebted to Royal Doulton Plc for allowing us to reproduce in colour a number of the rare items from 'Royal Doulton Figures' 1978. Lyle Publications Ltd. has no connection with Royal Doulton Plc and any of its associated companies or the Royal Doulton International Collectors Club. The contents of The Lyle Price Guide to Doulton have not been endorsed or approved in any way by Royal Doulton and they disclaim any responsibility for the book's contents.

Illustration on page 1 – Royal Doulton wall mask of Jester HN1630, introduced 1934, 10¾in. high.

The publishers wish to express their sincere thanks to the following for their involvement and assistance in the production of this volume:

Editor:	TONY CURTIS	Editorial:	ANNETTE CURTIS
		Art Production:	CATRIONA DAY
Text by:	EELIN McIVOR		ANGIE DEMARCO
	LIZ TAYLOR		NICKY FAIRBURN

LYLE PRICE GUIDE
DOULTON

(Royal Doulton Plc)

TONY CURTIS

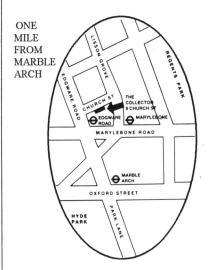

CONTENTS

ACKNOWLEDGEMENTS

DORIS AMES
SANDRA BADDELEY (Sir Henry Doulton Gallery)
BONHAMS, Montpelier Street, Knightsbridge, London, SW7 1HH
BILL & LILY BRETT
BERYL BURGESS (Toby Jug Museum, St Ives, Cornwall)
CANTERBURY AUCTION GALLERIES
CHRISTIE'S, 85 Old Brompton Road, London, SW7 3LD
ALEXANDER CLEMENT (Sir Henry Doulton Gallery)
DAVID COPE
FRED DEARDEN
GILLIAN DENMARK
LEAH & GERALD FITERSTEIN
HENRY GIBBONS
DOROTHY GREEN
P. HATFIELD, (Lambeth Archives Dept.)
PETER JACKMAN
GORDON LITHERLAND
JULIE MCKEOWN (Sir Henry Doulton Gallery)
PHILLIPS, Blenstock House. New Bond Street, London, W1Y 0AS
SYLVIA POWELL (DECORATIVE ARTS)
TOM POWER
SOTHEBY'S, 34 – 35 New Bond Street, London, W1A 2AA
PHILIP SPRINGTHORPE (Photographer)
LOUIS TAYLORS, Hanley, Stoke-on-Trent
KEN WHITBREAD (Photographer)
MICK YEWMAN

The publishers would like to express special thanks to all of the auction houses and specialist dealers and collectors who have given so generously of their time and expertise and in particular they would like to mention the help given by ROYAL DOULTON PLC in assisting in the compilation of this book.

NOTES ON PRICING

The purpose of the price guide to Doulton is to give both collectors and dealers an informed value of the numerous items which appear regularly on the open market through outlets such as antique fairs, auctions and markets as well as trade and private sources, including dealer's catalogues and private sales.

Prices given are for pieces in perfect condition, free of any restoration or damage. Items which have been repaired or professionally restored are worth considerably less than the perfect piece, usually between one third to one half less depending on the rarity of the individual item. A similar allowance should be made if selling into the antiques trade through auction or to a specialised dealer buying for resale.

Prices are based essentially on four main criteria, rarity, quality, desirability and aesthetics. A figure produced for only a brief period in the 1920's or 1930's will be highly sought after compared to a recent model made in much larger quantities, with the possible exception of low limited editions of recent manufacture which have been heavily over-subscribed.

Whilst it is true that the first half of the 1990's was a difficult period economically for collectors and dealers on both sides of the Atlantic, the same cannot be said for the second half. Good rare figures and jugs have increased considerably in value during the past couple of years, with some models changing hands at more than double the values of the mid 1990's. Collectors who held on to their collection during the recession are now enjoying a considerable increase in value.

Whilst every care has been taken to ensure the accuracy of the prices shown, a figure or jug is worth only what someone is prepared to pay for it and, like any volatile market, prices can go down as well as up, so the old collecting adage still holds good: Never buy for investment, buy only if you like the piece, then if the value increases that's a bonus.

THE HISTORY OF DOULTON

"**B**etter to bear with singularity than crush individuality" said Henry Doulton when critics complained about the variable output of his pottery studio.

He knew that the artists and potters who worked for him were producing treasures for ordinary people at reasonable prices and also for future generations of collectors. Even though some of the hundreds of thousands of designs and individual items that were produced under the Doulton name were calculated to appeal to the bizarre and overdecorated taste of the High Victorians, there were many others of such high quality and originality that they have never lost their artistic quality and appeal. A study of the trade catalogues of the Doulton Company gives a staggering glimpse into the enormous range of their products and the free scope which both John and Henry Doulton gave to the people who worked for them.

There never was a style 'trademark' in Doulton, each potter and artist was free to interpret influences and fashions in their own way and the result was an upsurge of creative talent which has never been equalled by any commercial enterprise in Britain.

In its Lambeth factory the company provided an opportunity for artistic creation and self expression to an army of men and women who otherwise would have lived and died in obscurity without exercising their enormous talents. Men like George Tinworth, an illiterate who became an R.A., or Frank Butler who was deaf and dumb and whose expertise in creating beautiful pieces of pottery enthralled visitors to the Doulton works, owed everything to the liberal minded attitudes of John and particularly Henry Doulton.

The Studio also provided an outlet for the talents of artistic women and paved the way for more employment equality between the sexes. The names of Hannah and Florence Barlow, Louisa Davis and the two Elizas, Simmance and Sayers, would never be remembered today if it had not been for the fact that they were allowed and encouraged to work at Lambeth.

It is to the credit of Henry Doulton in particular that this creativity burst into life for he was the archetypal Victorian businessman, forward thinking, energetic and entrepreneurial, who took over a well established business and turned it into a world famous name.

He was not however a woolly minded do-gooder, for his company first of all had to turn out a profit but still he was prepared, for the sake of an ideal, to sponsor and finance a pottery studio side by side with the money making commercial factory. In the 1860s the Lambeth Studio made a loss for several years until the public began to appreciate the quality and enormous originality of the work that was being produced there.

The Doulton story began with Henry's father John, a native of Fulham, who was reputed to be the best thrower of pint pots in London. He worked as an apprentice with John Dwight, called 'the father of English pottery', who was carrying on the ancient tradition of saltglaze pottery-making in Fulham. In 1815 young John, who had saved the considerable sum of £100, went into partnership in a pottery with a widow called Jones and a journeyman called Watts. They were established at Vauxhall, opposite the gate of the famous Vauxhall Pleasure Gardens, once the haunt of the fashionable beaux and belles of 18th century London.

The widow disappeared from the scene fairly quickly but Watts and Doulton continued in business. It is said that in the beginning their pottery sign board had "Watts and Doulton" on one side and "Doulton and Watts" on the other but after a short time they called themselves only Doulton and Watts until 1853 when Mr Watts retired.

By this time the firm had moved to Lambeth High Street, to a property with a large garden which was to become the nucleus of the famous Lambeth Pottery Works. It was to stay there until 1956 when it closed down because of rising transport costs and the clean air legislation. In its 19th century heyday however it made a fine sight on the south bank of the Thames because the original works were rebuilt as an

(Royal Doulton Plc)

Doulton's first premises, formerly Stiff & Sons, on the corner of Broad St. (now Black Prince Road) and the Albert Embankment, London, circa 1909.

Italianate Palace, modelled on the Palazzo Vecchio of Florence on the advice of Henry Doulton's friend, John Ruskin of "The Stones of Venice" fame. The 233 foot high factory chimney was disguised as a campanile.

While John Doulton and his original partners were running the business they concentrated on making earthenware beer bottles, chimney pots, ridge tiles and garden vases. Now and again however they would produce a good selling pot 'figure'; for example the model of George IV's unfortunate Queen Caroline, which they made in 1820, and also figures of contemporary heroes including Nelson and even of enemies like Napoleon, were very much in demand with the poorer class of customers at the time.

In 1832 while the country was afire with enthusiasm for the Reform Bill, which extended the male franchise, Doulton, and Watts, like several other companies, brought out what are known as Reform flasks. They were really stone glazed bottles for gin but the upper half was modelled on the figure of a popular politician of the time. Because they were designed for such a utilitarian purpose few of those flasks still exist but the few that do are highly prized – and priced – by collectors.

By the time Watts left the firm and it became Doulton and Company, Henry, John's second son, had joined his father in spite of his parent's wish that he become a Baptist preacher. The lure of pottery making was too much for Henry. His father proudly exhibited outside the door of their works a vast pottery urn, which was Henry's handiwork. It was reputed to be the largest stoneware vessel in the world and could hold 300 gallons. However, it also seems likely that the lure of

Salt-glazed stoneware jug depicting Lord Nelson by Doulton & Watts, Lambeth, circa 1830. $560 £350

business made preaching pale into insignificance for the energetic Henry who turned out to be a prime example of Victorian enterprise and ingenuity.

No idea was too novel for him to give it serious consideration. Edwin Chadwick, the pioneer of improved sanitation, was a friend of Henry's and persuaded him that a better sewage and water supply system was the only way of freeing Britain's crowded cities of the scourge of cholera that stalked them every summer. Chadwick's theories originally must have seemed the theorising of a crank, for at the beginning of the 19th century even doctors believed that the cholera infection was spread through the air – they never guessed it was water borne. Henry Doulton however listened to Chadwick and was one of the first to start making earthenware sewage and water pipes. Many of the drainpipes and conduits made during Henry Doulton's lifetime are still in use beneath city streets today.

He designed a self-adjusting joint for water pipes and before long was extending the firm's product lines into baths, lavatories, washbasins and other sanitary fitments to cope with the new 'bathroom' craze which was to sweep the country. This branch of the business was to culminate in a magnificent order for fitting out the bathrooms of the Savoy Hotel in London with 237 specially designed baths.

At the height of their production the Doulton Works were turning out one fifth of the sewer pipes made in Britain at a rate of ten miles a week and exporting them all over the world.

Ever inventive, Henry took a chemistry course and also designed airtight jars for keeping food and a screw top bottle. He recognised the enormous potential of the new industries and inventions that were to transform Victorian Britain into the modern age and devised chemical resistant earthenware for use in telephone and electrical systems.

It was Henry's idea to install steam power in the factory to drive the potters' wheels and by doing so he put his firm in the forefront of the pottery industry because it was a good ten years before any competitor followed his example.

The development of the company into art pottery would not have been possible without the sound financial base provided by the industrial and sanitary side. By the 1860s however John and Henry Doulton were presiding over a company of enormous capacity and world fame. At the time when their finances were beginning to be established on a very stable basis,

Henry was prepared to take a chance and founded a Pottery Studio in the corner of his works.

In doing so he was responding to a prevalent theory among the intelligentsia that art and industry should be able to co-exist. That theory was continued and fostered by the Doulton Company right till the end of the First World War and to a lesser extent after as well but by the 1930s the new generation of studio potters were rejecting the Victorian ideas of a creative collaboration between art and industry.

Henry Doulton was first approached by John Sparkes, head of the newly formed Lambeth School of Art, in the late 1850s with the proposition that some of the students should be allowed to try their hand at potting. At first the idea met with little response from John Doulton but his son was to return to it later and set aside a corner of the factory for a few Lambeth School of Art students. It is noticeable that many of them were people who would have worked at lowly or manual trades without this opportunity. Tinworth, a universally acknowledged artistic genius, was a wheelwright before Sparkes took him up and he and the famous Barlows were among the first intake to the Lambeth Studio.

Henry Doulton was ahead of his time too in his ability as a publicist for he was quick to realise the value of the exhibitions which were organised all over the world in the 19th century and, having an acute sense of what was going to be important, he never missed an opportunity to display his firm's goods. This was the medium that presented the work of his studio potters to the world.

Henry had joined his father's firm in

1835 and when the Great Exhibition was unveiled in Hyde Park in 1852, Doulton and Company exhibited, but the pieces on show were all industrial items except for a figure of Old Father Time and some terracotta garden vases.

By 1862 however the Lambeth Studio had been established in a small way and in the London Exhibition of that year Doulton exhibited their first piece of art pottery – a reproduction of a 16th century Rhenish salt cellar.

In the Paris Exhibition of 1867 however the work of George Tinworth was on the Doulton stand and it created a sensation which was followed at the London International Exhibition of 1871 where the robust and virile work of Hannah and Arthur Barlow was first displayed. Queen Victoria was so impressed by the Doulton ware in the exhibition that she ordered some to be sent to Buckingham Palace.

The Doulton name had now begun to have another meaning than just pipes and conduits. At the Vienna Exhibition of 1873 a distinctive cobalt blue glaze which the company was using was given the official name of 'Doulton blue' and in the Philadelphia Centennial Exhibition of 1876, which perhaps marked the zenith of the Lambeth Pottery, they won five first class awards. There was such a great interest in the pieces from the American public that a cult for Doulton began which continues to this day. American collectors are among the most enthusiastic and knowledgeable in the world. Their original enthusiasm was only intensified by the Chicago International Exhibition of 1893 where the firm showed 1,500 items from its Lambeth and its recently acquired Burslem factory.

Some of the items displayed over the years were of such magnificence that they stopped the public in its tracks. For example for the Glasgow Exhibition of 1888 Doulton made an Indian pavilion of glazed and enamelled terracotta with stained glass windows

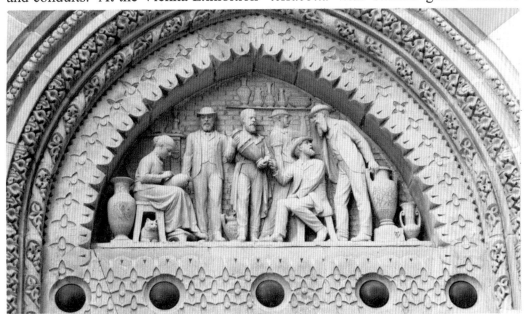

Terracotta panel above the entrance to Doulton House, modelled by George Tinworth, showing Sir Henry Doulton in the artists' studios.

which had also been manufactured by the company. The firm's success at international exhibitions continued into the 20th century, for at the Brussels Exhibition of 1958 they were the winners of the only Gold Medal awarded to a British pottery manufacturer.

(Royal Doulton Plc)

The Prince of Wales with Henry Doulton, 1885.

They expanded rapidly throughout the 19th century and in 1877 Henry Doulton bought an earthenware factory called Pinder Bourne and Company in Burslem, Staffordshire. In spite of antagonism and opposition from rival potteries there, who regarded him as a southern incomer and upstart, he set about energising the new acquisition with his own brand of magic and in 1882 the name was changed to Doulton and Company, Burslem. His firm now had major factories in London and in Staffordshire where they were able to draw on the long established potting skills of the local population. It was in Burslem that Doulton began to manufacture bone china in 1885 when a new wing was built onto the factory for that purpose. As in Lambeth, a Studio for creative artists and potters was established and the variety of their output was truly dazzling.

Sir Henry Doulton died in 1897, loaded with honours and success. He was given the Albert Medal by the Royal Society of Arts in 1885 and in 1887 he was knighted by Queen Victoria, the first potter ever to be awarded the honour of a knighthood.

Part of his achievement was the creation of an artistic environment that encouraged individual creation. It must have been exhilarating to be on the staff of the Studios belonging to Doulton because their artists were given a free hand, there were no official guidelines about what sort of thing they should be turning out, no production line theories of any kind.

This manner of handling artists produced results. Not only did they create exactly the sort of thing that the mass of the public wanted to buy but they also produced in enormous volume. Hannah Barlow, at her peak, made 30 different original pieces every week and hundreds of thousands of other individual pieces were turned out by the rest of the Doulton artists. They signed their work with their initials or monograms and took personal pride in their creations, a pride that was fostered and encouraged by their employer.

When the staff of the Lambeth Studio expanded from a handful of people to 200 by 1880 and later doubled by the end of the century, the firm enjoyed a world dominance in decorative pottery. Both factories were constantly trying to devise new ways of firing and producing exotic glazes or

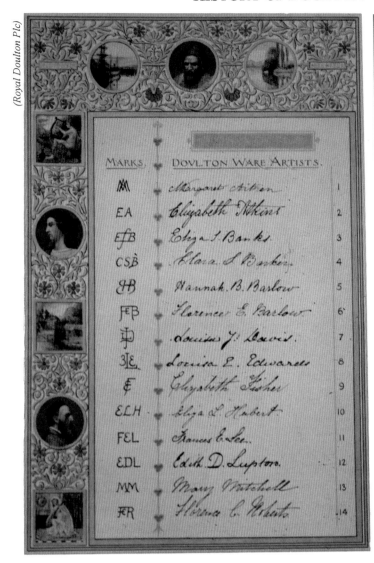

MARKS.	DOULTON WARE ARTISTS.	
ᴀᴀ	Margaret Aitkin	1
EA	Elizabeth Atkins	2
EⱭB	Eliza S. Banks	3
CSB	Clara S Barker	4
ℋB	Hannah. B. Barlow	5
FEB	Florence E. Barlow	6
ID	Louisa J. Davis	7
3E	Louisa E. Edwards	8
E	Elizabeth Fisher	9
ELH	Eliza L. Hubert	10
FEL	Frances E. Lee	11
EDL	Edith D. Lupton	12
MM	Mary Mitchell	13
FR	Florence C. Roberts	14

Hannah Barlow

Florence Barlow

A page from the Doulton archives listing the Artists' and Assistants' signatures with their individual marks.

experimenting with new colours. C.J. Noke who joined Doulton from the Worcester Pottery in 1889 and later became the Artistic Director of Burslem, concentrated on producing a range of experimental transmutation glazed wares as good as those made by Sevres, Copenhagen or Dresden. He devised the Titanian glaze which gave a Copenhagen style look to pottery. Noke also experimented in recreating some of the Oriental techniques of the past and his work resulted in the famous Flambé, Sung, Chinese jade and Chang pottery. In the 1890s he also guided the firm into one of its most successful lines, the production of figure models. The first of these, a range of

Shakespearean characters, were shown at the Chicago Exhibition in 1893.

As the Lambeth Studio was getting into full swing Henry Doulton converted a group of workers' houses into individual studios where his protégés were encouraged to work without managerial interference and this policy proved to be a hothouse for talent. Creativity was allowed its head and pieces were produced with leaves or lace pressed into the glaze as the artists' fancies took them. The potters also devised new techniques like *pâte sur pâte,* as used by Florence Barlow and Eliza Simmance, and their work reflects the styles and fashions of the day. Doulton designs over the years show the influence of Japanese and Primitive art as well as the rising Art Nouveau which they were among the first to popularise, producing a range of distinctive items for Liberty's.

Impasto Ware vase by K. Rodgers, 10in. high, circa 1885. $440   £275

Bone china Buddha decorated with Sung and lustre glazes, 4in. high, circa 1920. $1360   £850

Bone china vase featuring Pan playing his pipes, in Sung glazes by Charles Noke, 7in. high, circa 1925. $1120   £700

Play Goers, by George Tinworth, salt-glazed stoneware, 5in. high, circa 1884.
$2,400   £1,500

Bone china teapot with raised paste gilding and exotic birds, painted by J. Birbeck, 5½in. high, circa 1910.
$440   £275

The First World War brought a running down to the Lambeth Studio but it survived on a reduced scale under J. H. Nott, producing some notable items including a range of Persian inspired designs. The Second World War however marked its death knell and though it produced the well designed range of blue plaques for the LCC which mark houses in London where famous people lived, and the Festival of Britain brought a surge of short lived energy, the Studio finally closed in 1956. That closure marked a 90 year long association between art and industry in Lambeth. Burslem however continued and carried on the success story.

Another interesting aspect of the Doulton story is the fact that while they had a famous name for producing decorative pottery they were also turning out a huge variety of other

Vase with modelled dragon in relief and with carved foliage decoration, designed by Mary Ann Thompson and Jessie Bowditch, salt-glazed stoneware, 9in. high., 1880.   *$1,200   £750*

products. Not only did they continue to make sanitary and industrial goods, but they had a huge output of garden ornaments, especially in the 19th century when the age of the public park began. They made drinking fountains, garden seats, urns, edgings, pots and sundials for every sort of garden from that of a stately home to the suburban villa. After the First World War the spacious age of gardening declined but the Doulton artists then turned their attention to creating decorative things for the smaller garden, including garden gnomes, but some of the imaginative artefacts installed in urban housing estates of the 1920s and '30s were produced for them by academic sculptors like Gilbert Bayes.

The firm also specialised in architectural work and was particularly well known for decorative tiles which were used both to beautify the interiors and exteriors of buildings. The famous Oyster Bar in Edinburgh's Café Royal is a lovely example of Doulton tile work and many hospital wards, especially children's wards, throughout the country were decorated with tile pictures. Those that survive today are highly prized.

The great upsurge in building in the latter half of the 19th century gave the company an enormous boost and they found that terracotta was an invaluable building and decorative material. Designs made in terracotta could be easily mass reproduced and it was also longer lasting and less liable to atmospheric pollution damage than stone. Examples of terracotta work by Doulton can still be seen on London's Savoy Hotel and Royal Court Theatre. Doulton also made a huge range of advertising wares and collectors now look out for things like model feet they

Ginger jar with cover, Shape 1261, Bazaar scene painted by Charles Nixon, bone china, height 10in., 1921.

$800 £500

produced for Dr Scholl; for ceramic pump handles; ashtrays and stoneware whisky bottles. For many years these were a profitable sideline of a multifaceted business which today continues its diversification with ceramics for the aerospace and textile industries.

Today Royal Doulton P.L.C. is still the largest producer of ceramic products in the U.K. with interests in glass, industrial and sanitary wares, engineering and building materials as well as producing the world famous Royal Doulton decorative pieces and tableware at Burslem. The artists in the Doulton factory continue the long artistic tradition laid down by their distinguished predecessors. They are still carrying on Henry Doulton's dream–making collectors' pieces for future generations.

ADVERTISING WARES

Before the advent of plastics, ceramics were used on an enormous scale for the production of advertising items.

Doulton was involved with the beer and spirit trade from the beginning of the 19th century and they produced all manner of promotional items for these industries ranging from public house tiled or terracotta frontages and ceramic beer pump handles to ashtrays and spittoons for public bars.

Some of the other advertising artefacts produced by the company included perfume bottles moulded like figures and plaques painted with portraits of Queen Victoria, advertising soap or toothpaste.

Most of the pieces came from Doulton's standard range of shapes, adapted for advertising purposes simply by the addition of a trademark or motto. Some companies, however, did commission their own shapes. One of the more unusual advertising commissions came Doulton's way in the 1950s when they were asked to make a Toby jug depicting the American industrialist Clifford Cornell, head of the Cleveland Flux Company of Ohio. He was a great fan of Winston Churchill and commissioned Doulton to make a Toby jug of him imitating the one they had recently produced of Churchill. Another oddity was a moulded white china foot which was made to advertise Dr Scholl's Zino pads.

Ordinary tableware often carried advertising slogans as well and a further development of this was the badged ware made specially for hotels, shipping companies, railways and the like.

The collecting of Doulton ceramic advertising ware is a growing field and items are eagerly sought out by enthusiasts.

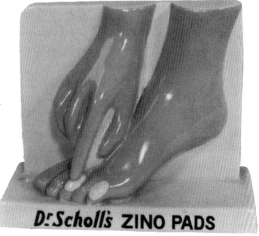

Dr Scholl's Zino Pads counter display sign by Doulton. $160 £100

Falstaff, a small character jug liqueur flask made for W. Walklate Ltd, 4in. high. $80 £50

Worthington's In Bottle, china jardiniere made by Royal Doulton, 20in. high. $800 £500

The Pickwick Collection, set of four character liqueur flasks made for Jim
Beam Whiskey, the handles in the form of bottle miniatures, 1983. $560 £350

Scotsman & Irishman whisky flasks in a
wooden tantalus, designed for Asprey & Co.
of New Bond St., London. $5200 £3250

Whisky flask in the form of a crow, made for
National Distillers of Kentucky, circa 1954.
$360 £200

The International Collection, a set of four character liqueur flasks made for
Pick-Kwik Wines and Spirits, John Bull (England), Captain Cook (Australia),
Samurai Warrior (Japan) and Uncle Sam (America), 1984. $560   £350

News Vendor, designed by W. Harper in a
limited edition of 2500 for the Newspaper
Society, 1986, 7in. high. $264   £165

Clifford Cornell Toby jugs, made in a limited
edition of 500 for the Cleveland Flux Company
of Ohio, 1956, 9¼in. high. $440   £275 each

Mae West character jug, part of
the Celebrity Collection
produced for American Express,
1983. $135 £85

Army Club cigarette display
figure by Doulton. $240 £150

Charrington's Toby produced by
Royal Doulton, inscribed on the
base *Charrington's 1939*, 23cm.
high. $760 $475

Stoneware matchstriker for
Doulton & Co. Ltd.   £130 £80

Rip Van Winkle, a small
character jug liqueur flask
made for W. Walklate Ltd,
4in. high, circa 1960. $90 £55

Worthington's India Pale Ale
matchstriker by Doulton. $70 £45

Mr Quaker character jug produced for Quaker Oats Ltd. to celebrate
the 100th anniversary of their registered mark, 1985. $470 £295

Dr Scholl's Zino Pads, counter display sign
made by Doulton, 8in. high. $160 £100

Poacher, a small character jug
adapted as a liqueur flask for
Walklate Ltd., 4in. high. $90 £55

McCallum, Kingsware character
jug produced in a limited edition
of 100 for D & T McCallum Whisky
Distillers, 1930. $1600 £1000

Whisky decanter made for
Watsons No. 10 Whisky, 9in.
high. $800 £500

Bull Dog Guinness jardiniere
manufactured by Doulton for
Robert Porter & Co., 5in.
high. $280 £175

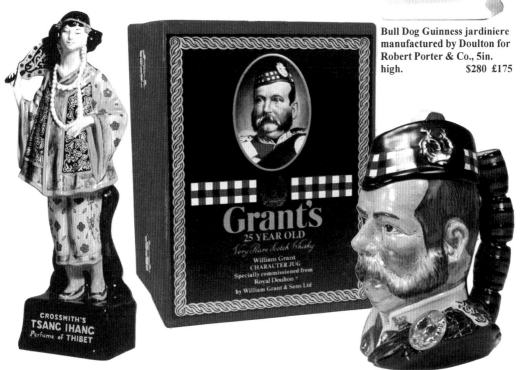

Grossmith's 'Tsang Ihang' perfume, counter display
sign, 11½in. high, 1923. $880 £550

William Grant character jug made for the whisky
distillers William Grant & Sons., 1986, in a limited
edition of 500. $640 £400

ASH BOWLS

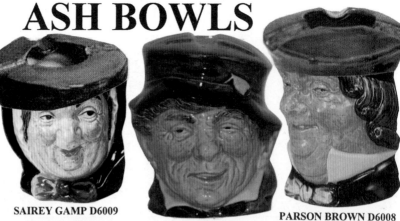

AULD MAC D6006
Designer: H. Fenton
Height: 3in., 7.5cm.
Issued: 1939-1960
Price: $160 £100

FARMER JOHN D6007
Designer: C. Noke
Height: 3in., 7.5cm.
Issued: 1939-1960
Price: $160 £100

OLD CHARLEY D5925
Designer: C. Noke
Height: 3in., 7.5cm.
Issued: 1938-1960
Price: $160 £100

SAIREY GAMP D6009

PADDY D5926

PARSON BROWN D6008

PADDY D5926
Designer: H. Fenton
Height: 3in. 7.5cm.
Issued: 1938-1960
Price: $160 £100

PARSON BROWN D6008
Designer: C. Noke
Height: 3in., 7.5cm.
Issued: 1939-1960
Price: $160 £100

SAIREY GAMP D6009
Designer: H. Fenton
Height: 3in., 7.5cm.
Issued: 1939-1960
Price: $160 £100

AULD MAC D6006

OLD CHARLEY D5925

FARMER JOHN D6007

ASH TRAYS

DICK TURPIN D5601
Designer: D. Biggs
Height: 2¾in., 7cm.
Issued: 1936-1960
Price: $128 $80

FAT BOY M44
Designer: L. Harradine
Height: 4in., 10cm.
Issued: 1932
Price: $160 £100

JOHN BARLEYCORN D5602
Designer: C. Noke
Height: 2¾in., 7cm.
Issued: 1936-1960
Price: $128 £80

OLD CHARLEY D5599
Designer: C. Noke
Height: 2¾in., 7cm.
Issued: 1936-1960
Price: $128 £80

ONE OF THE FORTY HN423
Designer: H. Tittensor
Height: 3¾in., 9.5cm.
Issued: 1921
Price: $500 £310

PARSON BROWN D5600
Designer: C. Noke
Height: 2¾in., 7cm.
Issued: 1936-1960
Price: $128 £80

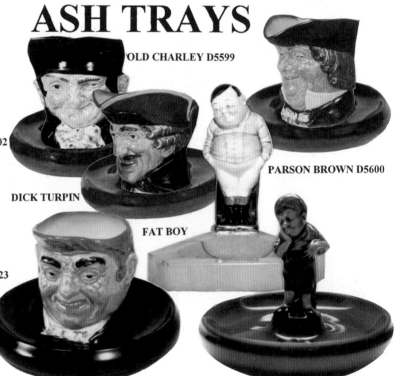

OLD CHARLEY D5599

PARSON BROWN D5600

DICK TURPIN

FAT BOY

JOHN BARLEYCORN D5602

ONE OF THE FORTY HN423

22

BOOKENDS

MR MICAWBER HN1615
Designed: H. Fenton
Height: 4in., 10cm.
Issued: 1934-c.1939
Price: $1200 $750

MR PICKWICK HN1623
Designer: H. Fenton
Height: 4in., 10cm.
Issued: 1934-c.1939
Price: $1200 £750

SAIREY GAMP HN1625
Designer: H. Fenton
Height: 4in., 10cm.
Issued: 1934-c.1939
Price: $1200 £750

TONY WELLER HN1616
Designer: H. Fenton
Height: 4in., 10cm.
Issued: 1934-c.1939
Price: $1200 £750

DOCTOR WATSON D7039
Designer: Martyn Alcock
Height: 7¼in., 18.5cm.
Issued: 1996
Price: $112 £70 (R.R.P.)

SHERLOCK HOLMES D7038
Designer: Martyn Alcock
Height: 7¼in., 18.5cm.
Issued: 1996
Price: $112 £70 (R.R.P.)

SAIREY GAMP HN1625   MR PICKWICK HN1623

TONY WELLER HN1616   MR MICAWBER HN1615

DOCTOR WATSON D7039   SHERLOCK HOLMES D7038

BOWLS

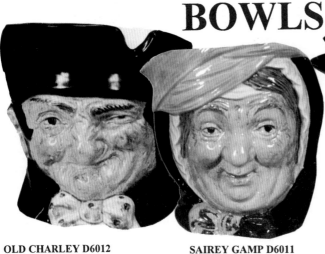

OLD CHARLEY D6012
Designer: C. Noke
Height: 2½in., 6.5cm.
Issued: 1939
Price: $480 £300

SAIREY GAMP D6011
Designer: H. Fenton
Height: 2½in., 6.5cm.
Issued: 1939
Price: $480 £300

TONY WELLER D6013
Designer: H. Fenton
Height: 2½in., 6.5cm.
Issued: 1939
Price: $480 £300

BUSTS

BUZ FUZ D6048
Height: 2½in., 6.4cm.
Issued: 1939-1960
Price: $120 £75

MR MICAWBER D6050
Height: 2½in., 6.4cm.
Issued: 1939-1960
Price: $120 £75

MR PICKWICK D6049
Height: 2½in., 6.4cm.
Issued: 1939-1960
Price: $120 £75

SAIREY GAMP D6047
Height: 2½in., 6.4cm.
Issued: 1939-1960
Price: $120 £75

SAM WELLER D6052
Height: 2½in., 6.4cm.
Issued: 1939-1960
Price: $120 £75

TONY WELLER D6051
Height: 2½in., 6.4cm.
Issued: 1939-1960
Price: $120 £75

MR MICAWBER

SAIREY GAMP

MR PICKWICK

TONY WELLER

SAM WELLER

BUZ FUZ

CHARACTER JUGS

It was the great Doulton designer Charles Noke who first saw the possibilities for a 20th century revival of the old Staffordshire Toby jug tradition and developed it with a completely new approach to the old 'face jug' concept.

He had in mind the creation of a series of characters from English legend, history and literature, which would be much more colourful than their prototypes but would, like them, have an immediate appeal for his own and future generations.

John Barleycorn D5327 $152   £95
This was the first character jug designed by C.J. Noke, introduced in 1934 and withdrawn in 1960.

Though Noke joined Doulton in 1889, it was not until the early 1930s that he had the time and opportunity to put his concept into production. The first such jug to appear was John Barleycorn, which was an instant success. It was soon followed by Old Charley, the Night Watchman, Dickens' Sairey Gamp, Parson Brown and Dick Turpin.

Other leading Doulton designers joined Noke in the production of these jugs, such as Leslie Harradine and Harry Fenton. Harradine was responsible for many Dickens' characters, while Fenton contributed in addition such figures as John Peel, Old King Cole and the Vicar of Bray. Later names associated with the genre are Max Henk (Long John Silver, Lord Nelson etc) and David Biggs (Town Crier, Veteran Motorist, and many others.)

The range has also been extended to include modern personalities from all walks of life from politicians to stars of stage and screen, pop stars, as well as contemporary types such as Golfer and Fireman.

Given the basic high quality of design and production, the value of each jug is often determined by its rarity, for many have a colourful history attached to their launch. Small variations in colour and design can also make an enormous difference.

The Clark Gable character jug was conceived as the first in a series of six celebrity jugs in 1983 (the others are Louis Armstrong, Mae West, Groucho Marx, W.C. Fields and Jimmy Durante). They were commissioned for the American market by American Express. About 150–200 were sent to the US as a trial, and immediately fell foul of the Clark Gable Association who informed the Retailers Association of America that they were issuing a writ against Doulton for copyright reasons. Doulton didn't argue, but immediately withdrew the jugs. Most were pulled back, leaving about 50 in circulation.

Groucho Marx D6710 designed by S. Taylor, introduced 1984. $136 £85

Clark Gable D6709 designed by S. Taylor, introduced 1984. $3200 £2000

For this reason, while others in the series fetch only £75–£100, Clark Gable will fetch a cool £2,000. The first Doulton clown jug was the red-haired version with a multi-coloured handle which was produced in the late 1930s. There is a visible difference in colouration between early examples and those produced during the war years when the supply of materials was restricted, so much so that the later ones have become known more or less unofficially as Brown haired clowns. The Red/Brown haired versions were in any case superseded after the Second World War by the White haired clown which was manufactured between 1951–55. The Red and Brown haired versions will fetch £1,650 while the White haired clown will fetch around £650. Only one Black haired clown has turned up at auction so far, where it fetched £12,000. This dates from the Red haired period of the late 1930s and seems to have been a one-off commission to Doulton by a family in memory of their grandfather, who had in fact been himself a black-haired clown.

Harry Fenton's 'Drake' jug was introduced in 1940. In the first version the rim is the character's hair, but in later versions it became his hat. The earlier jug, known as 'The Hatless Drake' carries the inscription 'Drake he was a Devon Man' and was produced only in limited numbers. Today, a 'hatless' Drake will sell for around £1,650, while the hatted version will fetch only about £85.

Drake D6115 (Hatless version) designed by Harry Fenton, introduced in 1940. $2640 £1650

Three versions of Clown, designed by H. Fenton. The red and black haired versions were introduced in 1937 and the white haired clown was introduced in 1951.

The normal Old King Cole character jug, D6036, designed by H. Fenton and issued 1939–1960 has a reddish brown crown and handle and as such is worth £165. With a yellow crown and a greenish coloured handle, issued 1939–1940, it is worth £1,450 and if it comes complete with a musical movement, D6014, issued in 1939, it is worth over £1,700.

Old King Cole D6036, designed by H. Fenton, introduced 1939, showing the more common version with a reddish brown crown and the much rarer version with a yellow crown and greenish handle.

'Blue' Pearly Boy designed by Harry Fenton, introduced 1947. $4,800 £3,000

'Blue' Pearly Girl designed by Harry Fenton, introduced 1947. $4,800 £3,000

'Arry and 'Arriet are favourite Doulton jugs designed by Harry Fenton, with somewhat complicated variations. These figures of a Cockney costermonger and his wife were introduced in the mid 1940s and withdrawn by 1960. 'Arry is predominantly brown in colour. In some variations however he is embellished by having brown or white buttons on his hat (a reference to the costermongers' custom of dressing up on high days and holidays as Pearly Kings and Queens) when he becomes Brown Pearly Boy, and can be worth £950. Even more rare is the version with pinkish white buttons on a brown hat with blue peak, when he becomes Blue Pearly Boy and fetches £3,000!

'Arriet is subject to slightly less complicated versions. Her basic form is a brown coat with green hat and handle and is worth £145. Her festive wear consists of a blue collar, and green boa on her mauve hat and she then becomes Blue Pearly Girl and will be worth £3,000.

The Churchill character jug, made during the Battle of Britain was one of the first jugs to be withdrawn. The first version was cream coloured with two black handles and bears the inscription 'Winston Spencer Churchill Prime Minster of Britain 1940'. It was withdrawn after only eighteen months however because, it is said, Churchill himself was not pleased with the likeness. Because so few were produced this jug is an extremely rare and desirable item, coveted by collectors throughout the world. The second version had natural colouring and bears the number D6170. The cream version, which was rather longer on the market before withdrawal, has fetched over £5,000, while one with natural colouring, which is even rarer, would be worth about £12,000.

Churchill (Natural) D6170, a two handled loving cup designed by Charles Noke, 1940.   *$18,750 £12,000*

Churchill (White) D6170, designed by Charles Noke, introduced 1940.
$8,000 £5,000

The Maori was a pilot jug which never went into production. It was made circa 1939 in two forms, one of which was more of a caricature than the other. Some examples did escape however and either version will fetch up to £15,000 Doulton was involved with the beer and spirit trade from the beginning of the 19th century and they produced all manner of promotional items for these industries ranging from public house tiled or terracotta frontages and ceramic beer pump handles to ashtrays and spittoons for public bars. The large Kingsware character jug, 'The McCallum', was made for D. & J. McCallum Whisky Distillers, circa 1930 and is worth £1,000.

The McCallum character jug issued in a limited edition of 1000 circa 1930

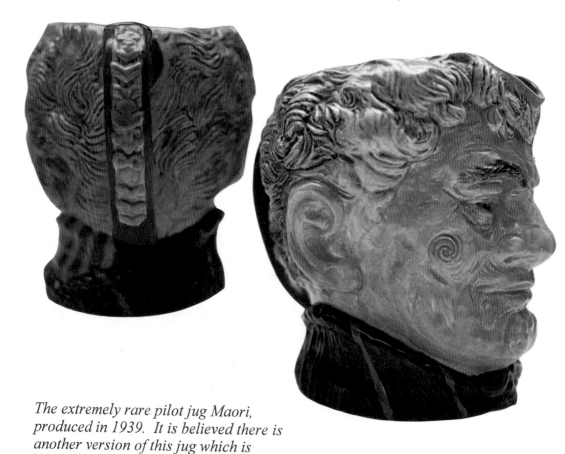

The extremely rare pilot jug Maori, produced in 1939. It is believed there is another version of this jug which is even rarer.

Other jugs worth keeping an eye open for are 'Ard of 'Earing D6588 designed by D. Biggs and worth about £950, the toothless version of Granny D5521 worth £550, Mephistopheles D5757 designed by Harry Fenton worth £850 and Smuts D6198 also designed by Harry Fenton and now worth £850.

Also worthy of note are Fortune Teller D6497 designed by G. Sharpe, Gladiator D6550 and Ugly Duchess D6599 designed by M. Henk, Gulliver D6560 and Punch & Judy Man D6590 designed by D. Biggs. All of these fine character jugs are worth well over £300.

'Ard of 'Earing D6588 designed by D. Biggs, introduced 1964. The hand is cleverly designed to form the handle.

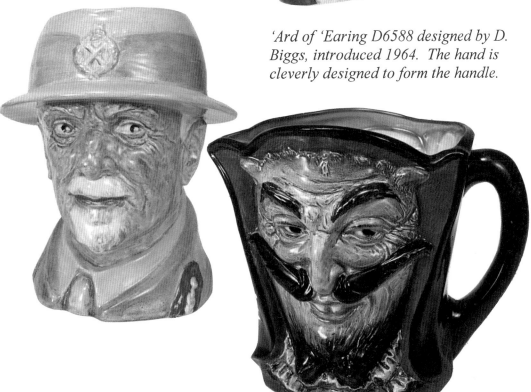

Smuts D6198, this character jug depicting Jan Christian Smuts, the South African statesman, was designed by Harry Fenton, introduced 1946.

Mephistopheles D5757 designed by H. Fenton, introduced 1937 until 1983 this remained the only two-sided character jug.

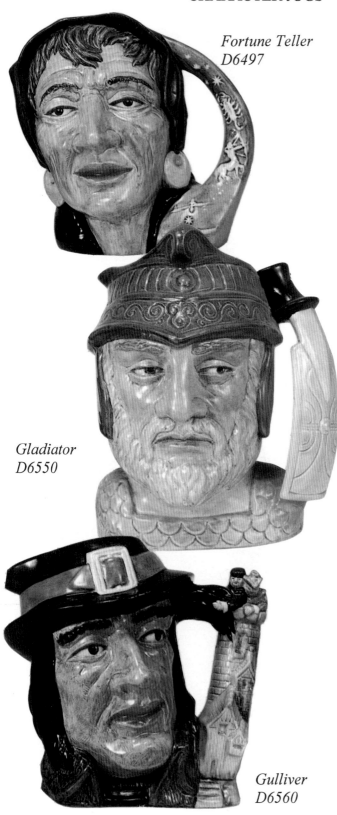

Fortune Teller
D6497

Gladiator
D6550

Gulliver
D6560

ABRAHAM LINCOLN D6936
In a limited edition of 2500
Designer: S.J. Taylor
Height: Large
Issued: 1992 only
Price: $264 £165

AIRMAN (THE) D6870
Designer: W.K. Harper
Height: Small
Issued: 1991-1996
Price: $72 £45

ALADDIN'S GENIE D6971
In a limited edition of 1500
Designer: David Biggs
Height: 7½in.,19cm.
Issued: 1994-1995
Price: $360 £225

ALBERT EINSTEIN D7023
Designer: S. Taylor
Height: 7in., 17.75cm.
Issued: 1996-1997
Price: $136 £85

ALFRED HITCHCOCK D6987
Designer: David Biggs
Height: 7in., 17.75cm.
Issued: 1995-1997
Price: $152 £95

ANGLER (THE) D6866
Designer: S. Taylor
Height: Small
Issued: 1990-1995
Price: $64 £40

ANNE BOLEYN D6644
Designer: D. Tootle
Height: Large
Issued: 1975-1990
Price: $152 £95

ANNE BOLEYN D6650
Designer: D. Tootle
Height: Small
Issued: 1980-1990
Price: $104 £65

ANNE BOLEYN D6651
Designer: D. Tootle
Height: Mini
Issued: 1980-1990
Price: $104 £65

ANNE OF CLEVES D6753
Designer: M. Abberley
Height: Small
Issued: 1987-1990
Price: $152 £95

ANNE OF CLEVES D6754
Designer: M. Abberley
Height: Mini
Issued: 1987-1990
Price: $152 £85

CHARACTER JUGS

AIRMAN (THE) D6870

ALFRED HITCHCOCK
D6987

ALBERT EINSTEIN D7023

ALADDIN'S GENIE
D6971

ANGLER (THE) D6866

ANNE OF CLEVES D6653 (Ears Up)

33

ANNE OF CLEVES D6653
Designer: M. Abberley
Height: Large
Issued: 1980 only
Price: $296 £185 (Ears Up)

ANNE OF CLEVES D6653
Designer: M. Abberley
Height: Large
Issued: 1980-1990
Price: $152 £95

ANNIE OAKLEY D6732
Designer: S. Taylor
Height: Medium
Issued: 1985-1988
Price: $104 £65

ANTIQUE DEALER
(Kevin Francis) D6809
In a limited edition of 5000
Designer: G. Blower
Height: Large
Issued: 1988-1992
Price: $136 £85

ANTONY AND CLEOPATRA
D6728 in a limited edition of
9500
Designer: M. Abberley
Height: Large
Issued: 1985-1992
Price: $152 £95

APOTHECARY D6567
Designer: M. Henk
Height: Large
Issued: 1963-1983
Price: $120 £75

APOTHECARY D6574
Designer: M. Henk
Height: Small
Issued: 1963-1983
Price: $72 £45

APOTHECARY D6581
Designer: M. Henk
Height: Mini
Issued: 1963-1983
Price: $96 £60

ARAMIS D6441
Designer: M.Henk
Height: Large
Issued: 1956-1991
Price: $136 $85

ARAMIS D6454
Designer: M .Henk
Height: Small
Issued: 1956-1991
Price: $64 £40

ARAMIS D6508
Designer: M. Henk
Height: Mini
Issued: 1960-1991
Price: $64 £40

ANNE BOLEYN

ANNE OF CLEVES

ARAMIS

CHARACTER JUGS

ANNIE OAKLEY D6732

ANTIQUE DEALER D6809

ANTONY AND CLEOPATRA D6728

ARAMIS D6828

APOTHECARY D6567

ARAMIS D6828
(Peter Jones)
In a Limited edition of 1000
Designer: M. Henk
Height: Large
Issued: 1988-1992
             Colour variation
Price: $136 £85

'ARD OF 'EARING D6588
Designer: D. Biggs
Height: Large
Issued: 1964-1967
Price: $1520 £950

'ARD OF 'EARING D6591
Designer: D. Biggs
Height: Small
Issued: 1964-1967
Price: $1040 £650

'ARD OF 'EARING D6594
Designer: D. Biggs
Height: Mini
Issued: 1964-1967
Price: $1040 £650

ARP WARDEN D6872
In a limited edition of 9500
Designer: S. J. Taylor
Height: Small
Issued: 1991
Price: $152 £95

'ARRIET D6208
Designer: H. Fenton
Height: Large
Issued: 1947-1960
Price: $232 £145

'ARRIET D6236
Designer: H. Fenton
Height: Small
Issued: 1947-1960
Price: $104 £65

'ARRIET D6250
Designer: H. Fenton
Height: Mini
Issued: 1947-1960
Price: $88 £55

'ARRIET D6256
Designer: H. Fenton
Height: Tiny
Issued: 1947-1960
Price: $152 £95

'ARRY D6207
Designer: H. Fenton
Height: Large
Issued: 1947-1960
Price: $232 £145

'ARRY D6235
Designer: H. Fenton
Height: Small
Issued: 1947-1960
Price: $104 £65

'ARRIET

'ARRY

'ARRY D6249
Designer: H. Fenton
Height: Mini
Issued: 1947-1960
Price: $88 £55

'ARRY D6255
Designer: H. Fenton
Height: Tiny
Issued: 1947-1960
Price: $152 £95

ATHOS D6439
Designer: M. Henk
Height: Large
Issued: 1956-1991
Price: $136 £85

ATHOS D6452
Designer: M. Henk
Height: Small
Issued: 1956-1991
Price: $64 £40

ATHOS D6509
Designer: M. Henk
Height: Mini
Issued: 1960-1991
Price: $64 £40

ATHOS D6827
(Peter Jones)
In a limited edition of 1000
Designer: M. Henk
Height: Large
Issued: 1988
             Colour variatio
Price: $136 £85

AUCTIONEER (Kevin Fra
D6838 in a limited edition o
5000
Designer: G. Blower
Height: Large
Issued: 1988-1992
Price: $160 £100

AULD MAC D5823
Designer: H. Fenton
Height: Large
Issued: 1937-1985
Price: $120 £75

AULD MAC D5824
Designer: H. Fenton
Height: Small
Issued: 1937-1985
Price: $56 £35

AULD MAC D6253
Designer: H. Fenton
Height: Mini
Issued: 1937-1985
Price: $56 £35

AULD MAC D6257
Designer: H.Fenton
Height: Tiny
Issued: 1946-1960
Price: $176 £110

CHARACTER JUGS

ATHOS D6439

'ARD OF 'EARING D6588

AULD MAC

ATHOS D6827

AUCTIONEER D6838

37

AUXILIARY FIREMAN D6887
In a limited edition of 9500
Designer: S. J. Taylor
Height: Small
Issued: 1991
Price: $152 £95

B

BACCHUS D6499
Designer: M. Henk
Height: Large
Issued: 1959-1991
Price: $104 £65

BACCHUS D6505
Designer: M. Henk
Height: Small
Issued: 1959-1991
Price: $64 £40

BACCHUS D6521
Designer: M. Henk
Height: Mini
Issued: 1960-1991
Price: $56 £35

BACCHUS

**BAHAMAS POLICEMAN
D6912** in a limited edition of
1000
Designer: W. K. Harper
Height: Large
Issued: 1992-1994
Price: $312 £195

BASEBALL PLAYER D6878
USA only
Designer: S.J. Taylor
Height: Small
Issued: 1991-1993
Price: $88 £55

BASEBALL PLAYER
Designer: David Biggs
Height: Large
Issued: 1970s
Price: $16000 £10000
This pilot jug was designed in
two colour variations, red &
blue, but never went into pro-
duction.

BEEFEATER

BEEFEATER D6206
Designer: H. Fenton
Height: Large
Issued: 1953-1996
Price $120 £75

BEEFEATER D6233
Designer: H. Fenton
Height: Small
Issued: 1953-1996
Price: $64 £40

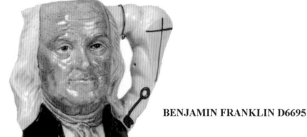

BENJAMIN FRANKLIN D6695

BEEFEATER D6251
Designer: H. Fenton
Height: Mini
Issued: 1953-1991
Price: $56 £35

CHARACTER JUGS

BEEFEATER (GR on handle)
D6206
Designer: H. Fenton
Height: Large
Issued: 1947-1953
Price: $152 £95

BEEFEATER (GR on yellow handle) D6206
Designer: H. Fenton
Height: Large
Issued: Circa 1947
Price: $3120 £1950

BEEFEATER (GR on yellow handle) D6206
Designer: H. Fenton
Height: Small
Issued: Circa 1947
Price: $1520 £950

BEEFEATER (GR on handle)
D6233
Designer: H. Fenton
Height: Small
Issued: 1947-1953
Price: $88 £55

BEEFEATER (GR on handle)
D6251
Designer: H. Fenton
Height: Mini
Issued: 1947-1953
Price: $104 £65

BEEFEATER D6806
(Collector's Club)
Designer: R. Tabbenor
Height: Tiny
Issued: 1988
Price: $104 £65

BEETHOVEN D7021
Designer: S. Taylor
Height: 7in., 17.75cm
Issued: 1996
Price: $144 £90 (R.R.P.)

BENJAMIN FRANKLIN D6695
Designer: E. Griffiths
Height: Small
Issued: 1982-1988
Price: $88 £55

BILL SHANKLEY (Liverpool Centenary Jug) D6914
In a limited edition of 5500
Designer: W. K. Harper
Height: Midi
Issued: 1992
Price: $88 £55

BILL SYKES D6981
In a limited edition of 2500
Designer: W. K. Harper
Height: Large
Issued: 1994-1997
Price: $176 £110

BOOTMAKER D6572

BEETHOVEN D7021

BLACKSMITH D6571

CHARACTER JUGS

BLACKSMITH D6571
Designer: D. Biggs
Height: Large
Issued: 1963-1983
Price: $120 £75

BLACKSMITH D6578
Designer: D. Biggs
Height: Small
Issued: 1963-1983
Price: $72 £45

BLACKSMITH D6585
Designer: D. Biggs
Height: Mini
Issued: 1963-1983
Price: $72 £45

BONNIE PRINCE CHARLIE D6858
Designer: W. K. Harper
Height: Large
Issued: 1990-1994
Price: $136 £85

BOOTMAKER D6572
Designer: D. Biggs
Height: Large
Issued: 1963-1983
Price: $120 £75

BOOTMAKER D6579
Designer: D. Biggs
Height: Small
Issued: 1963-1983
Price: $72 £45

BOOTMAKER D6586
Designer: D. Biggs
Height: Mini
Issued: 1963-1983
Price: $64 £40

BOWLS PLAYER, THE D6896
Designer: Stan Taylor
Height: 3⅜in., 9.5cm.
Issued: 1991-1995
Price: $46 £29

BUDDY HOLLY D7100
In a limited edition of 2500
Designer: D. Biggs
Height: Large
Issued: 1998
Price: $200 £125 (R.R.P.)

BUFFALO BILL D6735
Designer: S. Taylor
Height: Medium
Issued: 1985-1988
Price: $104 £65

BUFFALO BILL
Designer: Unknown
Height: Large
Issued: Unknown
Price: $16000 £10000
This was a pilot jug of which only one copy is known. The character was included in the 1985 Wild West series.

BOWLS PLAYER D6896

BUFFALO BILL D6735

BUSKER D6775

BUSKER D6775
Designer: S. Taylor
Height: Large
Issued: 1988-1991
Price: $136 £85

BUZ FUZ D5838
Designer: L Harradine and H. Fenton
Height: Intermediate
Issued: 1938-1948
Price: $192 £120

BUZ FUZ D5838
Designer: L. Harradine and H. Fenton
Height: Small
Issued: 1948-1960
Price: $104 £65

C

CABINET MAKER D7010
USA only. In a limited edition of 1500
Designer: Michael Abberley
Height: Large
Issued: 1995-1996
Price: $312 £195

CAP'N CUTTLE D5842
Designer: L. Harradine
Height: Intermediate
Issued: 1938-1945
Price: $192 £120

CAP'N CUTTLE D5842
Designer: L. Harradine
Height: Small
Issued: 1948-1960
Price: $104 £65

CAPTAIN AHAB D6500
Designer: G. Sharpe
Height: Large
Issued: 1959-1985
Price: $104 £65

CAPTAIN AHAB D6506
Designer: G. Sharpe
Height: Small
Issued: 1959-1985
Price: $72 £45

CAPTAIN AHAB D6522
Designer: G. Sharpe
Height: Mini
Issued: 1960-1985
Price: $64 £40

CAPTAIN BLIGH D6967
Designer: S.J. Taylor
Height: Large
Issued: 1995 Jug of the year
Price: $176 £110

CHARACTER JUGS

BUZ FUZ D5838

CAP'N CUTTLE

CAPTAIN HENRY MORGAN

CAPTAIN AHAB D6500

CAPTAIN BLIGH D6967

BLIGH OF THE BOUNTY

41

CAPTAIN HENRY MORGAN
D6467
Designer: G. Sharpe
Height: Large
Issued: 1958-1982
Price: $120 £75

CAPTAIN HENRY MORGAN
D6469
Designer: G. Sharpe
Height: Small
Issued: 1958-1982
Price: $72 £45

CAPTAIN HENRY MORGAN
D6510
Designer: G. Sharpe
Height: Mini
Issued: 1960-1982
Price: $72 £45

CAPTAIN HOOK D6597
Designer: M. Henk & D. Biggs
Height: Large
Issued: 1965-1971
Price: $520 £325

CAPTAIN HOOK D6601
Designer: M. Henk & D. Biggs
Height: Small
Issued: 1965-1971
Price: $360 £225

CAPTAIN HOOK D6605
Designer: M. Henk & D. Biggs
Height: Mini
Issued: 1965-1971
Price: $360 £225

CAPTAIN HOOK D6947
Designer: Martyn Alcock
Height: Large
Issued: 1994 only
Price: $192 £120

CARDINAL D5614
Designer: C. Noke
Height: Large
Issued: 1936-1960
Price: $136 £85

CARDINAL D6033
Designer: C. Noke
Height: Small
Issued: 1939-1960
Price: $104 £65

CARDINAL D6129
Designer: C. Noke
Height: Mini
Issued: 1940-1960
Price: $80 £50

CARDINAL D6258
Designer: C. Noke
Height: Tiny
Issued: 1947-1960
Price: $176 £110

CAPTAIN HOOK D6597

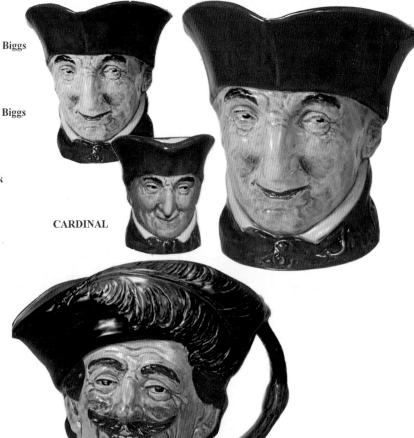

CARDINAL

CAVALIER D 6114

CHARACTER JUGS

CAROLLER D7007
RDICC USA only
Designer: Martyn Alcock
Height: Mini
Issued: 1995
Price: $104 £65

CATHERINE HOWARD D6645
Designer: P. Gee
Height: Large
Issued: 1978-1989
Price: $136 £85

CATHERINE HOWARD D6692
Designer: P. Gee
Height: Small
Issued: 1984-1989
Price: $120 £75

**CATHERINE HOWARD
D6693**
Designer: P. Gee
Height: Mini
Issued: 1984-1989
Price: $88 £55

**CATHERINE OF ARAGON
D6643**
Designer: A. Maslankowski
Height: Large
Issued: 1975-1989
Price: $136 £85

**CATHERINE OF ARAGON
D6657**
Designer: A. Maslankowski
Height: Small
Issued: 1981-1989
Price: $80 £50

**CATHERINE OF ARAGON
D6658**
Designer: A. Maslankowski
Height: Mini
Issued: 1981-1989
Price: $80 £50

CATHERINE PARR D6664
Designer: M. Abberley
Height: Large
Issued: 1981-1989
Price: $152 £95

CATHERINE PARR D6752
Designer: M. Abberley
Height: Mini
Issued: 1987-1989
Price: $192 £120

CATHERINE PARR D6751
Designer: M. Abberley
Height: Small
Issued: 1987-1989
Price: $176 £110

CAVALIER D6114
Designer: H. Fenton
Height: Large
Issued: 1940-1960
Price: $136 £85

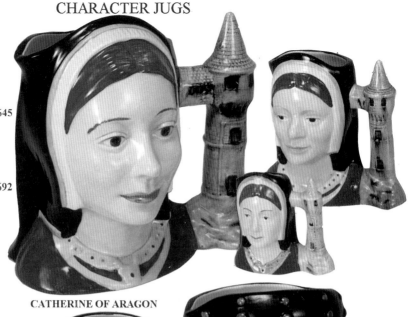

CATHERINE OF ARAGON

CATHERINE PARR

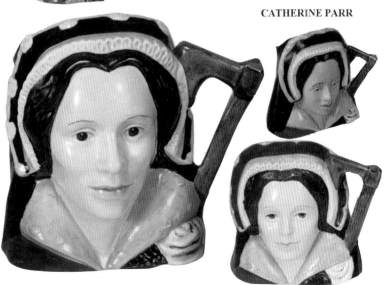

CATHERINE HOWARD

CHARACTER JUGS

CAVALIER D6173
Designer: H. Fenton
Height: Small
Issued: 1941-1960
Price: $88 £55

CAVALIER D 6114
Designer: H. Fenton
Height: Large (with goatee beard)
Issued: 1940-1942
Price: $2640 £1650

CHARLES DICKENS D6939
In a limited edition of 2500
Designer: W. K. Harper
Height: 7in., 17.75cm.
Issued: 1995-1997
Price: $400 £250

CHARLIE CHAPLIN D6949
In a limited edition of 5000
Designer: W. K. Harper
Height: Large
Issued: 1993-1996
Price: $176 £110

CHEF, THE D7103
Designer: D. Biggs
Height: Small
Issued: 1998
Price: $80 £50 (R.R.P.)

CHELSEA PENSIONER D6817
Designer: S. Taylor
Height: Large
Issued: 1989-1992
Price: $152 £95

CHIEF SITTING BULL AND GEORGE ARMSTRONG CUSTER D6712
In a limited edition of 9500
Designer: M. Abberley
Height: Large
Issued: 1984-1989
Price: $200 £125

CHOPIN D7030
Designer: S. Taylor
Height: 7in., 17.75cm.
Issued: 1996
Price: $144 £90 (R.R.P.)

CHRISTOPHER COLUMBUS D6911
In a limited edition of 7500
Designer: S.J. Taylor
Height: Small
Issued: 1992
Price: $88 £55

CHURCHILL (Natural) D6170
Two handled Loving Cup, very rare.
Designer: C. Noke
Height: Large
Issued: 1940-1941
Price: $18750 £12500

CLARK GABLE D6709

CHELSEA PENSIONER D6817

CITY GENT D6815

CHURCHILL (White) D6170
Two handled Loving Cup, rare
Designer: C. Noke
Height: Large
Issued: 1940-1941
Priced: $8000 £5000

CHURCHILL D6849
(Lawleys)
Designer: S. Taylor
Height: Small
Issued: 1989-1992
Price: $152 £95

CHURCHILL - JUG OF THE YEAR 1992 D6907
Designer: C. Noke & S. Taylor
Height: Large
Issued: 1992-1994
Price: $230 £145

CITY GENT D6815
Designer: S. Taylor
Height: Large
Issued: 1988-1991
Price: $120 £75

CLARK GABLE D6709
Designer: S. Taylor
Height: Large
Issued: 1984-
Price: $3200 £2000

CLOWN D5610
Designer: H. Fenton
Height: Large
          (Red Haired)
Issued: 1937-1942
Price: $2640 £1650

CLOWN D5610
Designer: H. Fenton
Height: Large
          (Brown Haired)
Issued: 1937-1942
Price: $2640 £1650

CLOWN D6322
Designer: H. Fenton
Height: Large
          (White Haired)
Issued: 1951-1955
Price: $1040 £650

CLOWN D5610
Designer: H. Fenton
Height: Large
          (Black Haired)
Issued: 1937-1942
Price: $18750 £12000

CLOWN D6834
Designer: S. Taylor
Height: Large
Issued: 1989-1995
Price: $120 £75

CHARACTER JUGS

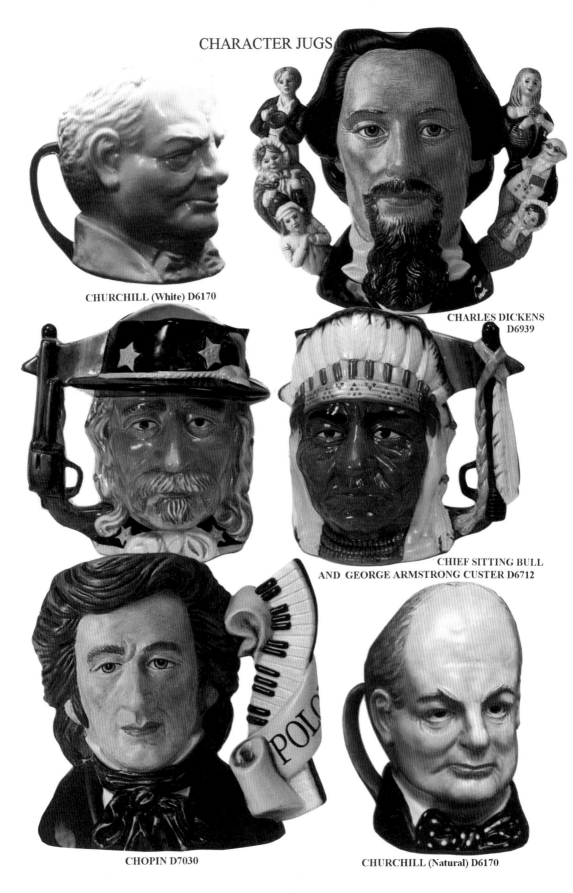

CHURCHILL (White) D6170

CHARLES DICKENS
D6939

CHIEF SITTING BULL
AND GEORGE ARMSTRONG CUSTER D6712

CHOPIN D7030

CHURCHILL (Natural) D6170

45

CHARACTER JUGS

COLLECTOR D6796 (Kevin Francis) in a limited edition of 5000
Designer: S. Taylor
Height: Large
Issued: 1988-1992
Price: $176 £110

COLUMBUS D6891
Designer: S. Taylor
Height: Large
Issued: 1991-1997
Price: $104 £65

CONFUCIUS D7003 (Flambé) In a limited edition of 1750
Designer: R. Tabbenor
Height: Large
Issued: 1995
Price: $312 £195 (R.R.P.)

COOK AND CHESHIRE CAT D6842
Designer: W. K. Harper
Height: Large
Issued: 1990-1991
Price: $232 £145

COUNT DRACULA D7053
Designer: D. Biggs
Height: 7¼in., 18.5cm.
Issued: 1997
Price: $160 £100 (R.R.P.)

CYRANO DE BERGERAC D7004
Designer: D. Biggs
Height: 7in., 17.75cm.
Issued: 1995-1997
Price: $136 £85

D

D'ARTAGNAN D6691
Designer: S. Taylor
Height: Large
Issued: 1982-1995
Priced: $136 £85

D'ARTAGNAN D6764
Designer: S. Taylor
Height: Small
Issued: 1988-1995
Price: $72 £45

D'ARTAGNAN D6765
Designer: S. Taylor
Height: Mini
Issued: 1988-1991
Price: $88 £55

DAVY CROCKETT/SANTA ANNA D6729
Designer: M. Abberley
Height: Large
Issued: 1985-1991
Price: $136 £85

CLOWN D6322

CLOWN D6834

CLOWN D6322

D'ARTAGNAN D6691

COLLECTOR D6796

CLOWN D5610

46

CYRANO DE BERGERAC
D7004

COLUMBUS D6891

DAVY CROKETT/SANTA
ANNA D6729

CONFUCIUS D7003 (Flambé)

COUNT DRACULA D7053

CHARACTER JUGS

DENNIS & GNASHER D7005
Designer: Simon Ward
Height: 7in., 17.75cm.
Issued: 1995
Price: $128 £80 (R.R.P.)

DESPERATE DAN D7006
Designer: Simon Ward
Height: 7in., 17.75cm.
Issued: 1995
Price: $128 £80 (R.R.P.)

DESPERATE DAN D7034
Designer: Simon Ward
Height: 4in., 10cm.
Issued: 1996
Price: $80 £50 (R.R.P.)

DICK TURPIN (First version) D5485
Designer: C. Noke & H. Fenton
Height: Large
Issued: 1935-1960
Price: $136 £85

DICK TURPIN (First version) D5618
Designer: C. Noke & H. Fenton
Height: Small
Issued: 1936-1960
Price: $88 £55

DICK TURPIN (First version) D6128
Designer: C. Noke & H. Fenton
Height: Mini
Issued: 1940-1960
Price: $72 £45

DICK TURPIN (Second version) D6528
Designer: D. Biggs
Height: Large
Issued: 1960-1981
Price: $120 £75

DICK TURPIN (Second version) D6535
Designer: D. Biggs
Height: Small
Issued: 1960-1981
Price: $72 £45

DICK TURPIN (Second version) D6542
Designer: D. Biggs
Height: Mini
Issued: 1960-1981
Price: $72 £45

DICK TURPIN (DIAMOND ANNIVERSARY) D6951
Designer: C. Noke
Height: Tiny
Issued: 1994
Price: $72 £45

DICK TURPIN
(Second version)

DICK TURPIN (First version)

DICK WHITTINGTON D6375
Designer: G. Blower
Height: Large
Issued: 1953-1960
Price: $360 £225

DICK WHITTINGTON D6846
(China Guild) In a limited edition of 6000
Designer: W. K. Harper
Height: Large
Issued: 1989
Price: $104 £65

DICKIE BIRD D7068
Designer: S.J. Taylor
Height: 4in., 10.1cm.
Issued: 1997
Price: $80 £50

DOC HOLLIDAY D6731
Designer: S. Taylor
Height: Medium
Issued: 1985-1988
Price: $104 £65

DON QUIXOTE D6455
Designer: G. Blower
Height: Large
Issued: 1960-1991
Price: $120 £75

DON QUIXOTE D6460
Designer: G. Blower
Height: Small
Issued: 1960-
Price: $72 £45

DON QUIXOTE D6511
Designer: G. Blower
Height: Mini
Issued: 1960-1991
Price: $64 £40

DRAKE D6115
Designer: H. Fenton
Height: Large (Hatless)
Issued: 1940-1941
Price: $2640 £1650

DRAKE D6115
Designer: H. Fenton
Height: Large
Issued: 1940-1960
Price: $135 £85

DRAKE D6174
Designer: H Fenton
Height: Small
Issued: 1941-1960
Price: $88 £55

DUKE OF WELLINGTON D6848 (U.K. Ceramics)
In a limited edition of 5000
Designer: W. K. Harper
Height: Large
Issued: 1989
Price: $176 £110

CHARACTER JUGS

DICK WHITTINGTON D6375

DON QUIXOTE D6455

DRAKE D6115
(Hatless)

DOC HOLLIDAY D6731

DICK WHITTINGTON D6846

DUKE OF WELLINGTON D6848

E

EARL MOUNTBATTEN OF BURMA D6851 (Lawleys)
In a limited edition of 9500
Designer: S. Taylor
Height: Small
Issued: 1989
Price: $152 £95

EARL MOUNTBATTEN OF BURMA D6944
In a limited edition of 5000
Designer: S. Taylor
Height: Large
Issued: 1993
Price: $215 £135

ELEPHANT TRAINER D6841
Designer: S. Taylor
Height: Large
Issued: 1990-1992
Price: $152 £95

ENGINE DRIVER D6823
(Lawleys)
In a limited edition of 5000
Designer: S. Taylor
Height: Small
Issued: 1987
Price: $104 £65

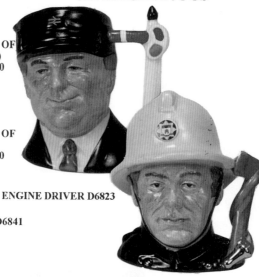

ENGINE DRIVER D6823

FIREMAN D6839 (Lawleys)

F

FALCONER D6533
Designer: M. Henk
Height: Large
Issued: 1960-1991
Price: $104 £65

FALCONER D6540
Designer: M. Henk
Height: Small
Issued: 1960-
Price: $64 £40

FALCONER D6547
Designer: M. Henk
Height: Mini
Issued: 1960-1992
Price: $55 £35

FALCONER D6800 (Peter Jones) in a limited edition of 1000
Designer: M. Henk
Height: Large
Issued: 1987-1991
Price: $152 £95

FALSTAFF D6287
Designer: H. Fenton
Height: Large
Issued: 1950-1995
Price: $104 £65

FALSTAFF D6385
Designer: H. Fenton
Height: Small
Issued: 1950-1995
Price: $55 £35

FAT BOY

FALSTAFF D6519
Designer: H. Fenton
Height: Mini
Issued: 1960-1992
Price: $55 £35

FALSTAFF D6795 (U.K. Fairs)
In a limited edition of 1500
Designer: H. Fenton
Height: Large
Issued: 1987
Price: $150 £95

FARMER JOHN D5788
Designer: C. Noke
Height: Large
Issued: 1938-1960
Price: $135 £85

FARMER JOHN D5789
Designer: C. Noke
Height: Small
Issued: 1938-1960
Price: £88 £55

FAT BOY D5840
Designer: L. Harradine & H. Fenton
Height: Intermediate
Issued: 1938-1948
Price: $190 £120

FAT BOY D5840
Designer: L. Harradine & H. Fenton
Height: Small
Issued: 1948-1960
Price: $105 £65

FAT BOY D6139
Designer: L. Harradine & H. Fenton
Height: Mini
Issued: 1940-1960
Price: $88 $55

FAT BOY D6142
Designer: L. Harradine & H. Fenton
Height: Tiny
Issued: 1940-1960
Price: $104 £65

FIREMAN D6697
Designer: R. Tabbenor
Height: Large
Issued: 1984-1991
Price: $120 £75

FIREMAN D6839 (Lawleys)
In a limited edition of 5000
Designer: S. Taylor
Height: Small
Issued: 1987
Price: $104 £65

FOOTBALL SUPPORTER (Arsenal) D6927
Designer: S. J. Taylor
Height: Midi
Issued: 1992-
Price: $62 £39

FALSTAFF D6287

FARMER JOHN D5788

FALCONER D6800

FALCONER D6533

FALSTAFF D6795

FIREMAN D6697

CHARACTER JUGS

FOOTBALL SUPPORTER
(Aston Villa) D6931
Designer: S. J. Taylor
Height: Midi
Issued: 1992-
Price: $62 £39

FOOTBALL SUPPORTER
(Celtic) D6925
Designer: S. J. Taylor
Height: Midi
Issued: 1992-
Price: $62 £39

FOOTBALL SUPPORTER
(Everton) D6926
Designer: S. J. Taylor
Height: Midi
Issued: 1992-
Price: $62 £39

FOOTBALL SUPPORTER
(Leeds) D6928
Designer: S. J. Taylor
Height: Midi
Issued: 1992-
Price: $62 £39

FOOTBALL SUPPORTER
(Liverpool) D6930
Designer: S. J. Taylor
Height: Midi
Issued: 1992-
Price: $62 £39

FOOTBALL SUPPORTER
(Man. U.) D6924
Designer: S. J. Taylor
Height: Midi
Issued: 1992-
Price: $62 £39

FOOTBALL SUPPORTER
(Rangers) D6929
Designer: S. J. Taylor
Height: Midi
Issued: 1992-
Price: $62 £39

FOOTBALL SUPPORTER
(Sheffield Wed.) D6958
Designer: S. J. Taylor
Height: Midi
Issued: 1992-
Price: $62 £39

FORTUNE TELLER D6497
Designer: G. Sharpe
Height: Large
Issued: 1959-1967
Price: $520 £325

FORTUNE TELLER D6503
Designer: G. Sharpe
Height: Small
Issued: 1959-1967
Price: $392 £245

FORTUNE TELLER D6523
Designer: G. Sharpe
Height: Mini
Issued: 1960-1967
Price: $376 £235

FORTUNE TELLER D6497

FRIAR TUCK D6321

GAOLER D6570

FRIAR TUCK D6321
Designer: H. Fenton
Height: Large
Issued: 1951-1960
Price: $392 £245

G

GAOLER D6570
Designer: D. Biggs
Height: Large
Issued: 1963-1983
Price: $120 £75

GAOLER D6577
Designer: D. Biggs
Height: Small
Issued: 1963-1983
Price: $72 £45

GAOLER D6584
Designer: D. Biggs
Height: Mini
Issued: 1963-1983
Price: $72 £45

GARDENER D6630
Designer: D. Biggs
Height: Large
Issued: 1973-1981
Price: $264 £165

GARDENER D6634
Designer: D. Biggs
Height: Small
Issued: 1973-1981
Price: $176 £110

GARDENER D6638
Designer: D. Biggs
Height: Mini
Issued: 1973-1981
Price: $152 £95

GARDENER D6868
Designer: S. Taylor
Height: Small
Issued: 1990-1995
Price: $64 £40

GENERAL CUSTER D7079
Designer: S. Taylor
Height: Large
Issued: 1997
Price: $160 £100 (R.R.P.)

GENERAL EISENHOWER
D6937
Designer: W. K. Harper
Height: Large
Issued: 1991 in a limited
             edition of 1000
Price: $312 £195

GENERAL GORDON D6869
Designer: W. K. Harper
Height: Large
Issued: 1991 in a limited
             edition of 1500
Price: $192 £120

CHARACTER JUGS

GARDENER D6868

GEORGE HARRISON D6727

FOOTBALL SUPPORTER (Aston Villa) D6931

FOOTBALL SUPPORTER (Leeds) D6928

**GEORGE WASHINGTON/
KING GEORGE III D6749**

CHARACTER JUGS

GENERAL PATTON D7026
Designer: Warren Platt
Height: 7in., 17.78cm.
Issued: 1996 in a limited
edition of 1000
Price: $312 £195

GENIE D6892
Designer: S. J. Taylor
Height: Large
Issued: 1991 only.
Price: $240 £150

GEOFFREY CHAUCER D7029
Designer: R. Tabbenor
Height: 7½in., 19cm.
Issued: 1996
Price: $478 £299 (R.R.P.)

GEORGE HARRISON D6727
Designer: S. Taylor
Height: Medium
Issued: 1984-1991
Price: $136 £85

GEORGE TINWORTH D7000
(Collectors Club only)
Designer: W. K. Harper
Height: 4¼in., 10.5cm.
Issued: 1995
Price: $120 £75

GEORGE WASHINGTON
D6669
Designer: S. Taylor
Height: Large
Issued: 1982-1994
Price: $136 £85

GEORGE WASHINGTON/
KING GEORGE III D6749
In a limited edition of 9500
Designer: M. Abberley
Height: Large
Issued: 1986
Price: $152 £95

GERONIMO D6733
Designer: S. Taylor
Height: Medium
Issued: 1985-1988
Price: $152 £95

GLADIATOR D6550
Designer: M. Henk
Height: Large
Issued: 1961-1967
Price: $560 £350

GLADIATOR D6553
Designer: M. Henk
Height: Small
Issued: 1961-1967
Price: $400 £250

GLADIATOR D6556
Designer: M. Henk
Height: Mini
Issued: 1961-1967
Price: $400 £250

GLENN MILLER D6970
Designer: W. K. Harper
Height: 7in., 17.75cm.
Issued: 1994
Price: $160 £100 (R.R.P.)

GEORGE TINWORTH D7000

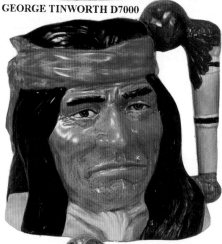

GERONIMO D6733

GLADIATOR D6550

GOLFER D6623
Designer: D. Biggs
Height: Large
Issued: 1971-1995
Price: $104 £65

GOLFER D6756
Designer: D. Biggs
Height: Small
Issued: 1987-1992
Price: $72 £45

GOLFER D6757
Designer: D. Biggs
Height: Mini
Issued: 1987-1991
Price: $72 £45

GOLFER D6784(John Sincl
In a limited edition of 1000
Designer: D. Biggs
Height: Large
Issued: 1987
Price: $152 £95

GOLFER D6865
Designer: S. Taylor
Height: Small
Issued: 1990-1995
Price: $64 £40

GONDOLIER D6589
Designer: D. Biggs
Height: Large
Issued: 1964-1969
Price: $520 £325

GONDOLIER D6592
Designer: D. Biggs
Height: Small
Issued: 1964-1969
Price: $360 £225

GONDOLIER D6595
Designer: D. Biggs
Height: Mini
Issued: 1964-1969
Price: $400 £250

GONE AWAY D6531
Designer: G. Sharpe
Height: Large
Issued: 1960-1982
Price: $120 £75

GONE AWAY D6538
Designer: G. Sharpe
Height: Small
Issued: 1960-1982
Price: $72 £45

GONE AWAY D6545
Designer: G. Sharpe
Height: Mini
Issued: 1960-1982
Price: $72 £45

GRADUATE,THE D6916
Designer: S. Taylor
Height: Small
Issued: 1993-1995
Price: $64 £40

CHARACTER JUGS

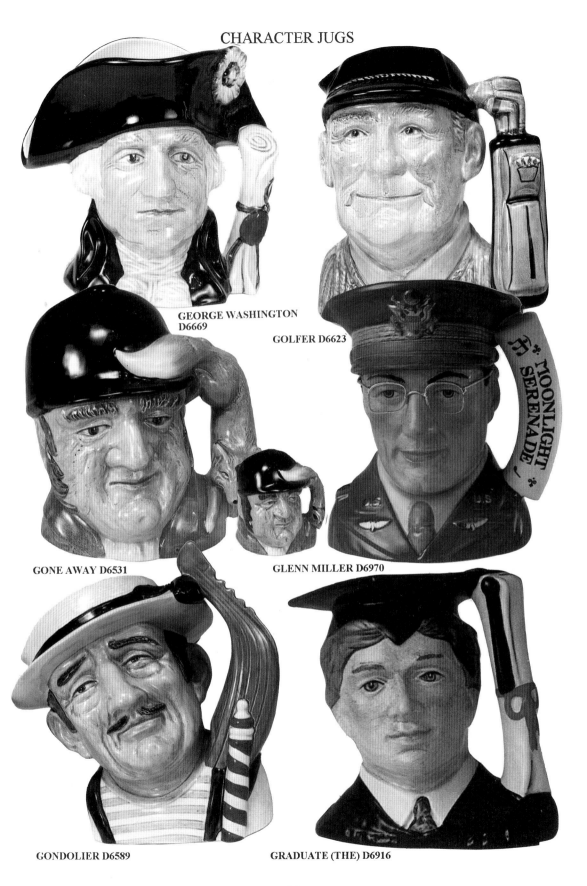

GEORGE WASHINGTON
D6669

GOLFER D6623

GONE AWAY D6531

GLENN MILLER D6970

GONDOLIER D6589

GRADUATE (THE) D6916

GRANNY D5521
Designer: H. Fenton &
M. Henk
Height: Large
Issued: 1935-1983
Price: $120 £75

GRANNY (Toothless version) D5521
Designer: H. Fenton &
M. Henk
Height: Large
Issued: 1935
Price: $880 £550

GRANNY D6384
Designer: H. Fenton &
M. Henk
Height: Small
Issued: 1953-1983
Price: $72 £45

GRANNY D6520
Designer: H. Fenton &
M. Henk
Height: Mini
Issued: 1960-1983
Price: $72 £45

GRANNY (DIAMOND AN-NIVERSARY) D6954
Designer: H. Fenton
Height: Tiny
Issued: 1994
Price: $72 £45

GREAT EXPLORERS SET D7081–D7086
Designer: Unknown
Height: 1½in., 3.8cm.
Issued: 1997
Price: £320 £200 (Set with wooden stand)

GROUCHO MARX D6710
Designer: S. Taylor
Height: Large
Issued: 1984-1987
Price: $136 £85

GUARDSMAN D6568
Designer: M. Henk
Height: Large
Issued: 1963-1983
Price: $136 £85

GUARDSMAN D6755
Designer: S. Taylor
Height: Large
Issued: 1986
Price: $128 £80 (R.R.P.)

GUARDSMAN D6575
Designer: M. Henk
Height: Small
Issued: 1963-1983
Price: $88 £55

GUARDSMAN D6582
Designer: M. Henk
Height: Mini
Issued: 1963-1983
Price: $80 £50

GUARDSMAN D6771
Designer: S. Taylor
Height: Small
Issued: 1986
Price: $72 £45 (R.R.P.)

GRANNY

GRANNY
(Toothless version)
D5521

GROUCHO MARX D6710

GUARDSMAN D6772
Designer: S. Taylor
Height: Mini
Issued: 1986-1992
Price: $72 £45

GULLIVER D6560
Designer: D. Biggs
Height: Large
Issued: 1962-1967
Price: $632 £395

GULLIVER D6563
Designer: D. Biggs
Height: Small
Issued: 1962-1967
Price: $472 £295

GULLIVER D6566
Designer: D. Biggs
Height: Mini
Issued: 1962-1967
Price: $385 £240

GUNSMITH D6573
Designer: D. Biggs
Height: Large
Issued: 1963-1983
Price: $136 £85

GUNSMITH D6580
Designer: D. Biggs
Height: Small
Issued: 1963-1983
Price: $88 £55

GUNSMITH D6587
Designer: D. Biggs
Height: Mini
Issued: 1963-1983
Price: $72 £45

GUY FAWKES D6861
Designer: W. K. Harper
Height: Large
Issued: 1990-1996
Price: $120 £75

H

H.G. WELLS D7095
In a limited edition of 2500
Designer: D. Biggs
Height: Large
Issued: 1998
Price: $160 £100

HAMLET D6672
Designer: M. Abberley
Height: Large
Issued: 1982-1988
Price: $136 £85

HAMPSHIRE CRICKETER D6739 (H.C.C. Club)
In a limited edition of 5000
Designer: H. Sales
Height: Medium
Issued: 1985
Price: $88 £55

CHARACTER JUGS

GUARDSMAN
D6568

GUARDSMAN D6575

GULLIVER D6560

GUY FAWKES D6861

GUARDSMAN D6755   GUARDSMEN D6771   GUNSMITH D6573

57

HANDEL D7080
Designer: S. Taylor
Height: Large
Issued: 1997
Price: $145 £90 (R.R.P.)

HENRY V D6671
Designer: R. Tabbenor
Height: Large
Issued: 1982-1988
Priced: $136 £85

HENRY VIII D6642
Designer: E. Griffiths
Height: Large
Issued: 1979-
Price: $96 £60 (R.R.P.)

HENRY VIII D6647
Designer: E. Griffiths
Height: Small
Issued: 1979-
Price: $51 £32 (R.R.P.)

HENRY VIII D6648
Designer: E. Griffiths
Height: Mini
Issued: 1979-1989
Price: $72 £45

HENRY COOPER D7050
Designer: S.J. Taylor
Height: 4in., 10.1cm.
Issued: 1996 in a limited
            edition of 9500
Price: $80 £50

HOME GUARD D6886
Designer: S. J. Taylor
Height: Small
Issued: 1991 in a limited
            edition of 9500
Price: $152 £95

I

IZAAK WALTON D6404
Designer: G. Blower
Height: Large
Issued: 1953-1982
Price: $136 £85

J

JANE SEYMOUR D6646
Designer: M. Abberley
Height: Large
Issued: 1979-1990
Price: $136 £85

JANE SEYMOUR D6747
Designer: M. Abberley
Height: Mini
Issued: 1986-1990
Price: $88 £55

JANE SEYMOUR D6746
Designer: M. Abberley
Height: Small
Issued: 1986-1990
Price: $104 £65

JARGE D6288
Designer: H. Fenton
Height: Large
Issued: 1950-1960
Price: $360 £225

HAMLET D6672

HAMPSHIRE CRICKETER D6739 (H.C.C. Club)

IZAAK WALTON D6404

JARGE D6295
Designer: H. Fenton
Height: Small
Issued: 1950-1960
Price: $200 £125

JESSE OWENS D7019
(Character Jug of the Year 1996)
Designer: S. Taylor
Height: 6¾in., 17cm.
Issued: 1996
Price: $176 £110

JESTER D5556
Designer: C. Noke
Height: Small
Issued: 1936-1960
Price: $104 £65

JESTER (DIAMOND AN-NIVERSARY) D6953
Designer: C. Noke
Height: Tiny
Issued: 1994
Price: $72 £45

JIMMY DURANTE D6708
Designer: D. Biggs
Height: Large
Issued: 1985-1986
Price: $136 £85

JOCKEY D6625
Designer: D. Biggs
Height: Large
Issued: 1971-1975
Price: $392 £245

JOCKEY D6877
Designer: S. Taylor
Height: Small
Issued: 1991-1996
Price: $72 £45

JOHN BARLEYCORN D5327
Designer: C. Noke
Height: Large
Issued: 1934-1960
Price: $152 £95

JOHN BARLEYCORN D7535
Designer: C. Noke
Height: Small
Issued: 1937-1960
Price: $88 £55

JOHN BARLEYCORN D6041
Designer: C. Noke
Height: Mini
Issued: 1939-1960
Price: $88 £55

JOHN BARLEYCORN (DIAMOND ANNIVERSARY) D6952
Designer: C. Noke & H.
            Fenton
Height: Tiny
Issued: 1994
Price: $72 £45

JANE SEYMOUR

JARGE

HENRY V D6671

HENRY VIII

CHARACTER JUGS

JOHN BARLEYCORN
D5327

JOCKEY D6625

JESTER D5556

JESSE OWENS D7019

JIMMY DURANTE D6708

JOCKEY D6877

60

CHARACTER JUGS

JOHN DOULTON D6656
(Collectors Club)
Designer: E. Griffiths
Height: Small
Issued: Showing 2pm.
              1983-1994
Price: $64 £40
Issued: Showing 8pm.
              1980-1982
Price: $104 £65

JOHN LENNON D6725
Designer: S. Taylor
Height: Medium
Issued: 1984-1991
Price: $136 £85

JOHN LENNON D6797 (John
Sinclair) In a limited edition of
1000
Designer: S. Taylor
Height: Medium
Issued: 1987
              Colour variation
Price: $240 £150

JOHN PEEL D5612
Designer: H. Fenton
Height: Large
Issued: 1936-1960
Price: $136 £85

JOHN PEEL D5731
Designer: H. Fenton
Height: Small
Issued: 1937-1960
Price: $88 £55

JOHN PEEL D6130
Designer: H. Fenton
Height: Mini
Issued: 1940-1960
Price: $80 £50

JOHN PEEL D6259
Designer: H. Fenton
Height: Tiny
Issued: 1947-1960
Price: $176 £110

JOHN SHORTER D6880
Designer: W. K. Harper
Height: Small
Issued: 1991 in a limited
              edition of 1500
              Australia only.
Price: $152 £95

JOHNNERS D7018
Designer: S. J. Taylor
Height: Small
Issued: 1995 in a limited
              edition of 9500
Price: $72 £45

JOHNNY APPLESEED D6372
Designer: H. Fenton
Height: Large
Issued: 1953-1969
Price: $360 £225

JOHN LENNON D6797

JOHN DOULTON D6656

JOHN LENNON D6725

JOHN PEEL D5612

JOHNNY APPLESEED D6372

61

JUGGLER D6835
Designer: S. Taylor
Height: Large
Issued: 1989-1991
Price: $152 £95

K

KING ARTHUR D7055
Designer: R. Tabbenor
Height: 7¼in., 18.5cm.
Issued: 1997
Price: $240 £150 (R.R.P.)

KING ARTHUR and GUINE-VERE D6836
In a limited edition of 9500
Designer: S. Taylor
Height: Large
Issued: 1989-1992
Price: $176 £110

KING CHARLES D6917
In a limited edition of 2500
Designer: W. K. Harper
Height: Large
Issued: 1992
Price: $400 £250

KING EDWARD VII D6923
Designer: W. K. Harper
Height: Small
Issued: 1992 R.D.I.C.C. only.
Price: $192 £120

KING PHILIP II of SPAIN D6822 (Lawleys)
In a limited edition of 9500
Designer: W. K. Harper
Height: Small
Issued: 1988-1992
Price: $136 £85

L

LAWYER D6498
Designer: M. Henk
Height: Large
Issued: 1959-1996
Price: $104 £65

LAWYER D6504
Designer: M. Henk
Height: Small
Issued: 1959-1996
Price: $56 £35

LAWYER D6524
Designer: M. Henk
Height: Mini
Issued: 1960-1991
Price: $56 £35

LEPRECHAUN D6847
Designer: W. K. Harper
Height: Large
Issued: 1990-1996
Price: $112 £70

LAWYER D6524

KING ARTHUR and GUINE-VERE D6836

LEPRECHAUN D6899
Designer: W. K. Harper
Height: Small
Issued: 1990-1996
Price: $56 £35

LEWIS CARROLL D7096
Designer: D. Biggs
Height: Large
Issued: 1998
Price: $160 £100 (R.R.P.)

LITTLE MESTER D6819 (John Sinclair) in a limited edition of 3500
Designer: S. Taylor
Height: Large
Issued: 1988-
Price: $120 £75

LOBSTER MAN D6617
Designer: D. Biggs
Height: Large
Issued: 1968-1991
Price: $104 £65

LOBSTER MAN D6620
Designer: D. Biggs
Height: Small
Issued: 1968-1991
Price: $64 £40

LOBSTER MAN D6652
Designer: D. Biggs
Height: Mini
Issued: 1980-1991
Price: $56 £35

LOBSTER MAN D6783
Designer: D. Biggs
Height: Large
Issued: 1987-1989
Colour variation
Price: $120 £75

LONDON BOBBY D6744
Designer: S. Taylor
Height: Large
Issued: 1986
Price: $128 £80 (R.R.P.)

LONDON BOBBY D6762
Designer: S. Taylor
Height: Small
Issued: 1986
Price: $72 £45 (R.R.P.)

LONDON BOBBY D6763
Designer: S. Taylor
Height: Mini
Issued: 1986-1991
Price: $64 £40

LONG JOHN SILVER D6335
Designer: M. Henk
Height: Large
Issued: 1960-
Price: $112 £70 (R.R.P.)

CHARACTER JUGS

LITTLE MESTER D6819

KING PHILIP II of
SPAIN D6822

KING ARTHUR D7055

LEPRECHAUN
D6847

LOBSTER MAN D6617

LONDON BOBBY D6744

CHARACTER JUGS

LONG JOHN SILVER D6386
Designer: M. Henk
Height: Small
Issued: 1960-
Price: $51 £32 (R.R.P.)

LONG JOHN SILVER D6512
Designer: M. Henk
Height: Mini
Issued: 1960-1992
Price: $56 £35

LORD MAYOR OF LONDON D6864
Designer: S. J. Taylor
Height: Large
Issued: 1990-1991
Price: $176 £110

LORD NELSON D6336
Designer: G. Blower
Height: Large
Issued: 1952-1969
Price: $392 £245

LOUIS ARMSTRONG D6707
Designer: D. Biggs
Height: Large
Issued: 1984-1987
Price: $152 £95

LUMBERJACK D6610
Designer: M. Henk
Height: Large
Issued: 1967-1983
Price: $120 £75

LUMBERJACK D6613
Designer: M. Henk
Height: Small
Issued: 1967-1983
Price: $72 £45

M

MACBETH D6667
Designer: M. Abberley
Height: Large
Issued: 1982-1988
Price: $136 £85

MCCALLUM
In a limited edition of 1000 for
D. & J. McCallum
Designer: Unknown
Height: 6½in., 17cm.
Issued: Early 1930s
Price: $1600 £1000

MAD HATTER D6598
Designer: M. Henk
Height: Large
Issued: 1965-1983
Price: $152 £95

MAD HATTER D6602
Designer: M. Henk
Height: Small
Issued: 1965-1983
Price: $104 £65

MAD HATTER D6606
Designer: M. Henk
Height: Mini
Issued: 1965-1983
Price: $104 £65

MAE WEST D6688
Designer: C. Davidson
Height: Large
Issued: 1983-1985
Price: $136 £85

MAORI
Designer: Unknown
Height: Large
Issued: c.1939
Price: $24000 £15000

MARCH HARE D6776
Designer: W. K. Harper
Height: Large
Issued: 1989-1991
Price: $176 £110

MARK TWAIN D6654
Designer: E. Griffiths
Height: Large
Issued: 1980-1990
Price: $104 £65

MARK TWAIN D6694
Designer: E. Griffiths
Height: Small
Issued: 1983-1990
Price: $72 £45

MARK TWAIN D6758
Designer: E. Griffiths
Height: Mini
Issued: 1987-1990
Price: $72 £45

MASTER (THE) D6898
Designer: S. Taylor
Height: Small
Issued: 1991-1995
Price: $64 £40

MEPHISTOPHELES D5757
Designer: H. Fenton
Height: Large
Issued: 1937-1948
Price: $1360 £850

MEPHISTOPHELES D5758
Designer: H. Fenton
Height: Small
Issued: 1937-1948
Price: $880 £550

MERLIN D6529
Designer: G. Sharpe
Height: Large
Issued: 1960-
Price: $112 £70 (R.R.P.)

MERLIN D6536
Designer: G. Sharpe
Height: Small
Issued: 1960-
Price: $51 £32 (R.R.P.)

LORD NELSON D6336

LONG JOHN SILVER D6335

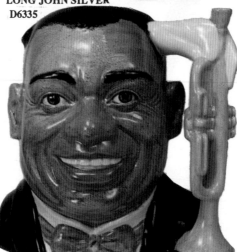

LOUIS ARMSTRONG D6707

CHARACTER JUGS

LUMBERJACK D6610

MACBETH D6667

MCCALLUM

MAE WEST D6688

MERLIN D6529

MAD HATTER D6598

MAORI

MARK TWAIN

MEPHISTOPHELES D5758

MEPHISTOPHELES D5757

CHARACTER JUGS

MERLIN D6543
Designer: G. Sharpe
Height: Mini
Issued: 1960-1992
Price: $56 £35

MICHAEL DOULTON D6808
Designer: W. K. Harper
Height: Small
Issued: 1988-1989
Price: $72 £45

MIKADO D6501
Designer: M. Henk
Height: Large
Issued: 1959-1969
Price: $520 £325

MIKADO D6507
Designer: M. Henk
Height: Small
Issued 1959-1969
Price: $392 £245

MIKADO D6525
Designer: M. Henk
Height: Mini
Issued: 1960-1969
Price: $360 £225

MINE HOST D6468
Designer: M. Henk
Height: Large
Issued: 1958-1982
Price: $120 £75

MINE HOST D6470
Designer: M. Henk
Height: Small
Issued: 1958-1982
Price: $72 £45

MINE HOST D6513
Designer: M. Henk
Height: Mini
Issued: 1960-1982
Price: $80 £50

MINNIE THE MINX D7036
Designer: Simon Ward
Height: 4in., 10cm.
Issued: 1996
Price: $80 £50 (R.R.P.)

MONTGOMERY D6908
In a limited edition of 2500
Designer: H. Fenton & S. Taylor
Height: Large
Issued: 1992-1995
Price: $200 £125

MONTY D6202
Designer: H. Fenton
Height: Large
Issued: 1946-1991
Price: $120 £75

MICHAEL DOULTON D6808

MASTER (THE) D6898

MINE HOST

MIKADO D6501

MONTY D6202

MOZART D7031
Designer: S. Taylor
Height: 7in., 17.75cm.
Issued: 1996
Price: $144 £90 (R.R.P.)

MR MICAWBER D5843
Designer: L. Harradine and
  H. Fenton
Height: Intermediate
Issued: 1938-1948
Price: $192 £120

MR MICAWBER D5843
Designer: L. Harradine and
  H. Fenton
Height: Small
Issued: 1948-1960
Price: $104 £65

MR MICAWBER D6138
Designer: L. Harradine and
  H. Fenton
Height: Mini
Issued: 1940-1960
Price: $72 £45

MR MICAWBER D6143
Designer: L. Harradine and
  H. Fenton
Height: Tiny
Issued: 1940-1960
Price: $104 £65

MR PICKWICK D6060
Designer: L. Harradine and
  H. Fenton
Height: Large
Issued: 1940-1960
Price: $200 £125

MR PICKWICK D5839
Designer: L. Harradine and
  H. Fenton
Height: Intermediate
Issued: 1938-1948
Price: $192 £120

MR PICKWICK D5839
Designer: L. Harradine
  and H. Fenton
Height: Small
Issued: 1948-1960
Price: $104 £65

MR PICKWICK D6254
Designer: L. Harradine
  and H. Fenton
Height: Mini
Issued: 1947-1960
Price: $72 £45

MR PICKWICK D6260
Designer: L. Harradine and
  H. Fenton
Height: Tiny
Issued: 1947-1960
Price: $175 £110

NEPTUNE

MR MICAWBER

MR PICKWICK D7025
(Collectors Club only)
Designer: W. K. Harper
Height: 4in., 10cm.
Issued: 1996
Price: $120 £75

MR QUAKER D6738 (Quaker Oats) In a limited edition of 3500
Designer: L. Harradine and
  H. Sales
Height: Large
Issued: 1985
Price: $472 £295

MRS CLAUS D6922
Designer: S. J. Taylor
Height: Mini
Issued: 1992 U.S.A. only
Price: $104 £65

MUTINY ON THE BOUNTY CAPTAIN BLIGH AND FLETCHER CHRISTIAN D7074, D7075
(Pair)
Designer: R. Tabbenor
Height: 4½in., 11.4cm.
Issued: 1997
Price: $192 £120 (Pair)

N

NAPOLEON D6941
In a limited edition of 2500
Designer: S. Taylor
Height: Large
Issued: 1993
Price: $176 £110

NAPOLEON AND JOSEPHINE D6750
Designer: M. Abberley
Height: Large
Issued: 1986 in a limited
  edition
Price: $136 £85

NEPTUNE D6548
Designer: M. Henk
Height: Large
Issued: 1961-1991
Price: $104 £65

NEPTUNE D6552
Designer: M. Henk
Height: Small
Issued: 1961-1991
Price: $72 £45

NEPTUNE D6555
Designer: M. Henk
Height: Mini
Issued: 1961-1991
Price: $64 £40

NIGHT WATCHMAN D6569
Designer: M. Henk
Height: Large
Issued: 1963-1983
Price: $120 £75

NIGHT WATCHMAN D6576
Designer: M. Henk
Height: Small
Issued: 1963-1983
Price: $88 £55

CHARACTER JUGS

MOZART D7031

MR PICKWICK
D7025

NAPOLEON AND JOSEPHINE
D6750

MR QUAKER D6738

MR PICKWICK D6060

NIGHT WATCHMAN D6583
Designer: M. Henk
Height: Mini
Issued: 1963-1983
Price: $72 £45

**NORTH AMERICAN INDIAN
D6611**
Designer: M. Henk
Height: Large
Issued: 1967-1991
Price: $104 £65

**NORTH AMERICAN INDIAN
D6611**
Designer: M. Henk
Height: Large
Issued: 1967
Price: $200 £125
(Special Back Stamp Canadian
Centennial)

**NORTH AMERICAN INDIAN
D6614**
Designer: M. Henk
Height: Small
Issued: 1967-1991
Price: $64 £40

**NORTH AMERICAN INDIAN
D6665**
Designer: M. Henk
Height: Mini
Issued: 1967-1992
Price: $56 £35

**NORTH AMERICAN INDIAN
D6786 (John Sinclair)**
In a limited edition of 1000
Designer: M. Henk
Height: Large
Issued: 1987-1991
Price: $136 £85

O

OLD CHARLEY D5420
Designer: C. Noke
Height: Large
Issued: 1934-1983
Price: $120 £75

OLD CHARLEY D5527
Designer: C. Noke
Height: Small
Issued: 1935-1983
Price: $64 £40

OLD CHARLEY D6046
Designer: C. Noke
Height: Mini
Issued: 1939-1982
Price: $56 £35

OLD CHARLEY D6144
Designer: C. Noke
Height: Tiny
Issued: 1940-1960
Price: $104 £65

NORTH
AMERICAN
INDIAN
D6611

NIGHT WATCHMAN
D6569

NORTH AMERICAN INDIAN D6786

OLD KING COLE D6036
Designer: H. Fenton
Height: Large
Issued: 1939-1960
Price: $264 £165

OLD KING COLE D6037
Designer: H. Fenton
Height: Small
Issued: 1939-1960
Price: $176 £110

**OLD KING COLE (Yellow
Crown) D6036**
Designer: H. Fenton
Height: Large
Issued: 1939-1940
Price: $2320 £1450

**OLD KING COLE (Yellow
Crown) D6037**
Designer: H. Fenton
Height: Small
Issued: 1939-1940
Price: $1520 £950

OLD SALT D6551
Designer: G. Sharpe
Height: Large
Issued: 1961-
Price: $112 £70 (R.R.P.)

OLD SALT D6554
Designer: G. Sharpe
Height: Small
Issued: 1961-
Price: $51 £32 (R.R.P.)

OLD SALT D6557
Designer: P. Gee
Height: Mini
Issued: 1984 only
Price: $56 £35

**OLD SALT D6782
Colourway**
Designer: G. Sharpe
Height: Large
Issued: 1987-1991
Price: $120 £75

OLIVER CROMWELL D6968
Designer: W. K. Harper
Height: 7in.,17.75cm.
Issued: 1994 in a limited
             edition of 2500
Price: $320 £200

OLIVER HARDY
In a limited edition of 3500
Paired with Stan Laurel
Designer: W.K. Harper
Height: 5in., 12.7cm.
Issued: 1995
Price: $120 £75

OTHELLO D6673
Designer: M. Abberley
Height: Large
Issued: 1982-1988
Price: $136 £85

CHARACTER JUGS

OLD CHARLEY D5420

OLD KING COLE

OLD SALT

OTHELLO D6673

OLD KING COLE (Yellow Crown) D6036

OLIVER CROMWELL D6968

71

P

PADDY D5753
Designer: H. Fenton
Height: Large
Issued: 1937-1960
Price: $136 £85

PADDY D5768
Designer: H. Fenton
Height: Small
Issued: 1937-1960
Price: $72 £45

PADDY D6042
Designer: H. Fenton
Height: Mini
Issued: 1939-1960
Price: $72 £45

PADDY D6145
Designer: H. Fenton
Height: Tiny
Issued: 1940-1960
Price: $104 £65

PARSON BROWN D5486
Designer: C. Noke
Height: Large
Issued: 1935-1960
Price: $136 £85

PARSON BROWN (White) D5486
Designer: C. Noke
Height: Large
Issued: Unknown
Price: $136 £85

PARSON BROWN D5529
Designer: C. Noke
Height: Small
Issued: 1935-1960
Price: $72 £45

PARSON BROWN (DIAMOND ANNIVERSARY) D6955
Designer: C. Noke
Height: Tiny
Issued: 1994
Price: $72 £45

PAUL McCARTNEY D6724
Designer: S. Taylor
Height: Medium
Issued: 1984-1991
Price: $136 £85

PEARLY BOY (Blue)
Designer: H. Fenton
Height: Large
Issued: 1947-
Price: $4800 £3000

PEARLY BOY (Blue)
Designer: H. Fenton
Height: Small
Issued: 1947-
Price: $2400 £1500

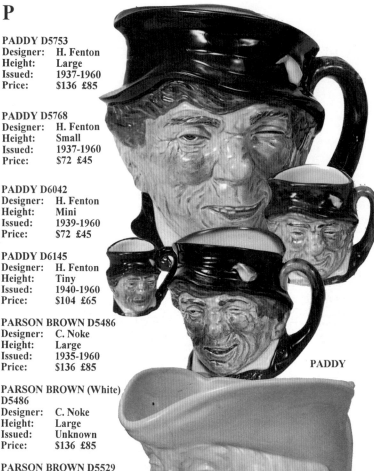

PADDY

PARSON BROWN D5486

PEARLY BOY (Blue)
Designer: H. Fenton
Height: Mini
Issued: 1947-1992
Price: $3200 £2000

PEARLY BOY (Brown buttons)
An early version of 'ARRY'
Designer: H. Fenton
Height: Large
Issued: 1947-
Price: $1520 £950

PEARLY BOY (Brown buttons)
An early version of 'ARRY
Designer: H. Fenton
Height: Small
Issued: 1947-
Price: $792 £495

PEARLY BOY (Brown buttons)
An early version of 'ARRY
Designer: H. Fenton
Height: Mini
Issued: 1947-1992
Price: $632 £395

PEARLY GIRL (Blue)
A very rare version of 'ARRIET
Designer: H. Fenton
Height: Large
Issued: 1947-
Price: $4800 £3000

PEARLY GIRL (Blue)
A very rare version of 'ARRIET
Designer: H. Fenton
Height: Small
Issued: 1947-
Price: $2800 £1750

PEARLY KING D6760
Designer: S. Taylor
Height: Large
Issued: 1987-1991
Price: $136 £85

PEARLY KING D6844
Designer: S. Taylor
Height: Small
Issued: 1990-1991
Price: $104 £65

PEARLY QUEEN D6759
Designer: S. Taylor
Height: Large
Issued: 1987-1991
Price: $136 £85

PEARLY QUEEN D6843
Designer: S. Taylor
Height: Small
Issued: 1990-1991
Price: $104 £65

PENDLE WITCH D6826 (Kevin Francis) in a limited edition of 5000
Designer: G. Blower
Height: Large
Issued: 1988-1992
Price: $200 £125

CHARACTER JUGS

EARLY GIRL (Blue)

PEARLY BOY (Blue)

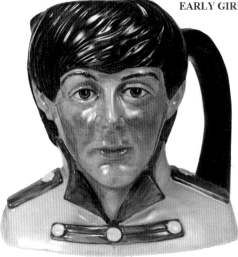

PAUL McCARTNEY D6724

PEARLY KING D6760

PEARLY QUEEN D6759

PENDLE WITCH D6826

**PHANTOM OF THE OPERA
D7017**
Designer: David Biggs
Height: Large
Issued: 1995 in a limited
edition of 2500
Price: $360 £225

PHARAOH D7028 (Flambé)
Designer: R. Tabbenor
Height: 8in., 20.3cm.
Issued: 1996 in a limited
editon of 1500
Price: $312 £195

PIED PIPER D6403
Designer: G. Blower
Height: Large
Issued: 1954-1981
Price: $136 £85

PIED PIPER D6462
Designer: G. Blower
Height: Small
Issued: 1957-1981
Price: $72 £45

PIED PIPER D6514
Designer: G. Blower
Height: Mini
Issued: 1960-1981
Price: $72 £45

PIPER, THE D6918
Designer: S. Taylor
Height: Large
Issued: 1992-1994
Price: $264 £165

PLUG D7035
Designer: Simon Ward
Height: 4in., 10cm.
Issued: 1997
Price: $80 £50

POACHER D6429
Designer: M. Henk
Height: Large
Issued: 1955-1995
Price: $96 £60

POACHER D6464
Designer: M. Henk
Height: Small
Issued: 1957-1995
Price: $56 £35

POACHER D6515
Designer: M. Henk
Height: Mini
Issued: 1960-1991
Price: $56 £35

POACHER D6781
Designer: M. Henk
Height: Large
Issued: 1987-1989
Colour variation
Price: $120 £75

POLICEMAN D6852 (Lawleys)
In a limited edition of 5000
Designer: S. Taylor
Height: Small
Issued: 1990
Price: $104 £65

PIED PIPER

PORTHOS

PORTHOS D6440
Designer: M. Henk
Height: Large
Issued: 1956-1991
Price: $136 £85

PORTHOS D6453
Designer: M. Henk
Height: Small
Issued: 1956-1991
Price: $72 £45

PORTHOS D6516
Designer: M. Henk
Height: Mini
Issued: 1960-1991
Price: $72 £45

PORTHOS D6828 (Peter Jones
In a limited edition of 1000
Designer: M. Henk
Height: Large
Issued: 1988
Colour variation
Price: $136 £85

POSTMAN D6801 (Lawleys)
Limited edition of 5000
Designer: S. Taylor
Height: Small
Issued: 1987-1988
Price: $192 £120

**PUNCH AND JUDY MAN
D6590**
Designer: D. Biggs
Height: Large
Issued: 1964 -1969
Price: $560 £350

**PUNCH AND JUDY MAN
D6593**
Designer: D. Biggs
Height: Small
Issued: 1964-1969
Price: $392 £245

**PUNCH AND JUDY MAN
D6596**
Designer: D. Biggs
Height: Mini
Issued: 1964-1969
Price: $360 £225

**PUNCH AND JUDY MAN
D6946**
In a limited edition of 2500
Designer: S. Taylor
Height: Large
Issued: 1993-1995
Price: $520 £325

Q

**QUEEN ELIZABETH 1st of
ENGLAND D6821 (Lawleys)**
In a limited edition of 5000
Designer: W. K. Harper
Height: Small
Issued: 1988-1992
Price: $136 £85

CHARACTER JUGS

PORTHOS D6828

PUNCH AND JUDY MAN D6590

POSTMAN D6801

PLUG D7035

PUNCH AND JUDY MAN D6946

POACHER D6429

75

QUEEN VICTORIA D6816
Designer: S. Taylor
Height: Large
Issued: 1988-1991
Price: $104 £65

QUEEN VICTORIA D6788
(China Guild)
In a limited edition of 3000
Designer: S. Taylor
Height: Large
Issued: 1988
Price: $136 £85

R

RED QUEEN D6777
Designer: W. K. Harper
Height: Large
Issued: 1987-1991
Price: $120 £75

RED QUEEN D6859
Designer: W. K. Harper
Height: Small
Issued: 1990-1991
Price: $88 £55

RED QUEEN D6860
Designer: W. K. Harper
Height: Mini
Issued: 1990-1991
Price: $80 £50

REGENCY BEAU D6559
Designer: D. Biggs
Height: Large
Issued: 1962-1967
Price: $880 £550

REGENCY BEAU D6562
Designer: D. Biggs
Height: Small
Issued: 1962-1967
Price: $600 £375

REGENCY BEAU D6565
Designer: D. Biggs
Height: Mini
Issued: 1962-1967
Price: $720 £450

RING MASTER D6863
Designer: S. J. Taylor
Height: Large
Issued: 1991-1993
Price: $136 £85

RING MASTER D6863
Designer: S. J. Taylor
Height: Large
Issued: 1990 in a limited
edition of 750
Canada only.
Price: $280 £175

RINGO STARR D6726
Designer: S. Taylor
Height: Medium
Issued: 1984-1991
Price: $136 £85

QUEEN
ELIZABETH 1st of
ENGLAND D6821

QUEEN VICTORIA
D6816

RED QUEEN D6777

RIP VAN WINKLE D6438
Designer: G. Blower
Height: Large
Issued: 1955- 1995
Price: $96 £60

RIP VAN WINKLE D6463
Designer: G. Blower
Height: Small
Issued: 1957-1995
Price: $56 £35

RIP VAN WINKLE D6517
Designer: G. Blower
Height: Mini
Issued: 1960-1991
Price: $56 £35

RIP VAN WINKLE D6788
(John Sinclair)
In a limited edition of 1000
Designer: G. Blower
Height: Large
Issued: 1987-1991
Colour variation
Price: $136 £85

**ROBIN HOOD (First version)
D6205**
Designer: H. Fenton
Height: Large
Issued: 1947-1960
Price: $136 £85

**ROBIN HOOD (First version)
D6234**
Designer: H. Fenton
Height: Small
Issued: 1947-1960
Price: $88 £55

**ROBIN HOOD (First version)
D6252**
Designer: H. Fenton
Height: Mini
Issued: 1947-1960
Price: $72 £45

**ROBIN HOOD (Second version)
D6527**
Designer: M. Henk
Height: Large
Issued: 1960-1992
Price: $104 £65

**ROBIN HOOD (Second version)
D6534**
Designer: M. Henk
Height: Small
Issued: 1960-1992
Price: $72 £45

**ROBIN HOOD (Second version)
D6541**
Designer: M. Henk
Height: Mini
Issued: 1960-1991
Price: $56 £35

REGENCY BEAU D6559

RIP VAN WINKLE
D6438

ROBIN HOOD
D6205 (First version)

ROBIN HOOD
D6527 (Second version)

RIP VAN WINKLE D6788

RINGO STARR D6726

CHARACTER JUGS

ROBIN HOOD D6998
Designer: W. K. Harper
Height: 7in., 17.75cm.
Issued: 1995 in a limited
        edition of 2500
Price: $400 £250 (R.R.P.)

ROBINSON CRUSOE D6532
Designer: M. Henk
Height: Large
Issued: 1960-1983
Price: $104 £65

ROBINSON CRUSOE D6539
Designer: M. Henk
Height: Small
Issued: 1960-1983
Price: $64 £40

ROBINSON CRUSOE D6546
Designer: M. Henk
Height: Mini
Issued: 1960-1983
Price: $64 £40

ROMEO D6670
Designer: D. Biggs
Height: Large
Issued: 1983-1988
Price: $136 £85

RONALD REAGAN D6718
(Republic Committee)
In a limited edition of 5000
Designer: E. Griffiths
Height: Large
Issued: 1984
Price: $472 £295

S

SAILOR (THE) D6875
Designer: W. K. Harper
Height: Small
Issued: 1991-1996
Price: $64 £40

ST. GEORGE D6618
Designer: M. Henk
Height: Large
Issued: 1968-1975
Price: $280 £175

ST. GEORGE D6621
Designer: M. Henk
Height: Small
Issued: 1968-1975
Price: $200 £125

SAIREY GAMP D5451
Designer: L. Harradine and
        H. Fenton
Height   Large
Issued: 1935-1986
Price: $104 £65

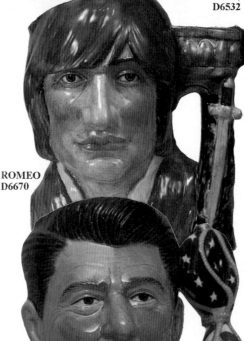

ROBINSON CRUSOE
D6532

ROMEO
D6670

RONALD REAGAN D6718

SAIREY GAMP D5528
Designer: L. Harradine and
        H. Fenton
Height: Small
Issued: 1935-1986
Price: $64 £40

SAIREY GAMP D6045
Designer: L. Harradine and
        H. Fenton
Height: Mini
Issued: 1939-1986
Price: $56 £35

SAIREY GAMP D6146
Designer: L. Harradine and
        H. Fenton
Height: Tiny
Issued: 1940-1960
Price: $104 £65

SAM WELLER D6140
Designer: L. Harradine and
        H. Fenton
Height: Mini
Issued: 1940-1960
Price: $72 £45

SAM WELLER D6064
Designer: L. Harradine and
        H. Fenton
Height: Large
Issued: 1940-1960
Price: $136 £85

SAM WELLER D5841
Designer: L. Harradine
        H. Fenton
Height: Intermediate
Issued: 1938-1948
Price: $192 £120

SAM WELLER D5841
Designer: L. Harradine and
        H. Fenton
Height: Small
Issued: 1948-1960
Price: $88 £55

SAM WELLER D6147
Designer: L. Harradine and
        H. Fenton
Height: Tiny
Issued: 1940-1960
Price: $104 £65

SAMSON and DELILAH D6787
In a limited edition of 9500
Designer: S. Taylor
Height: Large
Issued: 1988-1991
Price: $144 £95

SAMUEL JOHNSON D6289
Designer: H. Fenton
Height: Large
Issued: 1950-1960
Price: $312 £195

CHARACTER JUGS

SAILOR (THE) D6875

ST. GEORGE D6618

SAMSON and DELILAH D6787

SAIREY GAMP D5451   SAIREY GAMP D5528   SAM WELLER D6064

CHARACTER JUGS

SAMUEL JOHNSON D6296
Designer: H. Fenton
Height: Small
Issued: 1950-1960
Price: $192 £120

SANCHO PANZA D6456
Designer: G. Blower
Height: Large
Issued: 1957-1983
Price: $120 £75

SANCHO PANZA D6461
Designer: G. Blower
Height: Small
Issued: 1957-1983
Price: $72 £45

SANCHO PANZA D6518
Designer: G. Blower
Height: Mini
Issued: 1960-1983
Price: $72 £45

SANTA ANNA/DAVY CROCKETT D6729
In a limited edition of 9500
Designer: M. Abberley
Height: Large
Issued: 1985-1991
Price: $144 £95

SANTA CLAUS D6668
Designer: M. Abberley
Height: Large with Peg Doll Handle
Issued: 1981
Price: $136 £85

SANTA CLAUS D6675
Designer: M. Abberley
Height: Large with Reindeer Handle
Issued: 1982
Price: $136 £85

SANTA CLAUS D6690
Designer: M. Abberley
Height: Large with Sack of Toys Handle
Issued: 1983
Price: $232 £145

SANTA CLAUS D6704
Designer: M. Abberley
Height: Large
Issued: 1984-
Price: $128 £80 (R.R.P.)

SANTA CLAUS D6705
Designer: M. Abberley
Height: Small
Issued: 1984-
Price: $64 £40 (R.R.P.)

SANTA CLAUS D6706
Designer: M. Abberley
Height: Mini
Issued: 1984-1991
Price: $64 £40

SANTA CLAUS D6690

SANTA CLAUS D6675

SANTA CLAUS D6668

SCARAMOUCHE D6558
Designer: M. Henk
Height: Large
Issued: 1962-1967
Price: $840 £525

SCARAMOUCHE D6561
Designer: M. Henk
Height: Small
Issued: 1962-1967
Price: $560 £350

SCARAMOUCHE D6564
Designer: M. Henk
Height: Mini
Issued: 1962-1967
Price: $560 £350

SCARAMOUCHE D6774
(China Guild)
In a limited edition of 1500
Designer: S. Taylor
Height: Large
Issued: 1987
Price: $176 £110

SCARAMOUCHE D6814
Designer: S. Taylor
Height: Large
Issued: 1988-1991
Colour variation
Price: $176 £110

SCHUBERT D7056
Designer: S. J. Taylor
Height: 6½in., 16cm.
Issued: 1997
Price: $144 £90 (R.R.P.)

SHAKESPEARE D6938
Designer: W. K. Harper
Height: Small
Issued: 1993
Price: $64 £40

SHERLOCK HOLMES SET
(LAWLEYS) (Six in Set)
Designer:
Height: 1½in., 3.7cm.
Issued: 1996
Price: $320 £200 (Set)

SIMON THE CELLARER D5504
Designer: C. Noke and H. Fenton
Height: Large
Issued: 1935-1960
Price: $136 £85

SIMON THE CELLARER D5616
Designer: C. Noke and H. Fenton
Height: Small
Issued: 1936-1960
Price: $72 £45

SAMUEL JOHNSON D6289

SANCHO PANZA D6456

SCARAMOUCHE D6774

SANTA CLAUS D6704

SCARAMOUCHE D6558

SCARAMOUCHE D6814

CHARACTER JUGS

SCHUBERT D7056

SIMON THE CELLARER D5504

SIMPLE SIMON D6374

SHAKESPEARE D6938

SIR FRANCIS DRAKE D6805

SIR HENRY DOULTON D7057

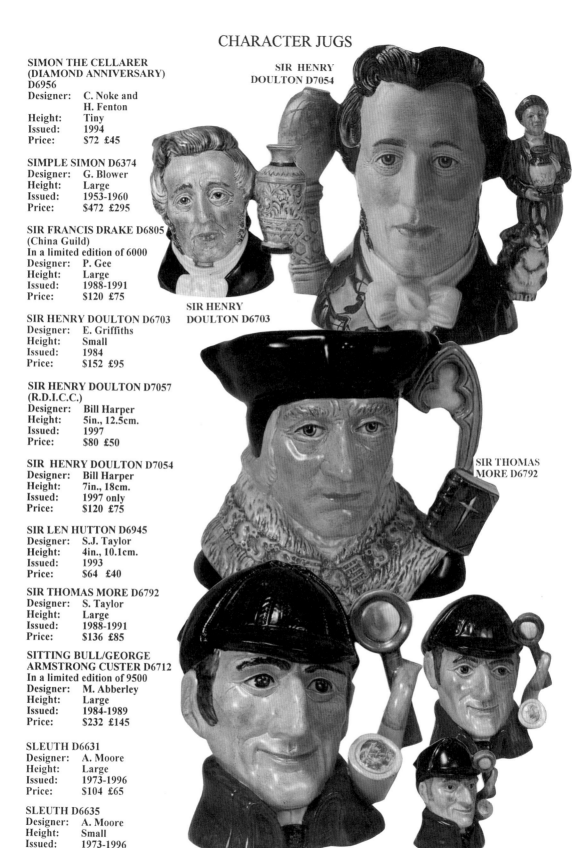

**SIMON THE CELLARER
(DIAMOND ANNIVERSARY)
D6956**
Designer: C. Noke and
             H. Fenton
Height: Tiny
Issued: 1994
Price: $72 £45

SIMPLE SIMON D6374
Designer: G. Blower
Height: Large
Issued: 1953-1960
Price: $472 £295

SIR FRANCIS DRAKE D6805
(China Guild)
In a limited edition of 6000
Designer: P. Gee
Height: Large
Issued: 1988-1991
Price: $120 £75

SIR HENRY DOULTON D6703
Designer: E. Griffiths
Height: Small
Issued: 1984
Price: $152 £95

**SIR HENRY DOULTON D7057
(R.D.I.C.C.)**
Designer: Bill Harper
Height: 5in., 12.5cm.
Issued: 1997
Price: $80 £50

SIR HENRY DOULTON D7054
Designer: Bill Harper
Height: 7in., 18cm.
Issued: 1997 only
Price: $120 £75

SIR LEN HUTTON D6945
Designer: S.J. Taylor
Height: 4in., 10.1cm.
Issued: 1993
Price: $64 £40

SIR THOMAS MORE D6792
Designer: S. Taylor
Height: Large
Issued: 1988-1991
Price: $136 £85

**SITTING BULL/GEORGE
ARMSTRONG CUSTER D6712**
In a limited edition of 9500
Designer: M. Abberley
Height: Large
Issued: 1984-1989
Price: $232 £145

SLEUTH D6631
Designer: A. Moore
Height: Large
Issued: 1973-1996
Price: $104 £65

SLEUTH D6635
Designer: A. Moore
Height: Small
Issued: 1973-1996
Price: $64 £40

SIR HENRY
DOULTON D7054

SIR HENRY
DOULTON D6703

SIR THOMAS
MORE D6792

SLEUTH

CHARACTER JUGS

SLEUTH D6639
Designer: A. Moore
Height: Mini
Issued: 1973-1992
Price: $72 £45

SLEUTH D6773 (Lawleys)
In a limited edition of 5000
Designer: S. Taylor
Height: Small
Issued: 1981-1991
Price: $120 £75

SMUGGLER D6616
Designer: D. Biggs
Height: Large
Issued: 1968-1981
Price: $136 £85

SMUGGLER D6619
Designer: D. Biggs
Height: Small
Issued: 1968-1981
Price: $72 £45

SMUTS D6198
Designer: H. Fenton
Height: Large
Issued: 1946-1948
Price: $1360 £850

SNAKE CHARMER D6912
Designer: S. J. Taylor
Height: Large
Issued: 1992 in a limited
    edition of 2500
Price: $312 £195

SNOOKER PLAYER (THE) D6879
Designer: S. Taylor
Height: Small
Issued: 1991-1995
Price: $64 £40

SNOWMAN D6972
Designer: Martin Alcock
Height: Mini
Issued: 1994 U.S.A. only
Price: £176 £110

SOLDIER (THE) D6816
Designer: W. K. Harper
Height: Small
Issued: 1991
Price: $72 £45

STAN LAUREL
In a limited edition of 3500
Paired with Oliver Hardy
Designer: Bill Harper
Height: 5in., 12.5cm.
Issued: 1995-1997
Price: $120 £75

STATUS QUO (RICK PARFITT) D6962 in a limited
edition of 2500
Designer: Unknown
Height: Midi
Issued: 1993
Price: $104 £65

SLEUTH D6773

SMUGGLER D6616

SMUTS D6198

STATUS QUO (FRANCIS ROSSI) D6961 in a limited edition of 2500
Designer: Unknown
Height: Midi
Issued: 1993
Price: $104 £65

STRAUSS II D7097
Designer: S. Taylor
Height: Large
Issued: 1998
Price: $160 £100 (R.R.P.)

T

TAM O'SHANTER D6632
Designer: M. Henk
Height: Large
Issued: 1973-1980
Price: $136 £85

TAM O'SHANTER D6636
Designer: M. Henk
Height: Small
Issued: 1973-1980
Price: $88 £55

TAM O'SHANTER D6640
Designer: M. Henk
Height: Mini
Issued: 1973-1980
Price: $88 £55

TCHAIKOVSKY D7022
Designer: S. Taylor
Height: 7in., 17.75cm.
Issued: 1996
Price: $144 £90 (R.R.P.)

THOMAS JEFFERSON D6943
Designer: S. J. Taylor
Height: Large
Issued: 1994 in a limited
    edition of 2500
Price: $264 £165

TOBY GILLETTE D6717
In a limited edition of three
Two owned by an American Col
lector and the other in the
Sir Henry Doulton Museum
Stoke-on-Trent
Designer: E. Griffiths
Height: Large
Issued: 1984
Price: $24000 £15000

TOBY PHILPOTS D5736
Designer: C. Noke
Height: Large
Issued: 1937-1969
Price: $136 £85

TOBY PHILPOTS D5737
Designer: C. Noke
Height: Small
Issued: 1937-1969
Price: $80 £50

SNOOKER PLAYER (THE) D6879

SOLDIER (THE) D6816

TCHAIKOVSKY D7022

TOBY GILLETTE D6717

CHARACTER JUGS

TOBY PHILPOTS D6043
Designer: C. Noke
Height: Mini
Issued: 1939-1969
Price: $72 £45

TONY WELLER D5531
Designer: L. Harradine and
H. Fenton
Height: Extra Large
Issued: c.1936
Price: $296 £185

TONY WELLER D5531
Designer: L. Harradine and
H. Fenton
Height: Large
Issued: c.1936-1960
Price: $136 £85

TONY WELLER D5530
Designer: L. Harradine and
H. Fenton
Height: Small
Issued: 1936-1960
Price: $72 £45

TONY WELLER D6044
Designer: L. Harradine
and H. Fenton
Height: Mini
Issued: 1939-1960
Price: $72 £45

TOUCHSTONE D5613
Designer: C. Noke
Height: Large
Issued: 1936-1960
Price: $232 £145

TOWN CRIER D6530
Designer: D. Biggs
Height: Large
Issued: 1960-1973
Price: $232 £145

TOWN CRIER D6537
Designer: D. Biggs
Height: Small
Issued: 1960-1973
Price: $152 £95

TOWN CRIER D6544
Designer: D. Biggs
Height: Mini
Issued: 1960-1973
Price: $176 £110

TOWN CRIER D6895
Designer: S. Taylor
Height: Large
Issued: 1991-1994
Price: $176 £110

TRAPPER D6609
Designer: M. Henk and D.
Biggs
Height: Large
Issued: 1967-1983
Price: $120 £75

TRAPPER D6609
Designer: M. Henk and D.
Biggs
Height: Large(Centennial
Back Stamp)
Issued: 1962-1983
Price: $190 £120

TRAPPER D6612
Designer: M. Henk and D.
Biggs
Height: Small
Issued: 1967-1983
Price: $88 £55

U

UGLY DUCHESS D6599
Designer: M. Henk
Height: Large
Issued: 1965-1973
Price: $560 £350

UGLY DUCHESS D6603
Designer: M. Henk
Height: Small
Issued: 1965-1973
Price: $400 £250

UGLY DUCHESS D6607
Designer: M. Henk
Height: Mini
Issued: 1965-1973
Price: $392 £245

**ULYSSES S. GRANT and
ROBERT E. LEE D6698**
Designer: M. Abberley
Height: Large
Issued: 1983-1986
Price: $264 £165

**UNCLE TOM COBBLEIGH
D6337**
Designer: M. Henk
Height: Large
Issued: 1952-1960
Price: $400 £250

V

VETERAN MOTORIST D6633
Designer: D. Biggs
Height: Large
Issued: 1973-1983
Price: $152 £95

VETERAN MOTORIST D6637
Designer: D. Biggs
Height: Small
Issued: 1973-1983
Price: $88 £55

VETERAN MOTORIST D6641
Designer: D. Biggs
Height: Mini
Issued: 1973-1983
Price: $104 £65

TOBY
PHILPOTS
D5736

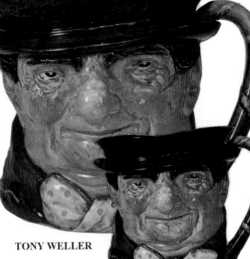

TONY WELLER

TOUCHSTONE D5613

TOWN CRIER D6530

TRAPPER D6609

ULYSSES S. GRANT and ROBERT E. LEE D6698

UNCLE TOM COBBLEIGH
D6337

UGLY DUCHESS D6599

VICAR OF BRAY D5615
Designer: C. Noke and H. Fenton
Height: Large
Issued: 1936-1960
Price: $200 £125

VICE AD. LORD NELSON D6932
Designer: S. J. Taylor
Height: Large
Issued: 1993 (Jug of the Year)
Price: $216 £135

VICTORIA & ALBERT (Pair) D7072, D7073
Designer: W.K. Harper
Height: 4in.,10.1cm.
Issued: 1997
Price: $200 £125 (Pair)

VIKING D6496
Designer: M. Henk
Height: Large
Issued: 1959-1975
Price: $232 £145

VIKING D6502
Designer: M. Henk
Height: Small
Issued: 1959-1975
Price: $144 £90

VIKING D6526
Designer: M. Henk
Height: Mini
Issued: 1959-1975
Price: $176 £110

VISCOUNT MONTGOMERY of ALAMEIN D6850 (Lawleys)
In a limited edition of 9500
Designer: S. Taylor
Height: Small
Issued: 1989-1992
Price: $176 £110

W

W. C. FIELDS D6674
Designer: D. Biggs
Height: Large
Issued: 1983-1985
Price: $152 £95

W. G. GRACE D6845 (Lawleys)
In a limited edition of 9500
Designer: S. Taylor
Height: Small
Issued: 1989
Price: $136 £85

W. G. GRACE D7032
Designer: S. J. Taylor
Height: 7in., 17.5cm.
Issued: 1996-97
Price: $176 £110

WALRUS AND CARPENTER D6600
Designer: M. Henk
Height: Large
Issued: 1965-1980
Price: $152 £95

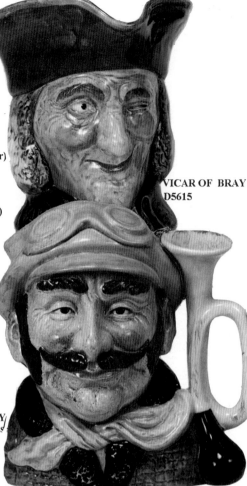

VICAR OF BRAY D5615

VETERAN MOTORIST D6633

VIKING D6496

WALRUS AND CARPENTER D6604
Designer: M. Henk
Height: Small
Issued: 1965-1980
Price: $104 £65

WALRUS AND CARPENTER D6608
Designer: M. Henk
Height: Mini
Issued: 1965-1980
Price: $104 £65

WILD BILL HICKOK D6736
Designer: M. Abberley
Height: Medium
Issued: 1985-1988
Price: $104 £65

WILLIAM GRANT
Limited edition of 500
Designer: Unknown
Issued: 1986
Price: $640 £400

WILLIAM SHAKESPEARE D6689
Designer: M. Abberley
Height: Large
Issued: 1983-1991
Price: $136 £85

WILLIAM SHAKESPEARE (Two handled) D6933
Designer: W. K. Harper
Height: Large
Issued: 1992 in a limited edition of 2500
Price: $400 £250

WINSTON CHURCHILL D6907
Designer: S. J. Taylor
Height: Large
Issued: 1992 Jug of the Year.
Price: $264 £165

WINSTON CHURCHILL D6934
Designer: S. Taylor
Height: Small
Issued: 1993
Price: $65 £40 (R.R.P.)

WITCH D6893
Designer: S. J. Taylor
Height: Large
Issued: 1991 only.
Price: $264 £165

WIZARD (THE) D6862
Designer: S. Taylor
Height: Large
Issued: 1990-1996
Price: $120 £75

WIZARD (THE) D6909
Designer: S. Taylor
Height: Small
Issued: 1990
Price: $64 £40 (R.R.P.)

CHARACTER JUGS

WALRUS AND CARPENTER
D6600

W. C. FIELDS D6674

W. G. GRACE D6845

W. G. GRACE D7032

WILLIAM GRANT

WILD BILL HICKOK D6736

WILLIAM SHAKESPEARE D6689

89

WYATT EARP D6711
Designer: S. Taylor
Height: Medium
Issued: 1985-1988
Price: $104 £65

Y

YACHTSMAN D6622
Designer: D. Biggs
Height: Large
Issued: 1971-1980
Price: $152 £95

YACHTSMAN D6820
Designer: S. Taylor
Height: Large
Issued: 1989-1991
Price: $120 £75

YEOMAN OF THE GUARD
D6873
Designer: S. Taylor
Height: Large
Issued: 1991-1997
Price: $152 £95

WIZARD (THE) D6862

WYATT EARP D6711

YACHTSMAN D6820

YACHTSMAN D6622

YEOMAN OF THE GUARD D6873

FLAMBÉ

The name Flambé describes the streaky, flame like effect of the deep blood red glaze which was produced by mixing copper oxide and other minerals and allowing certain amounts of oxygen to be admitted to the kiln during firing. The technique was first discovered by Bernard Moore, a chemist and innovator who worked in conjunction with Doulton at the turn of the century. After two years' experimentation the first examples of Flambé were shown at the St. Louis Exhibition of 1904 and it had a huge appeal. Although it is expensive to make, Flambé is still being produced.

Flambé tobacco jar with elephant finial, 6in. high, circa 1936. $560 £350

Fox, Model 102, sitting with head up, designed by C. Noke, introduced 1962, withdrawn 1965, 9½in. high. $250 £400

Geisha HN3229, designed by Pauline Parsons, 1989, 9½in. high. $240 £150

Monkeys, Model 486, embracing, 5½in. high. $240 £150

Peruvian Penguin on Rock, Model 585, designed by C. Noke, 1947, 9in. high. $560 £350

King Penguin and Chick,
Model 239, designed by C. Noke,
1947, 6in. high. $360 £225

Mallard, Model 654, designed
by C. Noke, introduced 1920,
withdrawn 1961, 4in. long.
$320 £200

Snarling Figure of a Panther,
9in. long, circa 1930. $640 £400

Wizard HN3121, designed by A.
Maslankowski, introduced 1990,
withdrawn 1995, 10in. high.
$360 £225

A large Royal Doulton flambé elephant
with trunk down, designed by C. Noke,
12in. high, circa 1930. $1600 £1000

MUSICAL JUGS

Apart from straightforward Character jugs, Doulton from time to time issued other novelty wares based on some of the more popular characters in their jug range. Among these were musical jugs which were produced between 1937 and circa 1948. Though to all intents and purposes they looked just like their character jug counterparts they were distinguished by an extended base to accommodate the Thorens Swiss musical movement. The air they played was relative to the character portrayed – Paddy, for example, played an Irish jig. As not many were produced the jugs are now quite rare.

OLD KING COLE D6014 'Old King Cole'

AULD MAC D5889
Designer: H. Fenton
Height: Large
Issued: 1938-c.1939
Price: $760 £475

OLD CHARLEY D5858
Designer: C. Noke
Height: Large
Issued: 1937-c.1939
Price: $760 £475

OLD KING COLE D6014
Designer: H. Fenton
Height: Large
Issued: 1939
Price: $1600 £1000

OLD KING COLE (Yellow Crown) D6014
Designer: H. Fenton
Height: Large
Issued: 1939
Price: $2800 £1750

PADDY D5887
Designer: H. Fenton
Height: Large
Issued: 1938-1939
Price: $760 £475

TONY WELLER D5888
Designer: L. Harradine and H. Fenton
Height: Large
Issued: 1938-1939
Price: $760 £475

TONY WELLER D5888
'Come Landlord Fill The Flowing Bowl'

OLD CHARLEY D5858
'Here's A Health Unto His Majesty'

AULD MAC D5889 'The Campbells Are Coming'   **PADDY D5887 'Irish Jig'**

OLD KING COLE (Yellow Crown) D6014 'Old King Cole'

NAPKIN RINGS

(Canterbury Auction Galleries)

SAM WELLER M61	**FAT BOY M59**	**SAIREY GAMP M62**
Issued: 1935-1939	Issued: 1935-1939	Issued: 1935-1939
Price: $400 £250	Price: $400 £250	Price: $400 £250
MR MICAWBER M58	**TONY WELLER M60**	**MR PICKWICK M57**
Issued: 1935-1939	Issued: 1935-1939	Issued: 1935-1939
Price: $400 £250	Price: $400 £250	Price: $400 £250

PUB JUGS

Pick Kwik promotional character jug for Dewar's Whisky, limited edition of 100, 1985-7. $360 £225

Pick Kwik Deluxe Wines promotional character jug, limited edition of 100, 1985-7. $280 £175

Pick Kwik Deluxe Wines promotional character jug, limited edition of 100, 1985-7. $360 £225

Greenlees Brothers,
Claymore Scotch Whisky by
Doulton. $800   £500

Charrington's Toby Stout
water jug by Doulton, 11cm
high. $350   £220

Greer's O.V.H. Scotch
Whisky jug by Doulton,
13½cm high. $350   £220

Melrose Highland Whisky
stoneware jug by Doulton,
20cm high. $800   £500

John Bull small size flagon made
for Jim Beam Whiskey, 5in. high,
1984. $135   £85

Palmeira House, Brighton,
Great Glen Pure Malt
Whisky, by Doulton, 37cm
high. $720   £450

Usher's Scotch Whisky
water jug by Doulton,
10½cm high. $350   £220

Doulton Lambeth stoneware harvest
water jug with applied slip scenes,
15½cm. high. $104   £65

D.C.L. Gold Medal Scotch
Whisky, by Doulton, 15cm
high. $400   £250

(Gordon R. Litherland)

Ushers Green Stripe Scotch
Whisky by Doulton, 15½cm
high. $560 £350

Thorne's Whisky jug by
Doulton, 15cm high.
        $720 £450

Vat 69 Liqueur Scotch
Whisky by Doulton, 14cm
high. $350 £220

'Wake up and get to
business', Watsons Scotch
Whisky, 23cm high.
        $1200 £800

Uncle Sam small size flagon
made for Jim Beam Whiskey,
5in. high, 1984. $136 £85

Bisquit's Brandy figure,
water jug made by Doulton,
27cm high. $720 £450

Blundell's Cabinet Whisky
by Doulton. $425 £265

Wm. Younger & Co., No. 3 Scotch
Ale jug by Royal Doulton, 8cm. high.
        $230 £145

Very Old Duniva Highland
Whisky by Doulton, 16cm
high. $640 £400

(Gordon R. Litherland)

Ainslie's Whisky jug, 'Ainslie's has risen to the top', 12cm high, by Royal Doulton. $640 £400

'Top Notch' King George IV Scotch Whisky jug by Royal Doulton, 15cm high.
$450 £275

Barnsley Brewery Co., 'Famous for mild and bitter ales' by Doulton, 17cm high. $1296 £81

Buz Fuz small sized character jug made for Pick Kwik Wines, limited edition of 100, 4in. high, 1985-7.
$240 £150

Claymore Scotch Whisky jug by Royal Doulton, 5in. high. $240 £150

Pickwick small sized character ju made for Pick Kwik Wines, limit edition of 100, 4in. high, 1985-7.
$320 £2

Bull Dog Bottled Beer of Robert Porter & Co., jug by Doulton, 16cm high. $800 £500

Pick Kwik promotional character jug for Dewar's Whisky, limited edition of 100, 1985-7. $320 £200

R. & H. Jenners & Son Coronation 1911, by Royal Doulton, 16½cm high. $800 £500

(Gordon R. Litherland)

PUB JUGS

Melrose Highland Whisky by Doulton, 20cm high. $800 £500

Charrington's Toby made by Royal Doulton, 23cm high. $800 £500

Schweppes Green Ginger Wine, 34cm high. $400 £250

The real Sandy MacDonald Scotch Whisky jug from the Stronachie Distillery by Royal Doulton, 7in. high. $960 £600

Stoneware water jug by Doulton, Lambeth, 6½in. high. $360 £225

Bass & Co. Pale Ale First Class, London 1867, Gold Medal Paris 1867, manufactured by Royal Doulton. $480 £300

(Gordon R. Litherland)

99

Claymore Scotch Whisky jug
by Royal Doulton, 14cm high.
$800 £500

King George IV Scotch Whisky
jug by Doulton. $260 £165

Watsons Old Scotch
Whisky, manufactured by
Doulton, 14½cm high.
$880 £550

R & H Jenner Southwark,
London, 1904 by Doulton,
16½cm high.
$800 £500

Pick-Kwik character jug, 4in
high, made in a limited edition
of 2000, circa 1982. $112 £70

Sporting Squire Kingsware
flask for Dewar's, circa 1909,
21cm high. $320 £200

Macnair Twinkle Scotch
Whisky by Doulton, 17cm
high. $650 £410

Flower's Ales and Stout jug by
Doulton, 10cm high.
$240 £150

Gaelic Old Smuggler Whisky
jug by Royal Doulton, 18cm
high. $480 £300

(Gordon R. Litherland)

Sunderland Highland Whisky
by Grant Mackay & Co., by
Doulton, 17cm high.
$1300 £800

Doulton Lambeth stoneware
water jug with silver rim,
15cm higin. $90 £55

Doulton Kingsware
Coronation flask for George V
and Queen Mary, 1911,
17cm high. $320 £200

Dirty Dicks Famous
Wines by Doulton, 23cm
high. $800 £500

Buz Fuz small size character
jug made for Pick-Kwik, Derby,
4in. high, 1984. $160 £100

R & H Jenner & Sons 'A
quart of ale is a dish for
a King'; 16½cm high.
$720 £450

Johnnie Walker Whisky,
manufactured by Doulton,
15½cm high. $880 £550

Simpson's Scotch Whisky
by Doulton, 15cm high.
$720 £450

Greenlee Brothers Claymore
Scotch Whisky by Royal
Doulton, 16½cm high. $800 £500

(Gordon R. Litherland)

Dewar's Whisky jug with applied lettering by Doulton, Lambeth, 7in. high. $150 £95

Bulldog Pilsener jug manufactured by Doulton for Robert Porter & Co., 5in. high. $280 £175

Pick Kwik jug with Jim Beam handle by Doulton, 1984. $104 £65

Blundell's Cabinet Whisky jug by Royal Doulton. $480 £300

M.B. Foster & sons Ltd 'Bottlers of Guinness's Stout' jug by Royal Doulton. $640 £400

Sir Edward Lees Scotch Whisky 'As supplied to the House of Commons', by Doulton. $400 $250

The World Supports Worthington's in Bottle, Oldest Burton Brewers by Doulton, 7in. high. $1200 £750

McCallum's Whisky is Perfection, by Royal Doulton, 15cm. high. $320 £200

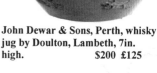

John Dewar & Sons, Perth, whisky jug by Doulton, Lambeth, 7in. high. $200 £125

(Gordon R. Litherland)

ROYAL DOULTON FIGURES

The first highly skilled figure maker who worked for Doulton was George Tinworth, the Lambeth sculptor, but his figure output was small.

However in 1889 Charles J. Noke left the Royal Worcester Company where he was already showing his prodigious talent as a sculptor and went to work for Doulton's at Burslem. The son of an antique dealer who appreciated the fine vases and figures made by Derby, Bow, Chelsea, Meissen and Sevres, he was fired with the ambition of recreating the once greatly admired Staffordshire figure making industry. For the Chicago Exhibition of 1893 he made several figures including 'Jack Point' and 'Lady Jester'.

(Royal Doulton Plc)

Charles J. Noke

During the next five years more figures followed, including Noke's 'Pierrot', 'Geisha' and the double figures 'Oh Law!' and 'Double Jester'. The latter figure today sells for £2,000 because it was only produced in small numbers.

These figures, though finely modelled, were of dull colours and did not sell well so Noke's figure making was suspended until around 1912 when he re-introduced a figure range which was released to the public in 1913 after Queen Mary, on a visit to Burslem, exclaimed "What a Darling!" at the sight of a figure called 'Bedtime' modelled by Charles Vyse.

'Bedtime' was re-christened 'Darling' and proved to be one of the most popular Doulton figures ever produced. It is still in production.

The colours of the new figures were bolder and a group of very talented sculptors worked on them. One of the most notable was Harry Tittensor. (1914-21), a local art master, His

(Royal Doulton Plc)

George Tinworth

'Europa and The Bull' today sells for £3,250 and his 'Princess Badoura' for a remarkable £13,250.

The work of Leslie Harradine, who began his career at the Lambeth Studio before emigrating to Canada but returned to work at Burslem after World War One, was filled with vitality. His 'Contentment' and 'The Goose Girl' showed his ability to capture movement and he also had a great talent for picking subjects which caught the public fancy. His 'Old Balloon Seller' is still in production today and is one of the most popular Doulton figures ever.

The quality of the range, which now numbers over 4,000, is superb. Limited editions of figures and wall masks were produced by Richard Garbe, an R.A. and Professor of Sculpture at the Royal College of Art, who modelled for Doulton between 1934 and 1939. His 'West Wind', which today fetches a price of £3,000, was produced in an edition of only 25 and originally sold for just over £8. Most of his wall masks, made of special porcelain with an ivory glaze, were in editions of 100.

Figure making still continues at Burslem with more than 300 still in production. The star of more recent times was Peggy Davies who was born and brought up in the pottery district of Burslem and, after studying at Burslem College of Art, began work as an assistant to Clarice Cliff. Her association with Doulton commenced in 1939 and, until her death in 1987 she produced an enormous range of figures ranging from her Kate Greenaway children to period characters from English history and a modelled head of Queen Elizabeth II.

Her work is notable for meticulous research which can be clearly seen in the 'Indian Brave' (today's price £2,000). She took great care in researching her subject, studying the anatomy of animals and people, as well as ensuring that all costume details were absolutely correct. Her 'Matador and The Bull' is a good example of this and today the figure sells for £10,250 to collectors. Her group, produced in an edition of 12, entitled 'The Marriage of Art and Industry', (today's price £3,000), showing a man and a woman, the tree of knowledge and doves of peace, was centrepiece for the Doulton stand at the Brussels Exhibition of 1958. It helped them win the only Grand Prix awarded to a pottery firm at the exhibition.

(Royal Doulton Plc)

Even figures, which were still in production until recently, can command large prices among collectors. An example is St. George by W. K. Harper. This is the third version of St. George produced by Doulton and was introduced in 1978. Its price at auction is £5,000.

(Royal Doulton Plc)

Valerie Annand

David Biggs

VALERIE ANNAND

A native of Glasgow, Valerie Annand now lives in South Wales and produced her first commission for Doulton, Loyal Friend, in 1990. She has since recreated the subjects of a number of French paintings, such as L'Ambitieuse and La Loge, as well as designing the Sporting Heritage and Four Seasons series.

DAVID BIGGS

David Biggs joined Doulton in 1958 when he answered an advertisement for a new tableware modeller. He worked under Max Henk, who invited him to produce sketches for possible character jugs in 1960. One of these, Town Crier, went into production as D6530. Thereafter he started to produce about four designs per year, one of the latest of which, Count Dracula, was Jug of the Year in 1997.

(Royal Doulton Plc)

(Royal Doulton Plc)

develop her artistic talents, and at 12 she won a scholarship to Burslem College of Art, where she learned to model. She worked for a time under Clarice Cliff before joining Doulton in 1939. After the war, she continued, as an independent artist, to create figures under contract for Doulton. These include many 'fair ladies', as well as complicated pieces such as Matador and Bull and The Palio.

MARGARET DAVIES

Margaret (Peggy) Davies was born in Burslem in the heart of the Potteries. Her childhood was dogged by ill-health, but this gave her time to

PETER GEE

Peter Gee joined Doulton as an apprentice modeller in 1973. His first figure, Rachel, was launched in 1981. He also worked in such varying styles as the Gainsborough and Reynolds Ladies series, and the cheeky Cockney Balloon Boy. In 1991 his figure Amy HN3316, was chosen as Figure of the Year.

(Royal Doulton Plc)

(Royal Doulton Plc)

ERIC GRIFFITHS

Born in North Wales, Eric Griffiths tried his hand at cartoon drawing and portrait painting before finding his metier as a modeller. He worked for a number of industrial concerns as chief designer or design consultant, before joining Doulton in 1972, where he later became Director of Sculpture.

Eric Griffiths

W. K. HARPER

Bill Harper, who started working freelance for Doulton in 1973, soon became the mainstay of their character figure designs. He has produced designs as different as the 'old dears' studies Eventide and Embroidering, and the London series, Bobby, Guardsman, etc. For the Prestige range in 1978 he designed the magnificent St. George and the Dragon.

W.K. Harper

(Royal Doulton Plc)

ADRIAN HUGHES

Adrian Hughes worked as an Art teacher before setting up his own studio in North Wales and starting to model freelance for Doulton in 1982. He has created many fine child studies, including the poignant evacuees for the Children of the Blitz series, and well as the first portrait figure of Winston Churchill.

(Royal Doulton Plc)

Adrian Hughes

ALAN MASLANKOWSKI

Of Polish extraction, Alan Maslankowski was born in Stoke-on-Trent, and, encouraged by his mother, who was a caster in a china factory, he took an early interest in modelling. With Doulton's sponsorship, he trained at the local art school, before working for several companies in Britain and the States, whilst at the same time also producing some figures for Doulton.

He returned to them as resident artist in 1990, and has since exercised his talents in such very different styles as the Sentiments series and portraits of Napoleon and the Duke of Wellington.

(Royal Doulton Plc)

Alan Maslankowski

LESLIE HARRADINE

Having worked at Lambeth as a modeller from 1902 to 1915, Leslie Harradine, a rather Bohemian young man with a taste for adventure and the outdoor life, emigrated to Canada. He returned to Britain to serve in the First World War, and thereafter Harry Noke tried to tempt him to return to Burslem. Harradine was unwilling to be tied down again to steady employment, but agreed to work freelance on figure designs. A hugely talented artist, he went on to produce some of Doulton's most notable figures, submitting at least one model a month for almost 40 years.

MARY NICOLL

The daughter of Gordon Nicoll RI, Mary studied at the Central School of Arts and Crafts in London and joined Royal Doulton under contract, working from her studio in Devon. From this area she drew inspiration for many of her figures, such as Lobster Man and

(Royal Doulton Plc)

Mary Nicoll

Sea Harvest. She died in 1974 at the tragically early age of 52.

PAULINE PARSONS

Following her training at Manchester School of Art, Pauline Parsons has been employed as a freelance by Doulton since 1977. She has executed many child studies and 'fair ladies', as well as working on the Images and Reflections series. It was one of her figures, Sleepy Darling, which in 1981 was chosen as the first figure designed especially for the Royal Doulton International Collectors' Club.

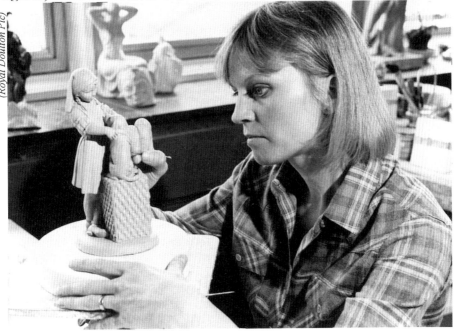

(Royal Doulton Plc)

Pauline Parsons

NADA PEDLEY

Born in Slovenia, Nada Pedley studied art in Germany and England and began modelling as a hobby. She has worked freelance for Doulton since 1988 and specialised in child figures, including the Age of Innocence collection. She lives and works in Sussex.

(Royal Doulton Plc)

Nada Pedley

(Royal Doulton Plc)

Robert Tabbenor

ROBERT TABBENOR

With no previous modelling experience, Robert Tabbenor joined Doulton as a trainee in 1973, studying under Eric Griffiths. His first figure All Aboard was accepted in 1982. Though he has since designed all types of figures, character studies continue to be his forte. He is now Studio Head at Doulton.

STAN TAYLOR

Born in Wales in 1926, Stan Taylor studied at the West of England College of Art in Bristol and became an art teacher. He submitted some of his work to Doulton for the consideration of Eric Griffiths in 1981 and his first accepted character jugs were D'Artagnan and George Washington. The Wild West series followed and then the London characters. Now retired from teaching, Stan Taylor continues to design for Doulton on a freelance basis.

DOUGLAS V. TOOTLE

Douglas Tootle trained at Burslem School of Art and joined Doulton in 1968. He modelled a number of 'fair ladies', such as Sweet Seventeen, and also designed large scale Prestige figures, such as Harlequin and Columbine. He left to go freelance in 1974, but has executed many commissions for the Images and Reflections series, as well as further 'fair ladies'.

ROYAL DOULTON FIGURES

A LA MODE HN2544
Designer: E.J. Griffiths
Height: 12¼ in., 31.1cm.
Issued: 1974-1977
Price: $440 £275

A PENNY'S WORTH HN2408
Designer: M. Nicoll
Height: 7in., 20cm.
Issued: 1986-1990
Price: $264 £165

ABDULLAH HN1410
Designer: L. Harradine
Height: 5¾ in., 14.6cm.
Issued: 1930-1938
Price: $1040 £650

ABDULLAH HN2104
Designer: L. Harradine
Height: 6in., 15.2cm.
Issued: 1953-1962
Colour variation
Price: $520 £325

ABIGAIL HN4044
Designer: Valerie Annand
Height: 8¼in., 21cm.
Issued: 1998
Price: $160 £100 (R.R.P.)

ACE, THE HN3398
Designer: Robert Tabbenor
Height: 10in., 25.5cm
Issued: 1991-1995
Price: $232 £145

A-COURTING HN2004
Designer: L. Harradine
Height: 7¼in., 18.4cm.
Issued: 1947-1953
Price: $520 £325

ACROSS THE MILES HN393
Designer: Alan Maslankowski
Height: 4in., 10cm.
Issued: 1996
Price: $64 £40 (R.R.P.)

ADELE HN2480
Designer: P. Davies
Height: 8in., 20cm.
Issued: 1987-1992
Price: $232 £145

ADORNMENT HN3015
Designer: P. Parsons
Height: 9½in., 24cm.
Issued: 1989 in a limited
edition of 750
Price: $1040 £650

ADRIENNE HN2152
Designer: P. Davies
Height: 7½in., 19.1cm.
Issued: 1964-1976
Price: $264 £165

ADELE HN2480

ACROSS THE MILES HN3934

A LA MODE HN2544

ADRIENNE HN2304

A PENNY'S WORTH HN2408

ACE, THE HN3398

ABDULLAH HN1410

111

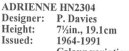

ADRIENNE HN2304
Designer: P. Davies
Height: 7½in., 19.1cm.
Issued: 1964-1991
            Colour variation
Price: $200 £125

AFFECTION HN2236
Designer: P. Davies
Height: 4½in., 11.4cm.
Issued: 1962-1994
Price: $152 £95

AFTERNOON TEA HN1747
Designer: P. Railston
Height: 5¾in., 14.6cm.
Issued: 1935-1981
Price: $560 £350

AFTERNOON TEA HN1748
Designer: P. Railston
Height: 5¼in., 13.3cm.
Issued: 1935-1949
            Colour variation
Price: $760 £475

AILEEN HN1645
Designer: L. Harradine
Height: 6in., 15.2cm.
Issued: 1934-1938
Price: $1040 £650

AILEEN HN1664
Designer: L. Harradine
Height: 6in., 15.2cm.
Issued: 1934-1938
            Colour variation
Price: $1040 £650

AILEEN HN1803
Designer: L. Harradine
Height: 6in., 15.2cm.
Issued: 1937-1949
            Colour variation
Price: $1040 £650

AJAX HN2908
Designer: S. Keenan
Height: 9¾in., 24.8cm.
Issued: 1980 in a limited
            edition of 950
Price: $560 £350

ALCHEMIST HN1259
Designer: L. Harradine
Height: 11½in., 29.2cm
Issued: 1927-1938
Price: $1360 £850

ALCHEMIST HN1282
Designer: L. Harradine
Height: 11¼in., 28.5cm.
Issued: 1928-1982
Price: $1040 £650

ALEXANDRA HN2398
Designer: P. Davies
Height: 7¾in., 19.7cm.
Issued: 1970-1976
Price: $264 £165

AILEEN HN1803

ALICE HN3368

ALCHEMIST
HN1282

AILEEN HN1645

AFTERNOON TEA HN1747

ROYAL DOULTON FIGURES

ALEXANDRA HN3286
Designer: D.V. Tootle
Height: 7¾in., 19.5cm.
Issued: 1990
Price: $232 £145 (R.R.P.)

ALEXANDRA (Pink) HN3292
Designer: D. V. Tootle
Height: 7¾in., 19.5cm.
Issued: 1994
Price: $232 £145 (R.R.P.)

ALFRED JINGLE HN541
Designer: L. Harradine
Height: 3¾in., 9.5cm.
Issued: 1922-1932
Price: $88 £55

ALFRED JINGLE M52
Designer: L. Harradine
Height: 3¾in., 9.5cm.
Issued: 1932-1982
Price: $72 £45

ALFRED THE GREAT HN3821
Designer: Douglas Tootle
Height: 9¼in., 24.5cm.
Issued: 1995-1997
Price: $440 £279

ALICE HN2158
Designer: P. Davies
Height: 5in., 12.7cm.
Issued: 1960-1980
Price: $232 £145

ALICE HN3368
Designer: Nada Pedley
Height: 8¼in., 21cm.
Issued: 1991-1996
Price: $240 £150

ALISON HN2336
Designer: P. Davies
Height: 7¼in., 19.1cm
Issued: 1966-1992
Price: $232 £145

ALISON HN3264
Designer: P. Davies
Height: 7½in., 19.1cm.
Issued: 1989-1993
Price: $200 £125

ALL-A-BLOOMING HN1457
Designer: L. Harradine
Height: 6½in., 16.5cm.
Issued: 1931-not known
Price: $1520 £950

ALL-A-BLOOMING HN1466
Designer: L. Harradine
Height: 6½in., 16.5cm.
Issued: 1931-1938
Price: $1200 £750

ALL ABOARD HN2940
Designer: R. Tabbenor
Height: 9¼in., 23.5cm
Issued: 1982-1986
Price: $264 $165

ALISON HN2336

ALEXANDRA
HN2398

ALEXANDRA
HN3286

ALFRED THE
GREAT HN3821

ALL ABOARD HN2940

AFFECTION HN2236

113

ROYAL DOULTON FIGURES

ALLURE HN3080
Designer: E. Griffiths
Height: 12¼in., 31cm.
Issued: 1987-1989
Price: $232 £145

ALMOST GROWN HN3425
Designer: Nada Pedley
Height: 4½in., 11.5cm.
Issued: 1993-1997
Price: $72 £45

ALWAYS & FOREVER HN3550
Designer: Adrian Hughes
Height: 4 ½in., 11.5cm.
Issued: 1993
Price: $56 £35 (R.R.P.)

AMANDA HN2996
Designer: R. Tabbenor
Height: 5¼in., 13.5cm.
Issued: 1986
Price: $64 £40 (R.R.P.)

AMANDA HN3406
Designer: R. Tabbenor
Height: 5¼in., 13.5cm.
Issued: 1993 U.S.A only
          Colour variation
Price: $104 £65

AMANDA HN3632
Designer: R. Tabbenor
Height: 5¼in., 13.5cm.
Issued: 1994
          Colour variation
Price: $104 £65

AMANDA HN3635
Designer: Robert Tabbenor
Height: 5¼in., 13.3cm.
Issued: 1995
Price: $104 £65

AMEN HN4021
Designer: D.V. Tootle
Height: 4¼in., 11cm.
Issued: 1997
Price: $48 £30 (R..R.P.)

AMY HN2958
Designer: Pauline Parsons
Height: 6in., 15cm.
Issued: 1982-1987
Price: $264 £165

AMY HN3316
Designer: Peter Gee
Height: 8in., 20.3cm.
Issued: 1991
Price: $880 £550

AMY HN3854
Designer: Tim Potts
Height: 8in., 20cm.
Issued: 1996
Price: $168 £105 (R.R.P.)

ALMOST GROWN
HN3425

AMY'S SISTER HN3445

ALLURE HN3080

AMANDA HN3406

AMANDA HN2996

AMY HN3854

ROYAL DOULTON FIGURES

AMY'S SISTER HN3445
Designer: Peter Gee
Height: 8in., 20cm.
Issued: 1993-1996
Price: $200 £125

AND ONE FOR YOU HN2970
Designer: A. Hughes
Height: 6½in., 16.5cm.
Issued: 1982-1985
Price: $200 £145

AND SO TO BED HN2966
Designer: P. Parsons
Height: 7½in., 19cm.
Issued: 1982-1985
Price: $264 £165

ANDREA HN3058
Designer: A. Hughes
Height: 5¼in., 13cm.
Issued: 1985-1995
Price: $80 £50

ANGEL HN3940
Designer: Alan Maslankowski
Height: 11½in., 29cm.
Issued: 1997
Price: $136 £85 (R.R.P.)

ANGELA (Style one) HN1204
Designer: L. Harradine
Height: 7¼in., 18.4cm.
Issued: 1926-1938
Price: $2000 £1250

ANGELA (Style one) HN1303
Designer: L. Harradine
Height: 7¼in., 18.4cm.
Issued: 1928-1938
            Colour variation
Price: $2000 £1250

ANGELA (Style two) HN2389
Designer: P. Davies
Height: 7½in., 19cm.
Issued: 1983-1986
Price: $264 £165

ANGELA HN3419
Designer: Nada Pedley
Height: 8½in., 21.5cm.
Issued: 1992 only (Michael
            Doulton Events)
Price: $312 £195

ANGELA HN3690
Designer: Nada Pedley
Height: 8in., 20.5cm.
Issued: 1995
Price: $232 £145

ANGELINA HN2013
Designer: L. Harradine
Height: 6¾in., 17.1cm.
Issued: 1948-1951
Price: $850 £550

ANDREA HN3058

ANGELA (Style one)
HN1204

AMY HN2958

AMY HN3316

ANGELA HN3419

ANGEL HN3940

115

ROYAL DOULTON FIGURES

ANN HN2739
Designer: D. Tootle
Height: 7¾in., 19.5cm.
Issued: 1983-1986
Price: $232 £145

ANN HN3259
Designer: D. V. Tootle
Height: 8in., 20cm.
Issued: 1990-1996
Price: $264 £165

ANNA HN4095
Designer: Nada Pedley
Height: 6½in., 17cm.
Issued: 1998
Price: $128 £80 (R.R.P.)

ANNA HN2802
Designer: P. Davies
Height: 5¾in., 14.6cm.
Issued: 1976-1982
Price: $216 £135

ANNABEL HN3273
Designer: R. Tabbenor
Height: 5½in., 14cm.
Issued: 1989-1992
Price: $280 £175

ANNABELLA HN1871
Designer: L. Harradine
Height: 5¼in., 13.3cm.
Issued: 1938-1949
Price: $880 £550

ANNABELLA HN1872
Designer: L. Harradine
Height: 5¼in., 13.3cm.
Issued: 1938-1949
             Colour variation
Price: $880 £550

ANNABELLA HN1875
Designer: L. Harradine
Height: 4¾in., 12cm.
Issued: 1938-1949
             Colour variation
Price: $880 £550

ANNE BOLEYN HN3232
Designer: Pauline Parsons
Height: 8¼in., 21cm.
Issued: 1993
Price: $360 £225 (R.R.P.)

ANNE OF CLEVES HN3356
Designer: Pauline Parsons
Height: 6½in., 16.5cm.
Issued: 1993-
Price: $392 £245 (R.R.P.)

ANNETTE HN1471
Designer: L. Harradine
Height: 6¼in.,15.9cm.
Issued: 1931-1938
Price: $600 £375

ANN HN3259

ANN HN2739

ANNE BOLEYN
HN3232

ANNE OF CLEVES
HN3356

ANNETTE HN3495

ANNETTE HN1472
Designer: L. Harradine
Height: 6in., 15.2cm.
Issued: 1931-1949
             Colour variation
Price: $520 £325

ANNETTE HN1550
Designer: L. Harradine
Height: 6¼in., 15.9cm.
Issued: 1933-1949
Price: $472 $295

ANNETTE HN3495
Designer: P. Davies
Height: 7¾in., 19.7cm.
Issued: 1993 only
             Colour variation
Price: $232 £145

ANNIVERSARY HN3648
Designer: Valerie Annand
Height: 8¾in., 22cm.
Issued: 1994
Price: $472 £295

ANTHEA HN1526
Designer: L. Harradine
Height: 6½in., 16.5cm.
Issued: 1932-1940
Price: $1040 £650

ANTHEA HN 1527
Designer: L. Harradine
Height: 6½in., 16.5cm.
Issued: 1932-1940
             Colour variation
Price: $1040 £650

ANTHEA HN1669
Designer: L. Harradine
Height: 6½in., 16.5cm.
Issued: 1934-1940
             Colour variation
Price: $1040 £650

ANTOINETTE (Style one) HN1850
Designer: L Harradine
Height: 8¼in., 21cm.
Issued: 1938-1949
Price: $1440 £900

ANTOINETTE (Style one) HN1851
Designer: L. Harradine
Height: 8¼in., 21cm.
Issued: 1938-1949
             Colour variation
Price: $1440 £900

ANTOINETTE (Style two) HN2326
Designer: P. Davies
Height: 6¼in., 15.9cm.
Issued: 1967-1978
Price: $264 £165

ROYAL DOULTON FIGURES

**ANTONY & CLEOPATRA
HN3114**
Designer: Robert Jefferson
Height: 12in., 30.5cm.
Issued: 1995-1997 in a lim-
            ited edition of 150
Price: $2400 £1500

APPLE MAID HN2160
Designer: L. Harradine
Height: 6½in., 16.5cm.
Issued: 1957-1962
Price: $472 £295

APRIL HN2708
Designer: P. Davies
Height: 7¾in., 19.7cm.
Issued: 1987
Price: $176 £110

APRIL HN3333
Designer: P. Davies
Height: 7½in., 19cm.
Issued: 1990 only
Price: $152 £95

APRIL HN3344
Designer: P. Davies
Height: 7½in., 19cm.
Issued: 1991 only
Price: $200 £125

APRIL HN3693
Designer: Nada Pedley
Height: 8in., 20cm.
Issued: 1995-1997
Price: $232 £145

APRIL SHOWER HN3024
Designer: R. Jefferson
Height: 4¾in., 12cm.
Issued: 1983-1986
Price: $360 £225

ARAB HN33
Designer: C. J. Noke
Height: 15¾in., 40cm.
Issued: 1913-1938
Price: $2800 £1750

ARAB HN343
Designer: C. J. Noke
Height: 16½in., 41.9cm.
Issued: 1919-1938
            Colour variation
Price: $2000 £1250

ARAB HN378
Designer: C. J. Noke
Height: 16½in., 41.9cm.
Issued: 1920-1938
            Colour variation
Price: $2480 £1550

ARAGORN HN2916
Designer: H. Sales
Height: 6¼in., 15.9cm.
Issued: 1979-1984
Price: $200 £125

APRIL HN2708

APRIL HN3333

ANNIVERSARY HN3648

ARAGORN HN2916

APRIL SHOWER HN3024

APRIL HN3693

ROYAL DOULTON FIGURES

ARIEL HN3831
Designer: Pauline Parsons
Height: 8¼in., 20.9cm.
Issued: 1997 in a limited edi
tion of 2000
Price: $312 £195

ARTFUL DODGER HN546
Designer: L. Harradine
Height: 3¾in., 9.5cm.
Issued: 1922-1932
Price: $104 £65

ARTFUL DODGER M55
Designer: L. Harradine
Height: 4¼in., 10.8cm.
Issued: 1932-1983
Price: $80 £50

AS GOOD AS NEW HN2971
Designer: A. Hughes
Height: 6½in., 16.5cm.
Issued: 1982-1985
Price: $232 £145

ASCOT HN2356
Designer: P. Davies
Height: 5¾in., 14.6cm.
Issued: 1968-1995
Price: $232 £145

ASCOT HN3471
Designer: Valerie Annand
Height: 8½in., 21.5cm.
Issued: 1994 in a limited
edition of 5000
Price: $360 £225 (R.R.P.

ASHLEY HN3420
Designer: Nada Pedley
Height: 8in., 20cm.
Issued: 1992
Price: $136 £85 (R.R.P.)

AT EASE HN2473
Designer: P. Davies
Height: 6in., 15.2cm.
Issued: 1973-1978
Price: $360 £225

AU REVOIR HN3723
Designer: A. Maslankowski
Height: 7¾in., 19.5cm.
Issued: 1995
Price: $128 £80 (R.R.P.)

AU REVOIR HN 3729
Designer: Alan Maslankowski
Height: 6½in., 16.5cm.
Issued: 1996
Price: $64 £40 (R.R.P.)

AUCTIONEER HN2988
Designer: R. Tabbenor
Height: 8in., 20.3cm.
Issued: 1986
Price: $392 £245

AUGUST HN3325
Designer: P. Davies
Height: 7½in., 19cm.
Issued: 1991
Price: $152 £95

AS GOOD AS NEW
HN2971

AUCTIONEER
HN2988

GRAND
ROYAL DOULTON
AUCTION
OVER 500 LOTS
INCLUDING THE RARE
RED HAIRED
CLOWN
CHARACTER JUG
MADE FROM
1937 TO 1942

ASHLEY HN3420

ASCOT HN2356

AT EASE HN2473

AUGUST HN3165
Designer: P. Davies
Height: 7¾in., 19.7cm.
Issued: 1987 only
Price: £200 £125

AUGUST HN3408
Designer: P. Davies
Height: 7½in., 19cm.
Issued: 1991 only
Price: $200 £125

AURORA HN3833
Designer: Pauline Parsons
Height: 7½in., 19.1cm.
Issued: 1996 in a limited
          edition of 2000
Price: $360 £225

AURORA HN3833
Designer: Pauline Parsons
Height: 7½in., 19.1cm.
Issued: 1997
Price: $240 £150

L'AUTOMNE HN3068
Designer: R. Jefferson
Height: 11½in., 29cm.
Issued: 1987 in a limited
          edition of 300
Price: $1200 £750

AUTUMN (Style one) HN314
Designer: Unknown
Height: 7¼in., 18.4cm.
Issued: 1918-1938
Price: $1360 £850

AUTUMN (Style one) HN474
Designer: Unknown
Height: 7½in., 19.1cm.
Issued: 1921-1938
Price: $1360 £850

AUTUMN (Style two) HN2087
Designer: P. Davies
Height: 7¼in., 18.4cm.
Issued: 1952-1959
Price: $600 £375

AUTUMN ATTRACTION HN3612
Designer: P. Davies
Height: 7in., 17.8cm.
Issued: 1993-1995
Price: $136 £85

AUTUMN BREEZES HN2131
(Red/orange/black)
Designer: Leslie Harradine
Height: 7½in., 19cm.
Issued: 1990-1994
Price: $232 £145

AUTUMN BREEZES HN2176
Designer: Leslie Harradine
Height: 4in., 10cm.
Issued: 1991-1995
Price: $120 £75

AUGUST HN3165

AUGUST HN3325

AUGUST HN3408

AUTUMN (Style two) HN2087

AUTUMN ATTRACTION HN3612

AUTUMN BREEZES HN2131

AUTUMN BREEZES HN2176

119

ROYAL DOULTON FIGURES

AUTUMN BREEZES HN2147
Designer: L. Harradine
Height: 7½in., 19.1cm.
Issued: 1955-1971
Colour variation
Price: $280 £175

AUTUMN BREEZES HN1934
Designer: L. Harradine
Height: 7½in., 19.1cm.
Issued: 1940-1997
Colour variation
Price: $232 £145

AUTUMN BREEZES HN1911
Designer: L. Harradine
Height: 7½in., 19.1cm.
Issued: 1939-1976
Price: $264 £165

AUTUMN BREEZES HN1913
Designer: L. Harradine
Height: 7½in., 19.1cm.
Issued: 1939-1971
Colour variation
Price: $264 £165

AUTUMN BREEZES HN3736
Designer: Leslie Harradine
Height: 7½in., 19cm.
Issued: 1998
Price: $240 £150

AUTUMN TIME HN3231
Designer: P. Parsons
Height: 8in., 20.3cm.
Issued: 1989
Price: $312 £195

AUTUMN TIME HN3621
Designer: V. Annand
Height: 8½in., 21.5cm.
Issued: 1994-1996
Price: $360 £225

AWAKENING HN1927
Designer: L. Harradine
Height: Unknown
Issued: 1940-1949
Price: $2320 £1450

AWAKENING HN2837 (Black)
Designer: P. Davies
Height: 8½in., 22cm.
Issued: 1981-86
Price: $200 £125

AWAKENING HN2875 (White)
Designer: P. Davies
Height: 8½in., 22cm.
Issued: 1981-
Price: $80 £50 (R.R.P.)

B

BABA HN1230
Designer: L. Harradine
Height: 3¼in., 8.3cm.
Issued: 1927-1938
Price: $792 £495

AUTUMN BREEZES
HN1911

AUTUMN BREEZES
HN1913

AUTUMN TIME HN3621

BABA HN1243
Designer: L. Harradine
Height: 3¼in., 8.3cm.
Issued: 1927-1938
Colour variation
Price: $792 £495

BABA HN1244
Designer: L. Harradine
Height: 3¼in., 8.3cm.
Issued: 1927-1938
Colour variation
Price: $792 £495

BABA HN1245
Designer: L. Harradine
Height: 3¼in., 8.3cm.
Issued: 1927-1938
Colour variation
Price: $792 £495

BABA HN1246
Designer: L. Harradine
Height: 3¼in., 8.3cm.
Issued: 1927-1938
Colour variation
Price: $792 £495

BABA HN1247
Designer: L. Harradine
Height: 3¼in., 8.3cm.
Issued: 1927-1938
Colour variation
Price: $792 £495

BABA HN1248
Designer: L. Harradine
Height: 3¼in., 8.3cm.
Issued: 1927-1938
Colour variation
Price: $792 £495

BABETTE HN1423
Designer: L. Harradine
Height: 5in., 12.7cm.
Issued: 1930-1938
Price: $880 £550

BABETTE HN1424
Designer: L. Harradine
Height: 5in., 12.7cm.
Issued: 1930-1938
Price: $880 £550

BABIE HN1679
Designer: L. Harradine
Height: 4¾in., 12cm.
Issued: 1935-1992
Price: $152 £95

BABIE HN1842
Designer: L. Harradine
Height: 4¾in., 12cm.
Issued: 1938-1949
Colour variation
Price: $312 £195

BABIE HN2121
Designer: L. Harradine
Height: 4¾in., 12cm.
Issued: 1983-1992
Price: $152 £95

ROYAL DOULTON FIGURES

BABY HN12
Designer: C. J. Noke
Height: Unknown
Issued: 1913-1938
Price: $2400 £1500

BABY BUNTING HN2108
Designer: P. Davies
Height: 5¼in., 13.3cm.
Issued: 1953-1959
Price: $472 £295

BACHELOR HN2319
Designer: M. Nicoll
Height: 7in., 17.8cm.
Issued: 1964-1975
Price: $392 £245

BALINESE DANCER HN2808
Designer: P. Davies
Height: 8¾in., 22.2cm.
Issued: 1982 in a limited
             edition of 750
Price: $880 £550

BALLAD SELLER HN2266
Designer: P. Davies
Height: 7½in., 19.1cm.
Issued: 1968-1973
Price: $360 £225

BALLERINA HN2116
Designer: P. Davies
Height: 7¼in., 18.4cm.
Issued: 1953-1973
Price: $360 £225

BALLERINA HN3828
Designer: D.V. Tootle
Height: 5½in., 14cm.
Issued: 1997
Price: $80 £50 (R.R.P.)

BALLET CLASS HN3134
Designer: P. Parsons
Height: 6in., 15.5cm.
Issued: 1987-1987
Price: $232 £145

BALLET CLASS HN3731
Designer: Alan Maslankowski
Height: 6in., 15cm.
Issued: 1996
Price: $64 £40 (R.R.P.)

BALLET SHOES HN3434
Designer: Alan Maslankowski
Height: 3¼in., 8cm.
Issued: 1993
Price: $64 £40 (R.R.P.)

BALLOON BOY HN2934
Designer: P. Gee
Height: 7½in., 19cm.
Issued: 1984-
Price: $160 £100 (R.R.P.)

BALLOON CLOWN HN2894
Designer: W. K. Harper
Height: 9¼in., 23cm.
Issued: 1986-1992
Price: $264 £165

BABIE HN1679

BABIE HN2121

BABETTE HN1423

BABA HN1247

BALLET CLASS HN3134

BALLERINA HN2116

BACHELOR HN2319

121

BALLET CLASS HN3731

BALLET SHOES HN3434

BALLOON CLOWN
HN2894

BALLOON GIRL HN2818
Designer: W. K. Harper
Height: 6½in., 16.5cm.
Issued: 1982-1997
Price: $200 £125

BALLOON LADY HN2935
Designer: P. Gee
Height: 8¼in., 21cm.
Issued: 1984-
Price: $176 £110 (R.R.P.)

BALLOON MAN HN1954
Designer: L. Harradine
Height: 7¼in., 18.4cm.
Issued: 1940-
Price: $232 £145 (R.R.P.)

BALLOON SELLER HN479
Designer: L. Harradine
Height: 9in., 22.9cm.
Issued: 1921-1938
Price: $1520 £950

BALLOON SELLER HN486
Designer: L. Harradine
Height: 9in., 22.9cm.
Issued: 1921-1938
Price: $720 £450

BALLOON SELLER HN548
Designer: L. Harradine
Height: 9in., 22.9cm.
Issued: 1922-1938
            Colour variation
Price: $720 £450

BALLOON SELLER HN583
Designer: L. Harradine
Height: 9in., 22.9cm.
Issued: 1923-1949
            Colour variation
Price: $600 £375

BALLOON SELLER HN697
Designer: L. Harradine
Height: 9in., 22.9cm.
Issued: 1925-1938
            Colour variation
Price: $880 $550

BALLOON SELLER HN2130
Designer: L. Harradine
Height: 4in., 10cm.
Issued: 1989-1992
Price: $232 £145

BARBARA HN1421
Designer: L. Harradine
Height: 7¾in., 19.7cm.
Issued: 1930-1938
Price: $1040 £650

BARBARA HN1432
Designer: L. Harradine
Height: 7¾in., 19.7cm.
Issued: 1930-1938
Price: $1040 £650

BALLOON BOY HN2934

BALINESE DANCER HN2808

BALLOON GIRL HN2818

BARBARA HN2962

BARBARA HN1421

BALLOON LADY
HN2935

BARBARA HN3441

BALLOON MAN HN1954

ROYAL DOULTON FIGURES

BARBARA HN1461
Designer: L. Harradine
Height: 7¾in., 19.7cm.
Issued: 1931-1938
  Colour variation
Price: $1040 £650

BARBARA HN2962
Designer: P. Parsons
Height: 8in., 20cm.
Issued: 1982-1984
Price: $264 £165

BARBARA HN3441
Designer: P. Gee
Height: 8in., 20cm.
Issued: 1992 in a special
  edition of 9500-1995
  (R.D.I.C.C.)
Price: $264 £165

**BARLIMAN BUTTERBUR
HN 2923**
Designer: D. Lyttleton
Height: 5¼in.,13cm.
Issued: 1982-1984
Price: $440 £275

BASKET WEAVER HN2245
Designer: M. Nicoll
Height: 5¾in., 14.6cm.
Issued: 1959-1962
Price: $520 £325

BATHER (Style one) HN 597
Designer: L. Harradine
Height: 7¾in., 19.7cm.
Issued: 1924-1938
Price: $1360 £850

BATHER (Style one) HN687
Designer: L. Harradine
Height: 7¾in., 19.7cm.
Issued: 1924-1949
  Colour variation
Price: $1040 $650

BATHER (Style one)HN781
Designer: L. Harradine
Height: 7¾in., 19.7cm.
Issued: 1926-1938
  Colour variation
Price: $1040 £650

BATHER (Style one) HN782
Designer: L. Harradine
Height: 7¾in., 19.7cm.
Issued: 1926-1938
  Colour variation
Price: $1040 £650

BATHER (Style one) HN1238
Designer: L. Harradine
Height: 7¾in., 19.7cm.
Issued: 1927-1938
  Colour variation
Price: $2000 £1250

BEDTIME HN1978

BARLIMAN BUTTERBUR
HN 2923

BATHER (Style one) HN687

BATHER (Style one) HN1238

BATHER (Style one) HN1708
Designer: L. Harradine
Height: 7¾in., 19.7cm.
Issued: 1935-1938
  Colour variation
Price: $2000 £1250

BATHER (Style two) HN773
Designer: L. Harradine
Height: 7½in., 19.1cm.
Issued: 1925-1938
Price: $2400 £1500

BATHER (Style two) HN774
Designer: L. Harradine
Height: 7¾in., 19.7cm.
Issued: 1925-1938
Price: $2400 £1500

BATHER (Style two) HN1227
Designer: L. Harradine
Height: 7½in., 19.1cm.
Issued: 1927-1938
  Colour variation
Price: $2400 £1500

BATHING BEAUTY HN3156
Designer: A. Hughes
Height: 9½in., 26cm.
Issued: 1988-1989
Price: $520 £325

BEACHCOMBER HN2487
Designer: M. Nicoll
Height: 6¼in., 15.9cm.
Issued: 1973-1976
Price: $232 £145

BEAT YOU TO IT HN2871
Designer: P. Davies
Height: 6½in., 16.5cm.
Issued: 1980-1987
Price: $392 £245

BEATRICE HN3263
Designer: P. Davies
Height: 7in., 17.8cm.
Issued: 1989
Price: $184 £115 (R.R.P.)

BEATRICE HN3631
U.S.A. edition
Designer: P. Davies
Height: 7in., 17.8cm.
Issued: 1994
Price: $200 £125 (R.R.P.)

BECKY HN2740
Designer: D. Tootle
Height: 8in., 20cm.
Issued: 1987-1992
Price: $232 £145

BEDTIME HN1978
Designer: L. Harradine
Height: 5¾in., 14.6cm.
Issued: 1945-1997
Price: $80 £50

ROYAL DOULTON FIGURES

BATHER (Style one)
HN1708

BATHER (Style two)
HN773

BEATRICE HN3631

BATHER (Style two)
HN1227

BEATRICE HN3263

BEAT YOU TO IT HN2871

BEACHCOMBER HN2487

BEDTIME HN2219
Designer: P. Gee
Height: 5¼in., 13.3cm.
Issued: 1992
Colour variation
Price: $125 £75

BEDTIME HN3418
Designer: N. Pedley
Height: 7¼in., 18.4cm.
Issued: 1992 in a limited
edition of 9500
Price: $312 £195

BEDTIME STORY HN2059
Designer: L. Harradine
Height: 4¾in., 12cm.
Issued: 1950-1996
Price: $312 £195

BEETHOVEN HN1778
Designer: R. Garbe
Height: 22in., 55.8cm.
Issued: 1933 in a limited
edition of 25
Price: $3200 £2000

BEGGAR (Style one) HN526
Designer: L. Harradine
Height: 6½in., 16.5cm.
Issued: 1921-1949
Price: $632 £395

BEGGAR (Style one) HN591
Designer: L. Harradine
Height: 6¾in., 17.2cm.
Issued: 1924-1949
Price: $632 £395

BEGGAR (Style two) HN2175
Designer: L. Harradine
Height: 6¾in., 17.2cm.
Issued: 1956-1972
Price: $632 £395

BELLE HN754
Designer: L. Harradine
Height: 6½in., 16.5cm.
Issued: 1925-1938
Price: $1040 £650

BELLE HN776
Designer: L. Harradine
Height: 6½in., 16.5cm.
Issued: 1925-1938
Price: $1040 £650

BELLE HN2340
Designer: P. Davies
Height: 4½in., 11.4cm.
Issued: 1968-1988
Price: $152 £95

BELLE HN3703
Designer: Valerie Annand
Height: 8in., 20cm.
Issued: 1996 (Figure of the
Year)
Price: $232 £145

BEDTIME HN3418

BEST FRIENDS HN3935

BELLE HN3703

BEGGAR (Style one) HN526

BEDTIME STORY HN2059

ROYAL DOULTON FIGURES

BELLE O' THE BALL HN1997
Designer: L. Harradine
Height: 6in., 15.2cm.
Issued: 1947-1978
Price: $472 £295

BENMORE HN2909
Designer: S. Keenan
Height: 9¼in., 23.5cm.
Issued: 1980 in a limited
edition of 950
Price: $520 £325

BERNICE HN2071
Designer: P. Davies
Height: 7¾in., 19.7cm.
Issued: 1951-1953
Price: $1200 £750

BESS HN2002
Designer: L. Harradine
Height: 7¼in., 18.4cm.
Issued: 1947-1969
Price: $392 £245

BESS HN2003
Designer: L. Harradine
Height: 7¼in., 18.4cm.
Issued: 1947-1950
Colour variation
Price: $392 £245

BEST FRIENDS HN3935
Designer: Alan Maslankowski
Height: 3in., 7.5cm.
Issued: 1997
Price: $80 £50 (R.R.P.)

BEST WISHES HN3426
Designer: Nada Pedley
Height: 6in., 15cm.
Issued: 1993-1995
Price: $136 £85

BETH HN2870
Designer: P. Davies
Height: 5¾in., 14.6cm.
Issued: 1980-1983
Price: $312 £195

BETSY HN2111
Designer: L. Harradine
Height: 7in., 17.8cm.
Issued: 1953-1959
Price: $472 £295

BETTY (Style one) HN402
Designer: L. Harradine
Height: 7½in., 19cm.
Issued: 1920-1938
Price: $2400 £1500

BETTY (Style one) HN403
Designer: L. Harradine
Height: 7½in., 19cm.
Issued: 1920-1938
Colour variation
Price: $2400 £1500

BELLE O' THE BALL HN1997

BELLE HN754

BEST WISHES HN3426

BENMORE HN2909

BESS HN2002

BETH HN2870

ROYAL DOULTON FIGURES

BETTY (Style one) HN435
Designer: L. Harradine
Height: 7½in., 19cm.
Issued: 1921-1938
            Colour variation
Price: $2400 £1500

BETTY (Style one) HN438
Designer: L. Harradine
Height: 7½in., 19cm.
Issued: 1921-1938
            Colour variation
Price: $2400 £1500

BETTY (Style one) HN477
Designer: L. Harradine
Height: 7½in., 19cm.
Issued: 1921-1938
            Colour variation
Price: $2400 £1500

BETTY (Style one) HN478
Designer: L. Harradine
Height: 7½in., 19cm.
Issued: 1921-1938
            Colour variation
Price: $2400 £1500

BETTY (Style two) HN1404
Designer: L. Harradine
Height: 4½in., 11.4cm.
Issued: 1930-1938
Price: $2000 £1250

BETTY (Style two) HN1405
Designer: L. Harradine
Height: 4½in., 11.4cm.
Issued: 1930-1938
            Colour variation
Price: $2000 £1250

BETTY (Style two) HN1435
Designer: L. Harradine
Height: 4½in., 11.4cm.
Issued: 1930-1938
            Colour variation
Price: $2000 £1250

BETTY (Style two) HN 1436
Designer: L. Harradine
Height: 4½in., 11.4cm.
Issued: 1930-1938
            Colour variation
Price: $2000 £1250

BIDDY HN1445
Designer: L. Harradine
Height: 5½in., 14cm.
Issued: 1931-1938
Price: $440 £275

BIDDY HN1500
Designer: L. Harradine
Height: 5½in., 14cm.
Issued: 1932-1938
Price: $472 £295

BIDDY HN1445

BILBO
HN2914

IDDY PENNY
FARTHING
HN1843

BIRTHDAY GIRL HN3423

BOLERO HN3076

BIDDY HN1513
Designer: L. Harradine
Height: 5½in., 14cm.
Issued: 1932- 1951
            Colour variation
Price: $312 £195

**BIDDY PENNY FARTHING
HN1843**
Designer: L. Harradine
Height: 9in., 22.9cm.
Issued: 1938-
Price: $232 £145 (R.R.P.)

BILBO HN2914
Designer: Harry Sales
Height: 4½in., 11.4cm.
Issued: 1979-1984
Price: $200 £125

BILL SYKES HN3785 (Resin)
Designer: Arthur Dobson
Height: 9in., 23cm.
Issued: 1996-1997
Price: $120 £75

BILL SYKES HN537
Designer: L. Harradine
Height: 3¾in., 9.5cm.
Issued: 1922-1932
Price: $96 £60

BILL SYKES M54
Designer: L. Harradine
Height: 4½in., 10.8cm.
Issued: 1932-1982
Price: $72 £45

BIRTHDAY GIRL HN3423
Designer: Nada Pedley
Height: 6in., 15cm.
Issued: 1993
Price: $104 £65 (R.R.P.)

ACKSMITH HN2782
Designer: W. K. Harper
Height: 9in., 22.5cm.
Issued: 1987-1991
Price: $312 £195

**BLACKSMITH OF
WILLIAMSBURG HN2240**
Designer: P. Davies
Height: 6¾in., 17.2cm.
Issued: 1960-1983
Price: $264 £165

BLIGHTY HN323
Designer: E. W. Light
Height: 11¼in., 28.5cm.
Issued: 1918-1938
Price: $2000 £1250

BLITHE MORNING HN2021
Designer: L. Harradine
Height: 7¼in., 18.4cm.
Issued: 1949-1971
Price: $296 £185

ROYAL DOULTON FIGURES

BLITHE MORNING HN2065
Designer: L. Harradine
Height: 7¼in., 18.4cm.
Issued: 1950-1973
            Colour variation
Price: $264 £165

BLOSSOM HN1667
Designer: L. Harradine
Height: 6¾in., 17.2cm.
Issued: 1934-1949
Price: $1840 £1150

BLUE BEARD (Style one) HN75
Designer: E. W. Light
Height: Unknown
Issued: 1917-1938
Price: $4400 £2750

BLUE BEARD (Style one) HN410
Designer: E. W. Light
Height: Unknown
Issued: 1920-1938
            Colour variation
Price: $4400 £2750

BLUE BEARD (Style two) HN1528
Designer: L. Harradine
Height: 11½in., 29.2cm.
Issued: 1932-1949
Price: $960 £600

BLUE BEARD (Style two) HN2105
Designer: L. Harradine
Height: 11in., 27.9cm.
Issued: 1953-1992
            Colour variation
Price: $472 £295

BLUE BIRD HN1280
Designer: L. Harradine
Height: 4¾in., 12cm.
Issued: 1928-1938
Price: $632 £395

BOATMAN HN2417
Designer: M. Nicoll
Height: 6½in., 16.5cm.
Issued: 1971-1987
Price: $280 £175

BOBBY HN2778
Designer: William K. Harper
Height: 9in., 23cm.
Issued: 1992-1995
Price: $200 £125

BOLERO HN3076
Designer: A. Hughes
Height: 13½in., 34.5cm.
Issued: 1985-1992
Price: $280 £175

BON APPETIT HN2444
Designer: M. Nicoll
Height: 6in., 15.2cm.
Issued: 1972-1976
Price: $232 £145

BLACKSMITH OF WILLIAMSBURG HN2240

BOBBY HN2778

BLITHE MORNING HN2021

BOATMAN HN2417

BON APPETIT HN2444

BLUE BEARD (Style two) HN2105

ROYAL DOULTON FIGURES

BON VOYAGE HN3866
Designer: Tim Potts
Height: 9in., 23cm.
Issued: 1998
Price: $44 £90

BONJOUR HN1879
Designer: L. Harradine
Height: 6¾in., 17.2cm.
Issued: 1938-1949
Price: $1200 £750

BONJOUR HN1888
Designer: L. Harradine
Height: 6¾in., 17.2cm.
Issued: 1938-1949
Colour variation
Price: $1200 £750

BONNIE LASSIE HN1626
Designer: L. Harradine
Height: 5¼in., 13.3cm.
Issued: 1934-1953
Price: $1200 £750

BO-PEEP (Style one) HN777
Designer: L. Harradine
Height: 6¾in., 17.2cm.
Issued: 1926-1938
Price: $2000 £1250

BO-PEEP (Style one) HN1202
Designer: L. Harradine
Height: 6¾in., 17.2cm.
Issued: 1926-1938
Colour variation
Price: $800 £500

BO-PEEP (Style one) HN1327
Designer: L. Harradine
Height: 6¾in., 17.2cm.
Issued: 1929-1938
Colour variation
Price: $2160 £1350

BO-PEEP (Style one) HN1328
Designer: L. Harradine
Height: 6¾in., 17.2cm.
Issued: 1929-1938
Colour variation
Price: $2160 £1350

BO-PEEP (Style two) HN1810
Designer: L. Harradine
Height: 5in., 12.7cm.
Issued: 1937-1949
Price: $440 £275

BO-PEEP (Style two) HN1811
Designer: L. Harradine
Height: 5in., 12.7cm.
Issued: 1937-1995
Colour variation
Price: $136 £85

BO-PEEP M82
Designer: L. Harradine
Height: 4in., 10.1cm.
Issued: 1939-1949
Price: $880 £550

BO-PEEP (Style two) HN1811

BONJOUR HN1879

BONNIE LASSIE HN1626

BO-PEEP M83
Designer: L. Harradine
Height: 4in., 10.1cm.
Issued: 1939-1949
Colour variation
Price: $880 £550

BOROMIR HN2918
Designer: Harry Sales
Height: 6¾in., 17.2cm.
Issued: 1980-1984
Price: $280 £175

BOUDOIR HN2542
Designer: E. J. Griffiths
Height: 12¼in., 31.1cm.
Issued: 1974-1977
Price: $440 £275

BOUQUET HN406
Designer: G. Lambert
Height: 9in., 22.9cm.
Issued: 1920-1938
Price: $2000 £1250

BOUQUET HN414
Designer: G. Lambert
Height: 9in., 22.9cm.
Issued: 1920-1938
Price: $2000 £1250

BOUQUET HN422
Designer: G. Lambert
Height: 9in., 22.9cm.
Issued: 1920-1938
Colour variation
Price: $2000 £1250

BOUQUET HN428
Designer: G. Lambert
Height: 9in., 22.9cm.
Issued: 1921-1938
Colour variation
Price: $2240 £1400

BOUQUET HN429
Designer: G. Lambert
Height: 9in., 22.9cm.
Issued: 1921-1938
Colour variation
Price: $2320 £1450

BOUQUET HN567
Designer: G. Lambert
Height: 9½in., 24.1cm.
Issued: 1923-1938
Colour variation
Price: $1840 £1150

BOUQUET HN794
Designer: G. Lambert
Height: 9in., 22.9cm.
Issued: 1926-1938
Colour variation
Price: $2000 £1250

BOWLS PLAYER HN3780
(Resin)
Designer: Joseph Jones
Height: 6in., 15cm.
Issued: 1996 only.
Price: $152 £95

ROYAL DOULTON FIGURES

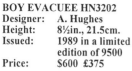

BOY EVACUEE HN3202
Designer: A. Hughes
Height: 8½in., 21.5cm.
Issued: 1989 in a limited
             edition of 9500
Price: $600 £375

**BOY FROM WILLIAMSBURG
HN2183**
Designer: P. Davies
Height: 5½in., 14cm.
Issued: 1969-1983
Price: $232 £145

BOY ON CROCODILE HN373
Designer: C. J. Noke
Height: 5in., 12.7cm.
Length: 14½in., 36.8cm.
Issued: 1920-1938
Price: $3200 £2000

BOY ON PIG HN1369
Designer: C. J. Noke
Height: 4in., 10.1cm.
Issued: 1930-1938
Price: $2400 £1500

BOY SCOUT HN3462
In a limited edition of 9500
Designer: Adrian Hughes
Height: 7¾in., 19.7cm.
Issued: 1994
Price: $312 £195

BOY WITH TURBAN HN586
Designer: L. Harradine
Height: 3¾in., 9.5cm.
Issued: 1923-1938
Price: $880 £550

BOY WITH TURBAN HN587
Designer: L. Harradine
Height: 3¾in., 9.5cm.
Issued: 1923-1938
Price: $880 £550

BOY WITH TURBAN HN661
Designer: L. Harradine
Height: 3¾in., 9.5cm.
Issued: 1924-1938
Price: $880 £550

BOY WITH TURBAN HN662
Designer: L. Harradine
Height: 3¾in., 9.5cm.
Issued: 1924-1938
             Colour variation
Price: $880 £550

BOY WITH TURBAN HN1210
Designer: L. Harradine
Height: 3¾in., 9.5cm.
Issued: 1926-1938
             Colour variation
Price: $880 £550

BOY WITH TURBAN HN1212
Designer: L. Harradine
Height: 3¾in., 9.5cm.
Issued: 1926-1938
Price: $880 £550

**BOY FROM WILLIAMSBURG
HN2183**

BOROMIR HN2918

BOUQUET HN567

BOY SCOUT HN3462

BOY EVACUEE HN3202

BOWLS PLAYER HN3780

131

ROYAL DOULTON FIGURES

BOY WITH TURBAN HN1213
Designer: L. Harradine
Height: 3¾in., 9.5cm.
Issued: 1926-1938
Colour variation
Price: $880 £550

BOY WITH TURBAN HN1214
Designer: L. Harradine
Height: 3½in., 8.9cm.
Issued: 1926-1938
Colour variation
Price: $880 £550

BOY WITH TURBAN HN1225
Designer: L. Harradine
Height: 3¾in., 9.5cm.
Issued: 1927-1938
Colour variation
Price: $880 £550

BREEZY DAYS HN3162
Designer: A. Hughes
Height: 8½in., 21.5cm.
Issued: 1988-1990
Price: $232 £145

BRETON DANCER HN2383
Designer: P. Davies
Height: 8½in., 21.5cm.
Issued: 1981 in a limited
edition of 750
Price: $632 £395

BRIDE (Style one) HN1588
Designer: L. Harradine
Height: 8¾in., 22.2cm.
Issued: 1933-1938
Price: $920 £575

BRIDE (Style one) HN1600
Designer: L. Harradine
Height: 8¾in., 22.2cm.
Issued: 1933-1949
Colour variation
Price: $680 £425

BRIDE (Style one) HN1762
Designer: L. Harradine
Height: 8¾in., 22.2cm.
Issued: 1936-1949
Colour variation
Price: $920 £575

BRIDE (Style one) HN1841
Designer: L. Harradine
Height: 9½in., 24.1cm.
Issued: 1938-1949
Colour variation
Price: $920 £575

BRIDE (Style two) HN2166
Designer: P. Davies
Height: 8in., 20.3cm.
Issued: 1956-1976
Price: $280 £175

BRIDE (Style three) HN2873
Designer: P. Davies
Height: 8in., 20.3cm.
Issued: 1980-1989
Price: $232 £145

BOY WITH TURBAN HN586

BOY WITH TURBAN HN1213

BOY WITH TURBAN HN662

BRIDE (Style three)
HN2873

BRETON DANCER HN2383

BRIDE (Style one) HN1841

BRIDE (White) HN3284
Designer: D. V. Tootle
Height: 8¼in., 21cm.
Issued: 1990-1997
Price: $232 £145 (R.R.P.)

BRIDE (Ivory) HN3285
Designer: D. V. Tootle
Height: 8¼in., 21cm.
Issued: 1990-1997
Price: $232 £145

BRIDE & GROOM HN3281
Designer: Robert Tabbenor
Height: 6¼in., 16cm.
Issued: 1991
Price: $64 £40 (R.R.P.)

BRIDESMAID (Style one) HN1433
Designer: L. Harradine
Height: 5¼in., 13.3cm.
Issued: 1930-1951
Price: $312 £195

BRIDESMAID (Style one) HN1434
Designer: L. Harradine
Height: 5in., 12.7cm.
Issued: 1930-1949
   Colour variation
Price: $360 £225

BRIDESMAID (Style one) HN1530
Designer: L. Harradine
Height: 5in., 12.7cm.
Issued: 1932-1938
   Colour variation
Price: $440 £275

BRIDESMAID (Style two) HN2148
Designer: P. Davies
Height: 5½in., 14cm.
Issued: 1955-1959
Price: $352 £220

BRIDESMAID (Style three) HN2196
Designer: P. Davies
Height: 5¼in., 13.3cm.
Issued: 1960-1976
Price: $192 £120

BRIDESMAID (Style four) HN2874
Designer: P. Davies
Height: 5¼in., 13.3cm.
Issued: 1980-1989
Price: $136 £85

BRIDESMAID M11
Designer: L. Harradine
Height: 3¾in., 9.5cm.
Issued: 1932-1938
Price: $472 £295

BRIDE (Ivory) HN3285

BRIDESMAID (Style one) HN1433

BRIDE (White) HN3284

BRIDESMAID (Style four) HN2874

BRIDESMAID (Style three) HN2196

BRIDE (Style two) HN2166

BRIDE & GROOM HN3281

BRIDESMAID M12
Designer: L. Harradine
Height: 3¾in., 9.5cm.
Issued: 1932-1945
Colour variation
Price: $472 £295

BRIDESMAID M30
Designer: L. Harradine
Height: 3¾in., 9.5cm.
Issued: 1932-1945
Colour variation
Price: $472 £295

BRIDESMAID HN3280
Designer: Robert Tabbenor
Height: 8½in., 21.5cm.
Issued: 1991
Price: $64 £40 (R.R.P.)

BRIDESMAID HN3476
Designer: Valerie Annand
Height: 5¼in., 13cm.
Issued: 1994 (In Canada
Flowergirl HN3479)
Price: $112 £70

BRIDGET HN2070
Designer: L. Harradine
Height: 7¾in., 19.7cm.
Issued: 1951-1973
Price: $280 £185

BRIGHT WATER HN3529
Designer: R. Jefferson
Height: 8½in., 21.5cm.
Issued: 1983-1986
Price: $48 £30

BROKEN LANCE HN2041
Designer: P. Davies
Height: 8¾in., 22.2cm.
Issued: 1949-1975
Price: $680 £425

BROTHER & SISTER HN3460
Designer: Adrian Hughes
Height: 7¾in., 19.5cm.
Issued: 1993
Price: $80 £50 (R.R.P.)

BROTHERS HN3191
Designer: Eric Griffiths
Height: 8¼in., 21cm.
Issued: 1991
Price: $80 £50 (R.R.P.)

BUDDIES HN2546
Designer: E.J.Griffiths
Height: 6in., 15.2cm.
Issued: 1973-1976
Price: $264 £165

BUDDIES HN3396
Designer: Alan Maslankowski
Height: 4¼in., 11cm.
Issued: 1992-1996
Price: $88 £55

BRIDGET HN2070

BRIDESMAID HN3280

BROTHERS HN3191

BRIDESMAID HN3476

BROKEN LANCE HN2041

BROTHER & SISTER HN3460

ROYAL DOULTON FIGURES

BUMBLE M76
Designer: L. Harradine
Height: 4in., 10.1cm.
Issued: 1939-1982
Price: $80 £50

BUNNY HN2214
Designer: P. Davies
Height: 5in., 12.7cm.
Issued: 1960-1975
Price: $232 £145

BUNNY'S BEDTIME HN3370
Designer: N. Pedley
Height: 6in., 15.2cm.
Issued: 1991 in a limited
edition of 9500
Price: $312 £195

BUTTERCUP HN2309
Designer: P. Davies
Height: 7in., 17.8cm.
Issued: 1964-1997
Price: $232 £145

BUTTERCUP HN2399
Designer: P. Davies
Height: 7½in., 19cm.
Issued: 1983-1997
Price: $232 £145

BUTTERCUP HN3268
Designer: Peggy Davies
Height: 3¾in., 9.5cm.
Issued: 1990-1965
Price: $104 £65

BUTTERFLY HN719
Designer: L. Harradine
Height: 6½in., 16.5cm
Issued: 1925-1938
Price: $2400 £1500

BUTTERFLY HN720
Designer: L. Harradine
Height: 6½in., 16.5cm.
Issued: 1925-1938
Colour variation
Price: $2400 £1500

BUTTERFLY HN730
Designer: L. Harradine
Height: 6½in., 16.5cm.
Issued: 1925-1938
Colour variation
Price: $2400 £1500

BUTTERFLY HN1203
Designer: L. Harradine
Height: 6½in., 16.5cm.
Issued: 1926-1938
Colour variation
Price: $2400 £1500

BUTTERFLY HN1456
Designer: L. Harradine
Height: 6½in., 16.5cm.
Issued: 1931-1938
Price: $2400 £1500

BUTTERCUP HN2399

BUTTERCUP HN2309

BUDDIES HN3396

BUTTERFLY HN1456   BUNNY'S BEDTIME HN3370

BUZ FUZ HN538
Designer: L. Harradine
Height: 3¾in., 9.5cm.
Issued: 1922-1932
Price: $104 £65

BUZ FUZ M53
Designer: L. Harradine
Height: 4in., 10.1cm.
Issued: 1932-1983
Price: $72 £45

C

CALLED LOVE, A LITTLE BOY HN1545
Designer: Unknown
Height: 3½in., 8.9cm.
Issued: 1933-1949
Price: $680 £425

CALUMET HN1428
Designer: C. J. Noke
Height: 6in., 15.2cm.
Issued: 1930-1949
Price: $880 £550

CALUMET HN1689
Designer: C. J. Noke
Height: 6½in., 16.5cm.
Issued: 1935-1949
         Colour variation
Price: $880 £550

CALUMET HN2068
Designer: C. J. Noke
Height: 6¼in., 15.9cm.
Issued: 1950-1953
Price: $880 £550

CAMELLIA HN2222
Designer: P. Davies
Height: 7¾in., 19.7cm.
Issued: 1960-1971
Price: $280 £175

CAMELLIAS HN3701
Designer: V. Annand
Height: 8½in., 21.5cm.
Issued: 1995
Price: $224 £140 (R.R.P.)

CAMILLA HN1710
Designer: L. Harradine
Height: 7in., 17.8cm.
Issued: 1935-1949
Price: $960 £600

CAMILLA HN1711
Designer: L. Harradine
Height: 7in., 17.8cm.
Issued: 1935-1949
         Colour variation
Price: $960 £600

CAMILLE HN1586
Designer: L. Harradine
Height: 6½in., 16.5cm.
Issued: 1933-1949
Price: $600 £375

CAMILLE HN1586

CAMILLA HN1710

CAMILLE HN1648

CAMELLIAS HN3701

CAMILLE HN3171

CALLED LOVE, A LITTLE BOY HN1545

ROYAL DOULTON FIGURES

CAMILLE HN1648
Designer: L. Harradine
Height: 6½in., 16.5cm.
Issued: 1934-1949
Colour variation
Price: $600 £375

CAMILLE HN1736
Designer: L. Harradine
Height: 6½in., 16.5cm.
Issued: 1935-1949
Colour variation
Price: $600 £375

CAMILLE HN3171
U.S.A. edition
Designer: P. Davies
Height: 7½in., 19cm
Issued: 1987
Price: $232 £145 (R.R.P.)

CAPTAIN (Style one) HN778
Designer: L. Harradine
Height: 7in., 17.8cm.
Issued: 1926-1938
Price: $2000 £1250

CAPTAIN (Style two) HN2260
Designer: M. Nicoll
Height: 9½in., 24.1cm.
Issued: 1965-1982
Price: $392 £245

CAPTAIN COOK HN2889
Designer: W. K. Harper
Height: 8in., 20.3cm.
Issued: 1980-1984
Price: $520 £325

CAPTAIN CUTTLE M77
Designer: L. Harradine
Height: 4in., 10.1cm.
Issued: 1939-1982
Price: $72 £45

CAPTAIN HOOK HN3636
(Resin)
Designer: Robert Tabbenor
Height: 9¼in., 23.5cm.
Issued: 1993-1996
Price: $120 £75

CAPTAIN MacHEATH HN464
Designer: L. Harradine
Height: 7in., 17.8cm.
Issued: 1921-1949
Price: $760 £475

CAPTAIN MacHEATH HN590
Designer: L. Harradine
Height: 7in., 17.8cm.
Issued: 1924-1949
Price: $760 £475

CAPTAIN MacHEATH HN1256
Designer: L. Harradine
Height: 7in., 17.8cm.
Issued: 1927-1949
Price: $760 £475

CAPTAIN (Style two) HN2260

CAPTAIN HOOK HN3636

CAPTAIÑ CUTTLE M77

CAPTAIN COOK HN2889

137

ROYAL DOULTON FIGURES

CAPTAIN, 2ND NEW YORK REGIMENT 1755 HN2755
Designer: E. J. Griffiths
Height: 10in., 25.4cm.
Issued: 1976 in a limited edition of 350
Price: $880 £550

CAREFREE (Black) HN3029
Designer: R. Jefferson
Height: 12¼in., 31cm.
Issued: 1986-1996
Price: $152 £95

CAREFREE (White) HN3026
Designer: R. Jefferson
Height: 12¼in., 31cm.
Issued: 1986
Price: $128 £80 (R.R.P.)

CARMEN (Style one) HN1267
Designer: L. Harradine
Height: 7in., 17.8cm.
Issued: 1928-1938
Price: $1040 £650

CARMEN (Style one) HN1300
Designer: L. Harradine
Height: 7in., 17.8cm.
Issued: 1928-1938 Colour variation
Price: $1760 £1100

CARMEN (Style two) HN2545
Designer: E. J. Griffiths
Height: 11½in., 29.2cm.
Issued: 1974-1977
Price: $440 £275

CARNIVAL HN1260
Designer: L. Harradine
Height: 8¼in., 21cm.
Issued: 1927-1938
Price: $2800 £1750

CARNIVAL HN1278
Designer: L. Harradine
Height: 8½in., 21.6cm.
Issued: 1928-1938
Price: $3200 £2000

CAROL HN2961
Designer: P. Parsons
Height: 7½in., 19cm.
Issued: 1982-1995
Price: $192 £120

CAROLINE HN3170
Designer: P. Davies
Height: 7½in., 19.5cm.
Issued: 1988-1992
Price: $232 £145

CAROLINE HN3694
Designer: Nada Pedley
Height: 8in., 20cm.
Issued: 1995
Price: $224 £140 (R.R.P.)

CAPTAIN, 2ND NEW YORK REGIMENT 1755 HN2755

CARNIVAL HN1260

CARMEN (Style one) HN1267

CARMEN (Style two) HN2545

CAROL HN2961

CAROLINE HN3694

ROYAL DOULTON FIGURES

CAROLYN HN2112
Designer: L. Harradine
Height: 7in., 17.8cm.
Issued: 1953-1965
Price: $440 £275

CAROLYN HN2974
Designer: A. Hughes
Height: 5½in., 14cm.
Issued: 1983-1986
Price: $280 £175

CARPENTER HN2678
Designer: M. Nicoll
Height: 8in., 20cm.
Issued: 1986-1992
Price: $360 £225

CARPET SELLER (Style one) HN1464
Designer: L. Harradine
Height: 9¼in., 23.5cm.
Issued: 1931-?
Price: $360 £225

CARPET SELLER (Style two) HN1464A
Designer: L. Harradine
Height: 9in., 22.9cm.
Issued: 1924-1969
Price: $360 £225

CARPET SELLER SITTING HN3277
Designer: R. Tabbenor
Height: 7½in., 19cm.
Issued: 1990-1995
Price: $158 £99

CARPET SELLER STANDING HN2776 (Flambé)
Designer: W.K. Harper
Height: 9in., 22.9cm.
Issued: 1990-1995
Price: $158 £99

CARPET VENDOR (Style one) HN38
Designer: C. J. Noke
Height: Unknown
Issued: 1914-1938
Price: $2400 £1500

CARPET VENDOR (Style one) HN38A
Designer: C. J. Noke
Height: Unknown
Issued: 1914-1938
Price: $2400 £1500

CARPET VENDOR (Style one) HN348
Designer: C. J. Noke
Height: Unknown
Issued: 1919-1938
Price: $2400 £1500

CAROLYN HN2112

CARPENTER HN2678

CARPET SELLER SITTING HN3277

CARPET SELLER STANDING HN2776

CARPET SELLER (Style one) HN1464

ROYAL DOULTON FIGURES

CARPET VENDOR (Style two)
HN76
Designer: C. J. Noke
Height: 5½in., 14cm.
Issued: 1917-1938
Price: $2400 £1500

CARPET VENDOR (Style two)
HN350
Designer: C. J. Noke
Height: 5½in., 14cm.
Issued: 1919-1938
Price: $2400 £1500

CARRIE HN2800
Designer: P. Davies
Height: 6in., 15.2cm.
Issued: 1976-1980
Price: $280 £175

CASSIM (Style one) HN1231
Designer: L. Harradine
Height: 3in., 7.6cm.
Issued: 1927-1938
Price: $800 £500

CASSIM (Style one) HN1232
Designer: L. Harradine
Height: 3in., 7.6cm.
Issued: 1927-1938
Price: $800 £500

CASSIM (Style two) HN1311
Designer: L. Harradine
Height: 3¾in., 9.5cm.
Issued: 1929-1938
Price: $800 £500

CASSIM (Style two) HN1312
Designer: L. Harradine
Height: 3¾in., 9.5cm.
Issued: 1929-1938
Price: $800 £500

CATHERINE HN3044
Designer: P. Parsons
Height: 5in.,12.5cm.
Issued: 1985-1996
Price: $80 £50

CATHERINE IIN3451
(U.S.A. only)
Designer: P. Parsons
Height: 5in., 12.7cm.
Issued: 1993-
             Colour variation
Price: $120 £75 (R.R.P.)

CATHERINE HOWARD
HN3449
In a limited edition of 6500
Designer: Pauline Parsons
Height: 8in., 20cm.
Issued: 1993
Price: $392 £245 (R.R.P.)

CATHERINE IN SPRING
HN3006
Designer: Peter Gee
Height: 8½in., 21.5cm.
Issued: 1985 Danbury Mint
             commission
Price: $360 £225

CATHERINE HN3451

CATHERINE HOWARD
HN3449

CATHERINE HN3044

CATHERINE OF ARAGON
HN3233

CELLIST HN2226

CATHERINE OF ARAGON
HN3233
In a limited edition of 6500
Designer: Pauline Parsons
Height: 6½in., 16.5cm.
Issued: 1993-
Price: $360 £225 (R.R.P.)

CATHERINE PARR HN3450
In a limited edition of 6500
Designer: Pauline Parsons
Height: Unknown
Issued: 1993
Price: $440 £275 (R.R.P.)

CAVALIER (Style one) HN369
Designer: Unknown
Height: Unknown
Issued: 1920-1938
Price: $1600 £1000

CAVALIER (Style two) HN2716
Designer: E. J. Griffiths
Height: 9¾in., 24.7cm.
Issued: 1976-1982
Price: $296 £185

CELESTE HN2237
Designer: P. Davies
Height: 6¾in., 17.2cm.
Issued: 1959-1971
Price: $264 £165

CELIA HN1726
Designer: L. Harradine
Height: 11½in., 29.2cm.
Issued: 1935-1949
Price: $1760 £1100

CELIA HN1727
Designer: L. Harradine
Height: 11½in., 29.2cm.
Issued: 1935-1949
Price: $1760 £1100

CELLIST HN2226
Designer: P. Davies
Height: 8in., 20.3cm.
Issued: 1960-1967
Price: $520 £325

CELLO HN2331
Designer: P. Davies
Height: 6in., 15.2cm.
Issued: 1970 in a limited
edition of 750
Price: $1040 £650

CELLO HN3707
In a limited edition of 1500
Designer: Valerie Annand
Height: 7in., 18cm.
Issued: 1996
Price: $760 £475

CENTURION HN2726
Designer: W. K. Harper
Height: 9¼in., 23.5cm.
Issued: 1982-1984
Price: $312 £195

CAVALIER (Style two) HN2716

CENTURION HN2726

CATHERINE PARR HN3450

CELLO HN2331

CERISE HN1607
Designer: L. Harradine
Height: 5¼in., 13.3cm.
Issued: 1933-1949
Price: $472 £295

CHARGE OF THE LIGHT BRIGADE HN3718
Designer: Alan Maslankowski
Height: 17in., 43cm.
Issued: 1995
Price: $13200 £8250
(R.R.P.)

CHARISMA HN3090
Designer: P. Parsons
Height: 12½in., 31.5cm.
Issued: 1987-1990
Price: $264 £165

CHARITY HN3087
Designer: E. J. Griffiths
Height: 8½in., 21.5cm.
Issued: 1987 in a limited
edition of 9500
Price: $312 $195

CHARLEY'S AUNT (Style one) HN35
Designer: A. Toft
Height: 6¾in., 17.2cm.
Issued: 1914-1938
Price: $640 £400

CHARLEY'S AUNT HN640
Designer: A. Toft
Height: 7in., 17.8cm.
Issued: 1924-1938
Colour variation
Price: $1520 £950

CHARLEY'S AUNT (Style two) HN1411
Designer: H. Fenton
Height: 8in., 20.3cm.
Issued: 1930-1938
Price: $1360 £850

CHARLEY'S AUNT (Style two) HN1554
Designer: H. Fenton
Height: 8in., 20.3cm.
Issued: 1933-1938
Price: $1360 £850

CHARLEY'S AUNT (Style three) HN1703
Designer: A. Toft
Height: 6in., 15.2cm.
Issued: 1935-1938
Price: $1040 £650

CHARISMA HN3090

CHARITY HN3087

CHARLEY'S AUNT (Style one) HN35

CHARLEY'S AUNT (Style two) HN1554

CHARLEY'S AUNT (Style two) HN1411

CHARMIAN HN1568

ROYAL DOULTON FIGURES

CHARLIE CHAPLIN HN2771
Designer: W. K. Harper
Height: 9in., 22..4cm.
Issued: 1989 in a limited
    edition of 5000
Price: $400 £250

CHARLOTTE HN2421
Designer: J. Bromley
Height: 6½in., 16.5cm.
Issued: 1972-1986
Price: $264 £165

CHARLOTTE HN2423
Designer: J. Bromley
Height: 6¾in., 17cm.
Issued: 1986-1992
Price: $264 £165

CHARLOTTE HN3658
Designer: Nada Pedley
Height: 7½in., 19cm.
Issued: 1995
Price: $232 £145

CHARLOTTE (Pink) HN3812
Designer: Alan Maslankowski
Height: 9¼in., 23.5cm.
Issued: 1996
Price: $200 £125 (R.R.P.)

**CHARLOTTE (Ivory/Gold)
HN3813**
Designer: Alan Maslankowski
Height: 9¼in., 23.5cm.
Issued: 1996-1997
Price: $200 £125 (R.R.P.)

CHARLOTTE HN4092
Designer: Nada Pedley
Height: 8½in., 21.5cm.
Issued: 1998
Price: $144 £90

CHARMIAN HN1568
Designer: L. Harradine
Height: 6½in., 16.5cm.
Issued: 1933-1938
Price: $880 £550

CHARMIAN HN1569
Designer: L. Harradine
Height: 6½in., 16.5cm.
Issued: 1933-1938
    Colour variation
Price: $880 £550

CHARMIAN HN1651
Designer: L. Harradine
Height: 6½in., 16.5cm.
Issued: 1934-1938
    Colour variation
Price: $880 £550

**CHELSEA PAIR (Woman)
HN577**
Designer: L. Harradine
Height: 6in., 15.2cm.
Issued: 1923-1938
Price: $680 £425

CHARLOTTE HN3813

CHARLIE CHAPLIN HN2771

CHARLOTTE (Pink) HN3812

CHARLOTTE HN2421

CHELSEA PAIR HN577

ROYAL DOULTON FIGURES

CHELSEA PAIR (Woman) HN578
Designer: L. Harradine
Height: 6in., 15.2cm.
Issued: 1923-1938
Colour variation
Price: $680 £425

CHELSEA PAIR (Man) HN579
Designer: L. Harradine
Height: 6in., 15.2cm.
Issued: 1923-1938
Price: $680 £425

CHELSEA PAIR (Man) HN580
Designer: L. Harradine
Height: 6in., 15.2cm.
Issued: 1923-1938
Colour variation
Price: $680 £425

CHELSEA PENSIONER HN689
Designer: L. Harradine
Height: 5¾in., 14.6cm.
Issued: 1924-1938
Price: $1200 £750

CHERIE HN2341
Designer: P. Davies
Height: 5½in., 14cm.
Issued: 1966-1992
Price: $152 £95

CHERRY BLOSSOM HN3092
Designer: P. Parsons
Height: 12¼in., 31cm.
Issued: 1987-1989
Price: $264 £165

CHERYL HN3253
Designer: D. Tootle
Height: 7½in.,19.1cm.
Issued: 1989-1994
Price: $280 £175

CHIC HN2997
Designer: R. Tabbenor
Height: 13in., 33cm.
Issued: 1987-1990
Price: $264 £165

CHIEF HN2892
Designer: W. K. Harper
Height: 7in., 17.8cm.
Issued: 1979-1988
Price: $264 £165

CHIEFTAIN HN2929
Designer: S. Keenan
Height: 8¾in., 22.2cm.
Issued: 1982 in a limited
edition of 950
Price: $600 £375

CHILD AND CRAB HN32
Designer: C. J. Noke
Height: 5¼in., 13.3cm.
Issued: 1913-1938
Price: $3600 £2250

CHERIE HN2341

CHERRY BLOSSOM HN3092

CHELSEA PAIR (Man) HN579

CHIEF HN2892

CHIC HN2997

CHILD FROM WILLIAMSBURG HN2154
Designer: P. Davies
Height: 5½in., 14cm.
Issued: 1964-1984
Price: $232 £145

CHILD STUDY (Style one) HN603A
Designer: L. Harradine
Height: 4¾in., 12cm.
Issued: 1924-1938
Price: $400 £250

CHILD STUDY (Style one) HN603B
Designer: L. Harradine
Height: 4¾in., 12cm.
Issued: 1924-1938
Colour variation
Price: $400 £250

CHILD STUDY HN606A
Designer: L. Harradine
Height: 5in., 12.7cm.
Issued: 1924-1938
Price: $312 £195

CHILD STUDY HN1441
Designer: L. Harradine
Height: 5in., 12.7cm.
Issued: 1931-1938
Price: $400 £250

CHILD STUDY (Style two) HN604A
Designer: L. Harradine
Height: 5½in., 14cm.
Issued: 1924-1938
Price: $400 £250

CHILD STUDY (Style two) HN604B
Designer: L. Harradine
Height: 5½in., 14cm.
Issued: 1924-1938
Colour variation
Price: $400 £250

CHILD STUDY (Style two) HN1442
Designer: L. Harradine
Height: 6¼in., 15.9cm.
Issued: 1931-1938
Price: $440 £275

CHILD STUDY(Style two) HN1443
Designer: L. Harradine
Height: 5in., 12.7cm.
Issued: 1931-1938
Price: $440 £275

CHILD STUDY (Style three) HN605A
Designer: L. Harradine
Height: 5½in., 14cm.
Issued: 1924-1938
Price: $360 £225

ROYAL DOULTON FIGURES

CHILD STUDY (Style three)
HN605B
Designer: L. Harradine
Height: 5½in., 14cm.
Issued: 1924-1938
Price: $360 £225

CHILD'S GRACE HN62
Designer: L. Perugini
Height: 6¾in., 17.2cm.
Issued: 1916-1938
Price: $1600 £1000

CHILD'S GRACE HN62A
Designer: L. Perugini
Height: 6¾in., 17.2cm.
Issued: 1916-1938
Colour variation
Price: $1600 £1000

CHILD'S GRACE HN510
Designer: L. Perugini
Height: 6¾in., 17.1cm.
Issued: 1921-1938
Price: $1600 £1000

CHINA REPAIRER HN2943
Designer: R. Tabbenor
Height: 6¾in., 17cm.
Issued: 1983-1988
Price: $280 £175

CHINESE DANCER HN2840
Designer: P. Davies
Height: 9in., 22.9cm.
Issued: 1980 in a limited
edition of 750
Price: $880 £550

CHITARRONE HN2700
Designer: P. Davies
Height: 7½in., 19.1cm.
Issued: 1974 in a limited
edition of 750
Price: $880 £550

CHLOE HN1470
Designer: L. Harradine
Height: 5½in., 14cm.
Issued: 1931-1949
Price: $520 £325

CHLOE HN1476
Designer: L. Harradine
Height: 5½in., 14cm.
Issued: 1931-1938
Colour variation
Price: $632 £395

CHLOE HN1479
Designer: L. Harradine
Height: 5½in., 14cm.
Issued: 1931-1949
Colour variation
Price: $520 £325

CHLOE HN1498
Designer: L. Harradine
Height: 6in., 15.2cm.
Issued: 1932-1938
Colour variation
Price: $720 £450

CHIEFTAIN HN2929

CHINA REPAIRER HN2943

CHILD FROM
WILLIAMSBURG
HN2154

CHITARRONE HN2700

CHINESE DANCER HN2840

CHLOE HN1765
Designer: L. Harradine
Height: 6in., 15.2cm.
Issued: 1936-1950
            Colour variation
Price: $560 £350

CHLOE HN1956
Designer: L. Harradine
Height: 6in., 15.2cm.
Issued: 1940-1949
            Colour variation
Price: $600 £375

CHLOE M9
Designer: L. Harradine
Height: 2¾in., 7cm.
Issued: 1932-1945
Price: $520 £325

CHLOE M10
Designer: L. Harradine
Height: 2¾in., 7cm.
Issued: 1932-1945
            Colour variation
Price: $520 £325

CHLOE M29
Designer: L. Harradine
Height: 2¾in., 7cm.
Issued: 1932-1945
            Colour variation
Price: $520 £325

CHOICE HN1959
Designer: L. Harradine
Height: 7¼in., 18.4cm.
Issued: 1941-1949
Price: $1280 £800

CHOICE HN1960
Designer: L. Harradine
Height: 7¼in., 18.4cm.
Issued: 1941-1949
Price: $1280 £800

CHOIR BOY HN2141
Designer: P. Davies
Height: 4¾in., 12cm.
Issued: 1954-1975
Price: $176 £110

CHORUS GIRL HN1401
Designer: L. Harradine
Height: 8½in., 21.6cm.
Issued: 1930-1938
Price: $2400 £1500

CHRISTENING DAY (Pink) HN3211
Designer: P. A. Northcroft
Height: 8½in., 21.5cm.
Issued: 1988-1990
Price: $232 £145

CHRISTENING DAY (Blue) HN3210
Designer: P. A. Northcroft
Height: 8½in., 21.5cm.
Issued: 1988-1990
Price: $232 £145

CHLOE HN1470

CHLOE HN1479

CHOICE HN1960

CHRISTINE HN3269

CHRISTINE (Style two) HN2792

ROYAL DOULTON FIGURES

CHRISTINE (Style one) HN1839
Designer: L. Harradine
Height: 7¾in., 19.7cm.
Issued: 1938-1949
Price: $1120 £700

CHRISTINE (Style one) HN1840
Designer: L. Harradine
Height: 7¾in., 19.7cm.
Issued: 1938-1949
            Colour variation
Price: $1120 £700

CHRISTINE (Style two) HN2792
Designer: P. Davies
Height: 7½in., 19.1cm.
Issued: 1978-1994
Price: $280 £175

CHRISTINE HN3269
Designer: Peggy Davies
Height: 4in.,10cm.
Issued: 1990-1994
Price: $120 £75

CHRISTINE HN3767
Designer: Nada Pedley
Height: 8in., 20cm.
Issued: 1996
Price: $216 £135 (R.R.P.)

CHRISTINE HN3905
Designer: Peggy Davies
Height: 7½in., 19cm.
Issued: 1998
Price: $206 £129

CHRISTMAS ANGEL HN3733
Designer: Alan Maslankowski
Height: 6in., 15cm.
Issued: 1996
Price: $64 £40 (R.R.P.)

CHRISTMAS CAROLS HN3727
Designer: Alan Maslankowski
Height: 6in., 15cm.
Issued: 1995
Price: $64 £40 (R.R.P.)

CHRISTMAS DAY HN3488
Designer: Alan Maslankowski
Height: 6in., 15cm.
Issued: 1993
Price: $64 £40 (R.R.P.)

CHRISTMAS LANTERN HN3943
Designer: Alan Maslankows
Height: 6in., 15.5cm.
Issued: 1997
Price: $64 £40 (R.R.P.)

CHRISTMAS MORN HN1992
Designer: P. Davies
Height: 7in., 17.8cm.
Issued: 1947-1996
Price: $232 £145

CHRISTMAS CAROLS HN3727

CHRISTMAS ANGEL HN3733

CHRISTINE HN3767

CHRISTMAS DAY HN3488

CHRISTMAS MORN HN1992

CHRISTMAS MORN HN3212
Designer: P. Davies
Height: 4in., 10cm.
Issued: 1988
Price: $104 £65 (R.R.P.)

**CHRISTMAS PARCELS
HN2851**
Designer: W. K. Harper
Height: 8¾in., 22.2cm.
Issued: 1978-1982
Price: $280 £175

**CHRISTMAS PARCELS
HN3493**
Designer: Alan Maslankowski
Height: 6in., 15cm.
Issued: 1994
Price: $64 £40

CHRISTMAS TIME HN2110
Designer: P. Davies
Height: 6½in.,16.5cm.
Issued: 1953-1967
Price: $520 £325

**CHRISTOPHER COLUMBUS
HN3392**
Designer: A. Maslankowski
Height: 12in., 13.5cm.
Issued: 1992 in a limited
edition of 1492
Price: $1200 £750

CICELY HN1516
Designer: L. Harradine
Height: 5¾in., 14.6cm.
Issued: 1932-1949
Price: $1200 £750

CIRCE HN1249
Designer: L. Harradine
Height: 7¾in., 19.7cm.
Issued: 1927-1938
Price: $2640 £1650

CIRCE HN1250
Designer: L. Harradine
Height: 7½in., 19.1cm.
Issued: 1927-1938
Price: $2640 £1650

CIRCE HN1254
Designer: L. Harradine
Height: 7½in., 19.1cm.
Issued: 1927-1938
Colour variation
Price: $2640 £1650

CIRCE HN1255
Designer: L. Harradine
Height: 7½in., 19.1cm.
Issued: 1927-1938
Colour variation
Price: $2640 £1650

CISSIE HN 1808
Designer: L. Harradine
Height: 5in., 12.7cm.
Issued: 1937-1951
Price: $400 £250

CHRISTMAS PARCELS
HN2851

CHRISTMAS PARCELS
HN3493

CISSIE HN1809

CHRISTOPHER COLUMBUS
HN3392

ROYAL DOULTON FIGURES

CISSIE HN1809
Designer: L. Harradine
Height: 5in., 12.7cm.
Issued: 1937-1993
          Colour variation
Price: $152 £95

CLAIRE HN3209
Designer: A. Hughes
Height: 8½in., 11.6cm.
Issued: 1990-1992
Price: $232 £145

CLAIRE HN3646
Designer: Nada Pedley
Height: 8in., 20.5cm.
Issued: 1994
Price: $136 £85 (R.R.P.)

CLARE HN2793
Designer: P. Davies
Height: 7½in., 19.1cm.
Issued: 1980-1984
Price: $280 £175

CLARIBEL HN1950
Designer: L. Harradine
Height: 4¾in., 12cm.
Issued: 1940-1949
Price: $440 £275

CLARIBEL HN1951
Designer: L. Harradine
Height: 4¾in., 12cm.
Issued: 1940-1949
Price: $440 £275

CLARINDA HN2724
Designer: W. K. Harper
Height: 8½in., 21.6cm.
Issued: 1975-1980
Price: $296 £185

CLARISSA (Style one) HN1525
Designer: L. Harradine
Height: 10in., 25.4cm.
Issued: 1932-1938
Price: $1040 £650

CLARISSA (Style one) HN1687
Designer: L. Harradine
Height: 9¾in., 24.8cm.
Issued: 1935-1949
          Colour variation
Price: $720 £450

CLARISSA (Style two) HN2345
Designer: P. Davies
Height: 7½in., 19.1cm.
Issued: 1968-1982
Price: $264 £165

CLEAR WATER HN3530
Designer: R. Jefferson
Height: 8¼in., 21cm.
Issued: 1983-1986
Price: $72 £45

(CLAIRE HN3646

CLARE HN2793

CLAIRE HN3209

CLARISSA (Style two) HN2345

CLARINDA HN2724

149

ROYAL DOULTON FIGURES

CLEMENCY HN1633
Designer: L. Harradine
Height: 7in., 17.8cm.
Issued: 1934-1938
Price: $880 £550

CLEMENCY HN1634
Designer: L. Harradine
Height: 7in., 17.8cm.
Issued: 1934-1949
Colour variation
Price: $880 £550

CLEMENCY HN1643
Designer: L. Harradine
Height: 7in., 17.8cm.
Issued: 1934-1938
Colour variation
Price: $880 £550

CLEOPATRA HN2868
Designer: P. Davies
Height: 7¼in., 18.4cm.
Issued: 1980 in a limited
edition of 750
Price: $1520 £950

CLOCKMAKER HN2279
Designer: M. Nicoll
Height: 7in., 17.8cm.
Issued: 1961-1975
Price: $472 £295

CLOTHILDE HN1598
Designer: L. Harradine
Height: 7¼in., 18.4in.
Issued: 1933-1949
Price: $960 £600

CLOTHILDE HN1599
Designer: L. Harradine
Height: 7¼in., 18.4cm.
Issued: 1933-1949
Colour variation
Price: $960 £600

CLOUD HN1831
Designer: R. Garbe
Height: 23In., 58.4cm.
Issued: 1937-1949
Price: $2400 £1500

CLOWN HN2890
Designer: W. K. Harper
Height: 9in., 22.9cm.
Issued: 1979-1988
Price: $312 £195

COACHMAN HN2282
Designer: M. Nicoll
Height: 7¼in., 18.4cm.
Issued: 1963-1971
Price: $472 £295

COBBLER (Style one) HN542
Designer: C. J. Noke
Height: 7½in., 19.1cm.
Issued: 1922-1939
Price: $760 £475

CLOTHILDE HN1598

CLOTHILDE HN1599

CLOCKMAKER HN2279

COBBLER (Style one) HN542

CLOWN HN2890

CLEOPATRA HN2868

ROYAL DOULTON FIGURES

COBBLER (Style one) HN543
Designer: C. J. Noke
Height: 7½in., 19.1cm.
Issued: 1922-1938
            Colour variation
Price: $760 £475

COBBLER (Style one) HN682
Designer: C. J. Noke
Height: 7½in., 19.1cm.
Issued: 1924-1938
            Colour variation
Price: $800 £500

COBBLER (Style two) HN681
Designer: C. J. Noke
Height: 8½in., 21.6cm.
Issued: 1924-1938
Price: $1120 £700

COBBLER (Style two) HN1251
Designer: C. J. Noke
Height: 8½in., 21.6cm.
Issued: 1927-1938
            Colour variation
Price: $1040 £650

COBBLER (Style two) HN1283
Designer: C. J. Noke
Height: 8½in., 21.6cm.
Issued: 1928-1949
            Colour variation
Price: $720 £450

COBBLER (Style three) HN1705
Designer: C. J. Noke
Height: 8in., 20.3cm.
Issued: 1935-1949
Price: $560 £350

COBBLER (Style three) HN1706
Designer: C. J. Noke
Height: 8½in., 21.6cm.
Issued: 1935-1969
            Colour variation
Price: $440 £275

COCKTAILS HN3070
Designer: A. Hughes
Height: 10¾in., 27.5cm.
Issued: 1985-1995
Price: $264 £165

COLLINETTE HN1998
Designer: L. Harradine
Height: 7¼in., 18.4cm.
Issued: 1947-1949
Price: $760 £475

COLLINETTE HN1999
Designer: L. Harradine
Height: 7¼in., 18.4cm.
Issued: 1947-1949
Price: $720 £450

COLONEL FAIRFAX HN2903
Designer: W. K. Harper
Height: 11½in., 29cm.
Issued: 1982-1986
Price: $792 £495

COCKTAILS HN3070

COBBLER (Style three) HN1706

COLLINETTE
HN1999

COLLINETTE HN1998

COBBLER (Style two) HN1283

COLONEL FAIRFAX HN2903

ROYAL DOULTON FIGURES

COLUMBINE (Style one)
HN1296
Designer: L. Harradine
Height: 6in., 15.2cm.
Issued: 1928-1938
Price: $1040 £650

COLUMBINE (Style one)
HN1297
Designer: L. Harradine
Height: 6in., 15.2cm.
Issued: 1928-1938
           Colour variation
Price: $1040 £650

COLUMBINE (Style one)
HN1439
Designer: L. Harradine
Height: 6in., 15.2cm.
Issued: 1930-1938
           Colour variation
Price: $1040 £650

COLUMBINE (Style two)
HN2185
Designer: P. Davies
Height: 7in., 17.8cm.
Issued: 1957-1969
Price: $312 £195

COLUMBINE HN2738
Designer: D. Tootle
Height: 12½in., 31cm.
Issued: 1982-
Price: $2000 £1250
           (R.R.P.)

COLUMBINE HN3288
Commissioned by Harrods in
1993.
U.S.A. edition
Designer: D. Tootle
Height: 12½in., 31.2cm.
Price: $2000 £1250

COMING OF SPRING HN1722
Designer: L. Harradine
Height: 12½in., 31.7cm.
Issued: 1935-1949
Price: $2640 £1650

COMING OF SPRING HN1723
Designer: L. Harradine
Height: 12½in., 31.7cm.
Issued: 1935-1949
           Colour variation
Price: $2640 £1650

CONFUCIUS HN3314 (Flambé)
Designer: P. Gee
Height: 9in., 22.9cm.
Issued: 1990-1995
Price: $400 £250

CONGRATULATIONS HN3351
Designer: Peter Gee
Height: 11in., 28cm.
Issued: 1991
Price: $168 £105 (R.R.P.)

COLUMBINE (Style two)
HN 2185

COLUMBINE HN3288

CONSTANCE HN1511

COLUMBINE HN2738

COLUMBINE (Style one)
HN1296

ROYAL DOULTON FIGURES

CONSTANCE HN1510
Designer: L. Harradine
Height: 6¾in., 17.1cm.
Issued: 1932-1938
Price: $1200 £750

CONSTANCE HN1511
Designer: L. Harradine
Height: 6¾in., 17.1cm.
Issued: 1932-1938
Colour variation
Price: $1200 £750

CONSTANCE (Blue) HN3930
Designer: Alan Maslankowski
Height: 8¾in., 22.5cm.
Issued: 1997 only
Price: $200 £125

CONSTANCE (Ivory/Gold) HN3933
Designer: Alan Maslankowski
Height: 8¾in., 22.5cm.
Issued: 1997 only
Price: $200 £125 (R.R.P.)

CONTEMPLATION HN2213
Designer: P. Davies
Height: 12in., 30cm.
Issued: 1982-1986
Price: $232 £145

CONTEMPLATION HN2241
Designer: P. Davies
Height: 12in., 30cm.
Issued: 1982-1986
Colour variation
Price: $232 £145

CONTENTMENT HN395
Designer: L. Harradine
Height: 7¼in., 18.4cm.
Issued: 1920-1938
Price: $1600 £1000

CONTENTMENT HN396
Designer: L. Harradine
Height: 7¼in., 18.4cm.
Issued: 1920-1938
Price: $1600 £1000

CONTENTMENT HN421
Designer: L. Harradine
Height: 7¼in., 18.4cm.
Issued: 1920-1938
Colour variation
Price: $1600 £1000

CONTENTMENT HN468
Designer: L. Harradine
Height: 7¼in., 18.4cm.
Issued: 1921-1938
Colour variation
Price: $1600 £1000

CONTENTMENT HN572
Designer: L. Harradine
Height: 7¼in., 18.4cm.
Issued: 1923-1938
Colour variation
Price: $1600 £1000

CONFUCIUS HN3314

CONGRATULATIONS HN3351

COMING OF SPRING HN1723

CONSTANCE (Ivory/Gold) HN3933

CONSTANCE (Blue) HN3930

CONTEMPLATION HN2213

ROYAL DOULTON FIGURES

CONTENTMENT HN685
Designer: L. Harradine
Height: 7¼in., 18.4cm.
Issued: 1923-1938
Colour variation
Price: $1920 £1200

CONTENTMENT HN686
Designer: L. Harradine
Height: 7¼in., 18.4cm.
Issued: 1924-1938
Colour variation
Price: $1920 £1200

CONTENTMENT HN1323
Designer: L. Harradine
Height: 7¼in., 18.4cm.
Issued: 1929-1938
Colour variation
Price: $1600 £1000

COOKIE HN2218
Designer: P. Davies
Height: 4¾in., 12cm.
Issued: 1958-1975
Price: $232 £145

COPPELIA HN2115
Designer: P. Davies
Height: 7¼in., 18.4cm.
Issued: 1953-1959
Price: $880 £550

COQUETTE HN20
Designer: W. White
Height: 9¼in., 23.5cm.
Issued: 1913-1938
Price: $3200 £2000

COQUETTE HN37
Designer: W. White
Height: 9¼in., 23.5cm.
Issued: 1913-1938
Price: $3200 £2000

CORALIE HN2307
Designer: P. Davies
Height: 7¼in., 18.4cm.
Issued: 1964-1988
Price: $264 £165

CORINTHIAN HN1973
Designer: H. Fenton
Height: 7¾in., 19.7cm.
Issued: 1941-1949
Price: $1600 £1000

CORPORAL, 1st HAMP-SHIRE REGIMENT 1778 HN2780
Designer: E. J. Griffiths
Height: 13in., 33cm.
Issued: 1975 in a limited edition of 350
Price: $800 £500

COQUETTE HN20

COUNTESS OF HARRINGTON HN3317

CORALIE HN2307

COPPELIA HN2115

CONTENTMENT HN1323

ROYAL DOULTON FIGURES

COUNTESS MARY HOWE
HN3007
Designer: P. Gee
Height: 9¼in., 23.5cm.
Issued: 1950 in a limited
             edition of 5000 -
             1994
Price: $560 £350

COUNTESS OF HARRINGTON
HN3317
Designer: Peter Gee
Height: 9½in., 24cm.
Issued: 1992 in a limited
             edition of 5000 -
             1995
Price: $520 £325

COUNTESS SPENCER HN3320
Designer: Peter Gee
Height: 9½in., 24cm.
Issued: 1993 in a limited
             edition of 5000 -
             1995
Price: $520 £325

COUNTRY GIRL HN3051
Designer: A. Hughes
Height: 7¾in., 19.5cm.
Issued: 1987-1991
Price: $200 £125

COUNTRY GIRL HN3856
Designer: Tim Potts
Height: 8in., 20cm.
Issued: 1996
Price: £120 £75 (R.R.P.)

COUNTRY GIRL HN3958
Designer: Alan Maslankowski
Height: 10¾in., 27.5cm.
Issued: 1998
Price: $136 £85 (R.R.P.)

COUNTRY LASS HN1991
Designer: L. Harradine
Height: 7¼in., 18.4cm.
Issued: 1975-1981
Price: $360 £225
Also called **MARKET DAY**
HN1991

COUNTRY LOVE HN2418
Designer: J Bromley
Height: 8in., 20.3cm.
Issued: 1990 in a limited
             edition of 12500 -
             1995
Price: $312 £195

COUNTRY MAID HN3163
Designer: P. Hughes
Height: 8¼in., 21cm.
Issued: 1988-1991
Price: $280 £175

COUNTRY ROSE HN3221
Designer: P. Davies
Height: 8½in., 21.5cm.
Issued: 1989
Price: $184 £115 (R.R.P.)

COUNTRY GIRL HN3051

COUNTRY LOVE HN2418

COUNTRY GIRL HN3856

COUNTRY ROSE HN3221

COUNTESS SPENCER HN3320

COUNTRY LASS HN1991

COURT SHOEMAKER HN1755
Designer: L. Harradine
Height: 6¾in., 17.2cm.
Issued: 1936-1949
Price: $1760 £1100

COURTIER HN1338
Designer: L. Harradine
Height: 4½in., 11.4cm.
Issued: 1929-1938
Price: $ 2400 £1500

COURTSHIP HN3525
Designer: Russell Willis
Height: 14¼in., 36cm.
Issued: 1982
Price: $632 £395 (R.R.P.)

COVENT GARDEN HN1339
Designer: L. Harradine
Height: 9in., 22.9cm.
Issued: 1929-1938
Price: $1600 £1000

COVENT GARDEN HN2857
Designer: W. K. Harper
Height: 10in., 25.5cm.
Issued: 1988-1990
Price: $312 £195

CRADLE SONG HN2246
Designer: P. Davies
Height: 5½in., 14cm.
Issued: 1959-1962
Price: $520 £325

CRAFTSMAN HN2284
Designer: M. Nicoll
Height: 8¼in., 21cm.
Issued: 1961-1965
Price: $800 $500

CRINOLINE HN21
Designer: G. Lambert
Height: 6¼in., 15.8cm.
Issued: 1913-1938
             Colour variation
Price: $1600 £1000

CRINOLINE HN8
Designer: G. Lambert
Height: 6¼in., 15.8cm.
Issued: 1913-1938
Price: $1760 £1100

CRINOLINE HN9
Designer: G. Lambert
Height: 6¼in., 15.8cm.
Issued: 1913-1938
             Colour variation
Price: $1840 £1150

CRINOLINE HN9A
Designer: G. Lambert
Height: 6¼in., 15.8cm.
Issued: 1913-1938
             Colour variation
Price: $2080 £1300

COURT SHOEMAKER HN1755

COURTSHIP HN3525

COVENT GARDEN HN1339

CRINOLINE HN21A
Designer: G. Lambert
Height: 6¼in., 15.8cm.
Issued: 1913-1938
             Colour variation
Price: $1125 £750

CRINOLINE HN413
Designer: G. Lambert
Height: 6¼in., 15.8cm.
Issued: 1920-1938
             Colour variation
Price: $1600 £1000

CRINOLINE HN566
Designer: G. Lambert
Height: 6¼in., 15.8cm.
Issued: 1923-1938
             Colour variation
Price: $1840 £1150

CRINOLINE HN628
Designer: G. Lambert
Height: 6¼in., 15.8cm.
Issued: 1924-1938
             Colour variation
Price: $2080 £1300

CRINOLINE LADY HN650
Designer: Unknown
Height: 3in., 7.6cm.
Issued: 1924-1938
Price: $1520 £950

CRINOLINE LADY HN651
Designer: Unknown
Height: 3in., 7.6cm.
Issued: 1924-1938
             Colour variation
Price: $1520 £950

CRINOLINE LADY HN652
Designer: Unknown
Height: 3in., 7.6cm.
Issued: 1924-1938
             Colour variation
Price: $1520 £950

CRINOLINE LADY HN653
Designer: Unknown
Height: 3in., 7.6cm.
Issued: 1924-1938
             Colour variation
Price: $1520 £950

CRINOLINE LADY HN654
Designer: Unknown
Height: 3in., 7.6cm.
Issued: 1924-1938
             Colour variation
Price: $1520 £950

CRINOLINE LADY HN655
Designer: Unknown
Height: 3in., 7.6cm.
Issued: 1924-1938
             Colour variation
Price: $1520 £950

CROQUET HN3470
Designer: Valerie Annand
Height: 8in., 20cm.
Issued: 1996 in a limited
           edition of 5000
Price: $312 £195 (R.R.P.)

CROUCHING NUDE HN457
Designer: Unknown
Height: 5½in., 14cm.
Issued: 1921-1938
Price: $1200 £750

CROUCHING NUDE HN604B
Designer: Leslie Harradine
Height: 5½in., 14cm.
Issued: 1921-1936
Price: $440 £275

CUP OF TEA HN2322
Designer: M. Nicoll
Height: 7in., 17.8cm.
Issued: 1964-1983
Price: $264 £165

CURLY KNOB HN1627
Designer: L. Harradine
Height: 6in., 15.2cm.
Issued: 1934-1949
Price: $1040 £650

CURLY LOCKS HN2049
Designer: P. Davies
Height: 4½in., 11.4cm.
Issued: 1949-1953
Price: $600 £375

CURTSEY HN57
Designer: E. W. Light
Height: 11in., 27.9cm.
Issued: 1916-1938
Price: $2240 £1400

CURTSEY HN57B
Designer: E. W. Light
Height: 11in., 27.9cm.
Issued: 1916-1938
           Colour variation
Price: $2000 £1250

CURTSEY HN66A
Designer: E. W. Light
Height: 11in., 27.9cm.
Issued: 1916-1938
           Colour variation
Price: $2000 £1250

CURTSEY HN327
Designer: E. W. Light
Height: 11in., 27.9cm.
Issued: 1918-1938
           Colour variation
Price: $1760 £1100

CURTSEY HN334
Designer: E. W. Light
Height: 11in., 27.9cm.
Issued: 1918-1938
           Colour variation
Price: $1760 £1100

CROUCHING NUDE HN457

CROQUET HN3470

CRINOLINE LADY HN651

CUP OF TEA HN2322

CURLY KNOB HN1627

ROYAL DOULTON FIGURES

CURTSEY HN363
Designer: E. W. Light
Height: 11in., 27.9cm.
Issued: 1919-1938
Colour variation
Price: $2240 £1400

CURTSEY HN371
Designer: E. W. Light
Height: 11in., 17.9cm.
Issued: 1920-1938
Colour variation
Price: $2240 £1400

CURTSEY HN518
Designer: E. W. Light
Height: 11in., 27.9cm.
Issued: 1921-1938
Colour variation
Price: $2240 £1400

CURTSEY HN547
Designer: E. W. Light
Height: 11in., 27.9cm.
Issued: 1922-1938
Colour variation
Price: $2240 £1400

CURTSEY HN629
Designer: E. W. Light
Height: 11in., 27.9cm..
Issued: 1924-1938
Colour variation
Price: $2240 £1400

CURTSEY HN670
Designer: E. W. Light
Height: 11in., 27.9cm.
Issued: 1924-1936
Colour variation
Price: $1760 £1100

CYMBALS HN2699
Designer: P. Davies
Height: 7½in., 19.1cm.
Issued: 1974 in a limited
edition of 750
Price: $880 £550

CYNTHIA HN1685
Designer: L. Harradine
Height: 5¾in., 14.6cm.
Issued: 1935-1949
Price: $1040 £650

CYNTHIA HN1686
Designer: L. Harradine
Height: 5¾in., 14.6cm.
Issued: 1935-1949
Colour variation
Price: $1000 £650

CYNTHIA HN1686A
Designer: L. Harradine
Height: 5¾in., 14.6cm.
Issued: 1935-1949
Colour variation
Price: $1040 £650

"DANCING EYES
AND SUNNY
HAIR" HN1543

CYMBALS
HN2699

CURTSEY
HN670

CYNTHIA HN2440

DANCING DELIGHT HN3078

CYNTHIA HN2440
Designer: P. Davies
Height: 7¼in., 18cm.
Issued: 1984-
Price: $232 £145

**CYRANO DE BERGERAC
HN3751**
Designer: David Biggs
Height: 8½in., 21.5cm.
Issued: 1995-1996
Price: $120 £75

D

DADDY'S GIRL HN3435
Designer: Alan Maslankowski
Height: 4in., 10cm.
Issued: 1993
Price: $56 £35 (R.R.P.)

DADDY'S JOY HN3294
Designer: Adrian Hughes
Height: 8in., 20.5cm.
Issued: 1990
Price: $312 £195

**DAFFY-DOWN-DILLY
HN1712**
Designer: L. Harradine
Height: 8¼in., 20.9cm.
Issued: 1935-1975
Price: $520 £325

**DAFFY-DOWN-DILLY
HN1713**
Designer: L. Harradine
Height: 8¼in., 20.9cm.
Issued: 1935-1949
Colour variation
Price: $560 £350

DAINTY MAY HN1639
Designer: L. Harradine
Height: 6in., 15.2cm.
Issued: 1934-1949
Price: $410 £275

DAINTY MAY HN1656
Designer: L. Harradine
Height: 6in., 15.2cm.
Issued: 1934-1949
Colour variation
Price: $560 £350

DAINTY MAY M67
Designer: L. Harradine
Height: 4in., 10.1cm.
Issued: 1935-1949
Price: $630 £395

DAINTY MAY M73
Designer: L. Harradine
Height: 4in., 10.1cm.
Issued: 1936-1949
Colour variation
Price: $800 £500

ROYAL DOULTON FIGURES

DAISY HN1575
Designer: L. Harradine
Height: 3¾in., 9.5cm.
Issued: 1933-1949
Price: $520 £325

DAISY HN1961
Designer: L. Harradine
Height: 3½in., 8.9cm.
Issued: 1941-1949
          Colour variation
Price: $520 £325

DAISY (Blue) HN3803
Designer: Alan Maslankowski
Height: 9¼in., 23.5cm.
Issued: 1996
Price: $200 £125 (R.R.P.)

DAISY (Ivory/Gold) HN3805
Designer: A. Maslankowski
Height: 9¼in., 23.5cm.
Issued: 1996
Price: $200 £125 (R.R.P.)

DAMARIS HN2079
Designer: P. Davies
Height: 7¼in., 18.4cm
Issued: 1951-1952
Price: $2000 £1250

DANCE, THE HN4025
Designer: D.V. Tootle
Height: 7in., 18cm.
Issued: 1998
Price: $96 £60 (R.R.P.)

DANCING DELIGHT HN3078
Designer: A. Hughes
Height: 12¾in., 32cm.
Issued: 1987-1989
Price: $264 £165

"DANCING EYES AND SUNNY HAIR" HN1543
Designer: Unknown
Height: 5in., 12.7cm.
Issued: 1933-1949
Price: $560 £350

DANCING FIGURE HN311
Designer: Unknown
Height: 17¾in., 45cm.
Issued: 1918-1938
Price: $2400 £1500

DANCING YEARS HN2235
Designer: P. Davies
Height: 6¾in., 17.2cm.
Issued: 1965-1971
Price: $440 £275

DANDY HN753
Designer: L. Harradine
Height: 6¾in., 17.2cm.
Issued: 1925-1938
Price: $1440 £900

CYRANO DE BERGERAC HN3751

DADDY'S GIRL HN3435

DAISY (Blue) HN3803

DAFFY-DOWN-DILLY HN1712

DANCING YEARS HN2235

ROYAL DOULTON FIGURES

DANIELLE HN3001
Designer: Peter Gee
Height: 7¼in., 15.5cm.
Issued: 1990-1995
Price: $176 £110

DAPHNE HN2268
Designer: P. Davies
Height: 8¼in., 21cm.
Issued: 1963-1975
Price: $280 £175

DAPPLE GREY HN2521
Designer: W.M. Chance
Height: 7in., 17.7cm.
Issued: 1938-1960
Price: $2000 £1250

DARBY HN1427
Designer: L. Harradine
Height: 5½in., 14cm.
Issued: 1930-1949
Price: $440 £275

DARBY HN2024
Designer: L. Harradine
Height: 5¾in., 14.6cm.
Issued: 1949-1959
Price: $440 £275

DARLING (Style one) HN1
Designer: C. Vyse
Height: 7¾in., 19.5cm.
Issued: 1913-1928
Price: $1600 £1000

DARLING (Style one) HN1319
Designer: C. Vyse
Height: 7½in., 19.1cm.
Issued: 1929-1959
            Colour variation
Price: $240 £150

DARLING (Style one) HN1371
Designer: C. Vyse
Height: 7½in., 19.1cm.
Issued: 1930-1938
            Colour variation
Price: $960 £600

DARLING (Style one) HN1372
Designer: C. Vyse
Height: 7¾in., 19.7cm.
Issued: 1930-1938
            Colour variation
Price: $960 £600

DARLING (Style two) HN1985
Designer: C. Vyse
Height: 5¼in., 13.3cm.
Issued: 1946-
Price: $72 £45 (R.R.P.)

DARLING HN3613
Designer: C. Vyse
Height: 5¼in., 13.3cm.
Issued: 1993
            Colour variation
Price: $152 £95

D'ARTAGNAN HN3638 (Resin)
Designer: Robert Tabbenor
Height: 9in., 23cm.
Issued: 1993-1996
Price: $120 £75

D'ARTAGNAN HN3638

DANIELLE HN3001

DARLING (Style one) HN1319

DARLING HN3613

DARLING (Style two)
HN1985

DARBY HN1427

DAPPLE GREY HN2521

ROYAL DOULTON FIGURES

DAVID COPPERFIELD M88
Designer: L. Harradine
Height: 4¼in., 10.8cm.
Issued: 1949-1983
Price: $60 £45

DAWN HN1858
Designer: L. Harradine
Height: 10in., 25.4cm.
Issued: 1938-?
Price: $2400 £1500

DAWN HN1858A
Designer: L. Harradine
Height: 9¾in., 24.7cm.
Issued: ?-1949
Colour variation
Price: $2400 £1500

DAWN HN3258
Designer: Douglas Tootle
Height: 8in., 20cm.
Issued: 1990-1992
Price: $232 £145

DAWN HN3600
Designer: Nada Pedley
Height: 7½in., 19cm.
Issued: 1993
Price: $128 £80 (R.R.P.)

DAYBREAK HN3107
Designer: R. Jefferson
Height: 11¾in., 30cm.
Issued: 1987-1989
Price: $264 £165

DAYDREAMS HN1731
Designer: L. Harradine
Height: 5¾in., 14.6cm.
Issued: 1935-1996
Price: $232 £145

DAYDREAMS HN1732
Designer: L. Harradine
Height: 5½in., 14cm.
Issued: 1935-1949
Colour variation
Price: $600 £375

DAYDEAMS HN1944
Designer: L. Harradine
Height: 5½in., 14cm.
Issued: 1940-1949
Colour variation
Price: $632 £395

DEAUVILLE HN2344
Designer: P. Davies
Height: 8¼in., 20.9cm.
Issued: 1982 in a limited
edition of 1500
Price: $400 £250

DEBBIE HN2385
Designer: P. Davies
Height: 5½in., 14cm.
Issued: 1969-1982
Price: $176 £110

DAYBREAK HN3107

DAWN HN1858

DEAUVILLE HN2344

DAWN HN3600

DEBBIE HN2400

DAYDREAMS HN1731

161

ROYAL DOULTON FIGURES

DEBBIE HN2400
Designer: P. Davies
Height: 6in., 15cm.
Issued: 1983-1995
Price: $120 £75

DEBORAH HN3644
(1995 Figure of the Year)
Designer: Nada Pedley
Height: 7½in., 19cm.
Issued: 1995
Price: $232 £145

DEBUT HN3046
Designer: P. Parsons
Height: 12¼in., 31cm
Issued: 1987-1989
Price: $264 £165

DEBUTANTE HN2210
Designer: P. Parsons
Height: 5in., 12.7cm.
Issued: 1963-1967
Price: $392 £245

DECEMBER HN2696
Designer: P. Davies
Height: 7¾in., 19.7cm.
Issued: 1987
Price: $232 £145

DECEMBER HN3329
Designer: P. Davies
Height: 7½in., 19cm.
Issued: 1991
Price: $152 £95

DEIRDRE HN2020
Designer: L. Harradine
Height: 7in., 17.8cm.
Issued: 1949-1955
Price: $600 £375

DELICIA HN1662
Designer: L. Harradine
Height: 5¾in., 14.6cm.
Issued: 1934-1938
Price: $1040 £650

DELICIA HN1663
Designer: L. Harradine
Height: 5¾in., 14.6cm.
Issued: 1934-1938
Colour variation
Price: $1040 £650

DELICIA HN1681
Designer: L. Harradine
Height: 5¾in., 14.6cm.
Issued: 1935-1938
Colour variation
Price: $1040 £650

DELIGHT HN1772
Designer: L. Harradine
Height: 7in., 17.8cm.
Issued: 1936-1967
Price: $360 £225

DEBUT HN3046

DECEMBER HN3329

DELIGHT HN1772

DELIGHT HN1773

DEMURE HN 3045

DENISE HN2273

DELIGHT HN1773
Designer: L. Harradine
Height: 6¾in., 17.2cm.
Issued: 1936-1949
Colour variation
Price: $640 £400

DELPHINE HN2136
Designer: P. Davies
Height: 7¾in., 18.4cm.
Issued: 1954-1967
Price: $360 £225

DEMURE HN3045
Designer: P. Parsons
Height: 12½in., 31.5cm.
Issued: 1987-1989
Price: $264 £165

DENISE HN2273
Designer: P. Davies
Height: 7in., 17.8cm.
Issued: 1964-1971
Price: $880 £550

DENISE M34
Designer: Unknown
Height: 4½in., 11.4cm.
Issued: 1933-1945
Price: $880 £550

DENISE M35
Designer: Unknown
Height: 4½in., 11.4cm.
Issued: 1933-1945
Colour variation
Price: $880 £550

DENISE HN2477
Designer: P. Davies
Height: 7¾in., 19.5cm.
Issued: 1987-1996
Price: $136 £85

DERRICK HN1398
Designer: L. Harradine
Height: 8in., 20.3cm.
Issued: 1930-1938
Price: $760 £475

DESDEMONA HN3676
In a limited edition of 5000
Designer: Pauline Parsons
Height: 9in., 23cm.
Issued: 1995
Price: $360 £225

DESPAIR HN596
Designer: Unknown
Height: 4½in., 11.4cm.
Issued: 1924-1938
Price: $960 £600

DETECTIVE HN2359
Designer: E. J. Griffiths
Height: 9¼in., 23.5cm.
Issued: 1977-1983
Price: $352 £220

DEVOTION HN3228
Designer: P. Parsons
Height: 9½in., 24cm.
Issued: 1989-1995
Price: $264 £165

DEVOTION HN3467
Designer: Peter Gee and A. Hughes
Height: 2½in., 6.5cm.
Issued: 1996
Price: $56 £35 (R.R.P.)

DIANA HN1716
Designer: L. Harradine
Height: 5¾in., 14.6cm.
Issued: 1935-1949
Price: $440 £275

DIANA HN1717
Designer: L. Harradine
Height: 5¾in., 14.6cm.
Issued: 1935-1949
Colour variation
Price: $440 £275

DIANA HN1986
Designer: L. Harradine
Height: 5¾in., 14.6cm.
Issued: 1946-1975
Colour variation
Price: $312 £195

DIANA HN2468
Designer: P. Davies
Height: 8in., 20cm.
Issued: 1987
Price: $184 £115 (R.R.P.)

DIANA HN3266
Designer: P. Davies
Height: 8in., 20.3cm.
Issued: 1990
Price: $264 £165

DIANA HN3310
Designer: Peggy Davies
Height: 4½in., 11.5cm.
Issued: 1991-1995
Price: $120 £75

DIANA THE HUNTRESS HN2829
Designer: R. Jefferson
Height: 11¼in., 28.5cm.
Issued: 1986 in a limited edition of 300
Price: $2000 £1250

DIANE HN3604 (R.D.I.C.C.)
Designer: Nada Pedley
Height: 8¾in., 22cm.
Issued: 1994 Only
Price: $264 £165

DICK SWIVELLER M90
Designer: L. Harradine
Height: 4¼in., 10.8cm.
Issued: 1949-1982
Price: $80 $50

DENISE HN2477

DERRICK HN1398

DEVOTION HN3228

DIANA HN3266

DIANA HN2468

DETECTIVE HN2359

163

DICK TURPIN HN3272
Designer: G. Tongue
Height: 12in., 30.5cm.
Issued: 1989 in a limited
             edition of 5000
Price: $632 £395

DICK TURPIN HN3637
Designer: Robert Tabbenor
Height: 9in., 23cm.
Issued: 1993-1996
Price: $160 £100

DIGGER (Australian) HN322
Designer: E. W. Light
Height: 11¼in., 28.5cm.
Issued: 1918-1938
Price: $2000 £1250

DIGGER (Australian) HN353
Designer: E. W. Light
Height: 11¼in., 28.5cm.
Issued: 1919-1938
Price: $2000 £1250

DIGGER (Zealand) HN321
Designer: E. W. Light
Height: 11¼in., 28.5cm.
Issued: 1918-1938
Price: $2000 £1250

DILIGENT SCHOLAR HN26
Designer: W. White
Height: 7in., 17.8cm.
Issued: 1913-1938
Price: $3200 $2000

DIMITY HN2169
Designer: L. Harradine
Height: 5¾in., 14.6cm.
Issued: 1956-1959
Price: $340 £225

DINKY DO HN1678
Designer: L. Harradine
Height: 4¾in., 12cm.
Issued: 1934-1996
             Colour variation
Price: $104 £65

DINKY DO HN2120
Designer: L. Harradine
Height: 4¾in., 12cm.
Issued: 1983-1996
Price: $88 £55

DINKY DO HN3618
Designer: L. Harradine
Height: 4¾in., 12cm.
Issued: 1994 Only
             Colour variation
Price: $104 £65

DINNERTIME HN3726
Designer: Alan Maslankowski
Height: 4½in., 11.5cm.
Issued: 1995
Price: $80 £50 (R.R.P.)

DICK TURPIN HN3637

DILIGENT SCHOLAR HN26

DINNERTIME HN3726

"DO YOU WONDER..."
HN1544

DICK TURPIN HN3272

ROYAL DOULTON FIGURES

DISCOVERY HN3428
(R.D.I.C.C.)
Designer: A. Munslow
Height: 12in., 30.5cm.
Issued: 1992 in a special
        edition for Expo 92
Price: $240 £150

"DO YOU WONDER..."
HN1544
Designer: Unknown
Height: 5in., 12.7cm.
Issued: 1933-1949
Price: $632 £395

DOCTOR HN2858
Designer: W. K. Harper
Height: 7½in., 19.1cm.
Issued: 1979-1992
Price: $260 £175

DOLLY HN355
Designer: C. J. Noke
Height: 7¼in., 18.4cm.
Issued: 1919-1938
Price: $3200 £2000

DOLLY VARDEN HN1514
Designer: L. Harradine
Height: 8½in., 21.6cm.
Issued: 1932-1938
Price: $1040 £650

DOLLY VARDEN HN1515
Designer: L. Harradine
Height: 8½in., 21.6cm.
Issued: 1932-1949
Price: $880 £550

DONNA HN2939
Designer: P. Gee
Height: 7¾in., 19.5cm.
Issued: 1982-1994
Price: $147 £95

DORCAS HN1490
Designer: L. Harradine
Height: 7in., 17.8cm.
Issued: 1932-1938
Price: $600 £375

DORCAS HN1491
Designer: L. Harradine
Height: 6¾in., 17.2cm.
Issued: 1932-1938
Price: $600 £375

DORCAS HN1558
Designer: L. Harradine
Height: 6¾in., 17.2cm.
Issued: 1932-1952
        Colour variation
Price: $560 £350

DOREEN HN1363
Designer: L. Harradine
Height: 5¼in., 13.3cm.
Issued: 1929-1938
Price: $1040 £650

DINKY DO HN1678

DINKY DO HN2120

DINKY DO HN3618

DOLLY VARDEN HN1515

DOCTOR HN2858

DONNA HN2939

DISCOVERY HN3428

DOREEN HN1389
Designer: L. Harradine
Height: 5¼in., 13.3cm.
Issued: 1930-1940
             Colour variation
Price: $1040 £650

DOREEN HN1390
Designer: L. Harradine
Height: 5¾in., 14.6cm.
Issued: 1929-1940
             Colour variation
Price: $1040 £650

DORIS KEENE as CAVALLINI
(Style one) HN90
Designer: C. J. Noke
Height: 11in., 27.9cm.
Issued: 1918-1936
Price: $2400 £1500

DORIS KEENE as CAVALLINI
(Style one) HN467
Designer: C. J. Noke
Height: 11in., 27.9cm.
Issued: 1921-1936
             Colour variation
Price: $2800 £1750

DORIS KEENE as CAVALLINI
(Style two) HN96
Designer: C. J. Noke
Height: 10¾in., 27.8cm.
Issued: 1918-1936
Price: $2320 £1450

DORIS KEENE as CAVALLINI
(Style two) HN345
Designer: C. J. Noke
Height: 10½in., 26.6cm.
Issued: 1919-1949
             Colour variation
Price: $2000 £1250

DOROTHY HN3098
Designer: P. Parsons
Height: 7in., 18cm.
Issued: 1987-1990
Price: $392 £245

DOUBLE JESTER HN365
Designer: C. J. Noke
Height: Unknown
Issued: 1920-1938
Price: $3200 £2000

DRAGON (Flambé) HN3552
Designer: Robert Tabbenor
Height: 5¼in., 13.3cm.
Issued: 1993 Only
Price: $265 £165

DREAM WEAVER HN2283
Designer: M. Nicoll
Height: 8¼in., 21cm.
Issued: 1972-1976
Price: $232 £145

DREAMING HN3133
Designer: P. Parsons
Height: 9in., 22.5cm.
Issued: 1987-1995
Price: $200 £125

DREAMING HN3133

DREAM WEAVER HN2283

DREAMLAND HN1473

DRUMMER BOY HN2679

DULCIE HN2305

ROYAL DOULTON FIGURES

DREAMLAND HN1473
Designer: L. Harradine
Height: 4¾in., 12cm.
Issued: 1931-1938
Price: $3200 £2000

DREAMLAND HN1481
Designer: L. Harradine
Height: 4¾in., 12cm.
Issued: 1931-1938
            Colour variation
Price: $3200 £2000

DRESSING UP HN2964
Designer: P. Parsons
Height: 7½in., 19cm.
Issued: 1982-1985
Price: $312 £195

DRESSING UP HN3300
Designer: N. Pedley
Height: 6¾in., 17.1 cm.
ssued: 1991 in a limited
            edition of 9500
Price: $264 £165

DRUMMER BOY HN2679
Designer: M. Nicoll
Height: 8½in., 21.6cm.
Issued: 1976-1982
Price: $560 £350

**DRYAD OF THE PINES
HN1869**
Designer: R. Garbe
Height: 23in., 58.4cm.
Issued: 1938-1949
Price: $2400 £1500

DUCHESS OF YORK HN3086
Designer: E. J. Griffiths
Height: 8½in., 21.5cm.
Issued: 1986 in a limited
            edition of 1500
Price: $630 £395

**DUKE OF WELLINGTON
HN3432**
Designer: Alan Maslankowski
Height: 12in., 30.5cm.
Issued: 1992 in a limited
            edition of 1500
Price: $1592 £995 (R.R.P.)

DULCIE HN2305
Designer: P. Davies
Height: 7¼in., 18.4cm.
Issued: 1981-1984
Price: $265 £165

DULCIMER HN2798
Designer: P. Davies
Height: 6½in., 16.5cm.
Issued: 1975 in a limited
            edition of 750
Price: $880 £550

DULCINEA HN1343
Designer: L. Harradine
Height: 5½in., 14cm.
Issued: 1929-1938
Price: $2400 £1500

DRESSING UP HN3300

DULCIMER HN2798

DUCHESS OF YORK HN3086

**DUKE OF WELLINGTON
HN3432**

ROYAL DOULTON FIGURES

DULCINEA HN1419
Designer: L. Harradine
Height: 5½in., 14cm.
Issued: 1930-1938
Colour variation
Price: $2400 £1500

DUNCE HN6
Designer: C. J. Noke
Height: 10½in., 26.7cm.
Issued: 1913-1938
Price: $1575 £1250

DUNCE HN310
Designer: C. J. Noke
Height: 10½in., 26.7cm.
Issued: 1918-1938
Colour variation
Price: $2000 £1250

DUNCE HN357
Designer: C. J. Noke
Height: 10½in., 26.7cm.
Issued: 1919-1938
Colour variation
Price: $2000 £1250

E

EASTER DAY HN1976
Designer: P. Davies
Height: 7¼in., 18.4cm.
Issued: 1945-1951
Price: $600 £375

EASTER DAY HN2039
Designer: P. Davies
Height: 7¼in., 18.4cm.
Issued: 1949-1969
Colour variation
Price: $472 £295

EASTERN GRACE HN3138
Designer: P. Parsons
Height: 12in., 30.5cm.
Issued: 1988-1989
Price: $360 £225

EDITH HN2957
Designer: P. Parsons
Height: 5¾in., 14.5cm.
Issued: 1982-1985
Price: $310 £195

ELAINE HN2791 (Blue)
Designer: P. Davies
Height: 7½in., 19.1cm.
Issued: 1980
Price: $216 £135 (R.R.P.)

ELAINE HN3214
Designer: P. Davies
Height: 3¾in., 9.5cm.
Issued: 1988
Price: $104 £65 (R.R.P.)

ELAINE (Pink) HN3307
Designer: Peggy Davies
Height: 7¼in., 18cm.
Issued: 1990
Price: $224 £140 (R.R.P.)

ELAINE HN3214

EDITH HN2957

ELAINE (Pink) HN3307

ELAINE HN2791

EASTER DAY HN2039

DULCINEA HN1343

168

ROYAL DOULTON FIGURES

ELEANOR HN3906
Designer: Peggy Davies
Height: 8in., 20.5cm.
Issued: 1998
Price: $206 £129 (R.R.P.)

ELEANOR OF PROVENCE
HN2009
Designer: P. Davies
Height: 9½in., 24.1cm.
Issued: 1948-1953
Price: $680 £425

ELEANORE HN1753
Designer: L. Harradine
Height: 7in., 17.8cm.
Issued: 1936-1949
Price: $1360 £850

ELEANORE HN1754
Designer: L. Harradine
Height: 7in., 17.8cm.
Issued: 1936-1949
           Colour variation
Price: $1360 £850

ELEGANCE HN2264
Designer: P. Davies
Height: 7¼in., 18.4cm.
Issued: 1961-1985
Price: $264 £165

ELFREDA HN2078
Designer: L. Harradine
Height: 7¼in., 18.4cm.
Issued: 1951-1955
Price: $920 £575

ELIZA HN2543
Designer: E. J. Griffiths
Height: 11¼in., 28.6cm.
Issued: 1974-1975
Price: $400 £250

ELIZA HN2543A
Designer: E. J. Griffiths
Height: 11¾in., 29.8cm.
Issued: 1975-1977
           Colour variation
Price: $400 £250

ELIZA HN3179
Designer: D. Tootle
Height: 7½in., 19cm.
Issued: 1988-1992
Price: $264 £165

ELIZA (Green) HN3798
Designer: A. Maslankowski
Height: 9¾in., 24.5cm.
Issued: 1996-1997
Price: $160 £100

ELIZA (Ivory/Gold) HN3801
Designer: A. Maslankowski
Height: 9¾in., 24.5cm.
Issued: 1996-1997
Price: $160 £100

ELIZA (Green) HN3798

ELIZA (Ivory/Gold) HN3801

ELFREDA HN2078

ELIZA HN2543

ELEANOR OF PROVENCE
HN2009

ROYAL DOULTON FIGURES

ELIZA FARRELL, COUNTESS OF DERBY HN3442
Designer: Peter Gee
Height: 7½in., 19cm.
Issued: 1992-1994
Price: $302 £195

ELIZABETH HN2946
Designer: B. Franks
Height: 8in., 20cm.
Issued: 1982-1986
Price: $360 £225

ELIZABETH HN2465
Designer: John Bromley
Height: 8½in., 21.5cm.
Issued: 1990
Price: $224 £140 (R.R.P.)

ELIZABETH FRY HN2
Designer: C. Vyse
Height: 17in., 43.2cm.
Issued: 1913-1938
Price: $3200 £2000

ELIZABETH FRY HN2A
Designer: C. Vyse
Height: 17in., 43.2cm.
Issued: 1913-1938
Price: $3200 £2000

ELLEN HN3020
Designer: P. Parsons
Height: 3½in., 9cm.
Issued: 1984-1987
Price: $392 £245

ELLEN (Blue) HN3816
Designer: Alan Maslankowski
Height: 8¾in., 22.5cm.
Issued: 1997 Only
Price: $160 £100

ELLEN (Ivory/Gold) HN3819
Designer: Alan Maslankowski
Height: 8¾in., 22.5cm.
Issued: 1997 Only
Price: $160 £100

ELLEN TERRY as QUEEN CATHERINE HN379
Designer: C. J. Noke
Height: 12½in., 31.7cm.
Issued: 1920-1949
Price: $2320 £1450

ELSIE MAYNARD HN639
Designer: C. J. Noke
Height: 7in., 17.8cm.
Issued: 1924-1949
Price: $760 £475

ELSIE MAYNARD HN2902
Designer: W. K. Harper
Height: 11¼in., 28.5cm.
Issued: 1982-1986
Price: $630 £395

ELSIE MAYNARD HN639

ELIZA FARRELL, COUNTESS OF DERBY HN3442

ELLEN (Blue) HN3816

ELIZABETH FRY HN2

ELIZABETH HN2946

170

ELYSE HN2429
Designer: P. Davies
Height: 5⅝in., 14.6cm.
Issued: 1972-1995
Price: $232 £145

ELYSE(Green) HN2474
Designer: P. Davies
Height: 6¾in., 17cm.
Issued: 1987
Price: $240 £150 (R.R.P.)

EMBROIDERING HN2855
Designer: W. K. Harper
Height: 7¼in., 18.4cm.
Issued: 1980-1990
Price: $280 £175

EMILY HN3204
Designer: Adrian Hughes
Height: 8¼in., 21cm.
Issued: 1989-1994
Price: $200 £125

EMILY(Pink) HN3808
Designer: Alan Maslankowski
Height: 9in., 23cm.
Issued: 1996-1997
Price: $200 £125

EMILY HN3688
(R.D.I.C.C.)
Designer: Nada Pedley
Height: 8¼in., 21cm.
Issued: 1995 Only
Price: $232 £145

EMILY (Ivory/Gold) HN3809
Designer: Alan Maslankowski
Height: 9in., 23cm.
Issued: 1996-1997
Price: $160 £125

EMILY (Green Dress) HN4093
Designer: Nada Pedley
Height: 8½in., 21cm.
Issued: 1998
Price: $200 £100 (R.R.P.)

EMILY IN AUTUMN HN3004
Designer: Peter Gee
Height: 8in., 20.5cm.
Issued: 1986 Danbury Mint
            commission
Price: $360 £225

EMIR HN1604
Designer: C. J. Noke
Height: 7½in., 19.1cm.
Issued: 1933-1949
Price: $840 £525

EMIR HN1605
Designer: C. J. Noke
Height: 7¼in., 18.4cm.
Issued: 1933-1949
Price: $760 £475
(Also called Ibrahim HN2095)

EMILY HN3808

EMILY HN3809

EMBROIDERING HN2855

ELSIE MAYNARD HN2902

ELYSE (Green) HN2474

ROYAL DOULTON FIGURES

EMMA HN2834
Designer: P. Davies
Height: 5¾in., 14.6cm.
Issued: 1977-1981
Price: $310 £195

EMMA HN3208
Designer: Adrian Hughes
Height: 4½in., 11.5cm.
Issued: 1990
Price: $104 £65 (R.R.P.)

EMMA HN3714
Designer: Valerie Annand
Height: 8½in., 21.5cm.
Issued: 1997
Price: $152 £95 (R.R.P.)

EMMA HN3843
In a limited edition of 3500
Designer: Pauline Parsons
Height: 8¼in., 21cm.
Issued: 1998
Price: $320 £200 (R.R.P.)

ENCHANTING EVENING HN3108
Designer: R. Jefferson
Height: 11¾in., 30cm.
Issued: 1987-1992
Price: $232 £145

ENCHANTMENT HN2178
Designer: P. Davies
Height: 7½in., 19.1cm.
Issued: 1957-1982
Price: $232 £145

ENCORE HN2751
Designer: D. Tootle
Height: 10in., 25.5cm.
Issued: 1988-1989
Price: $232 £145

ENGLAND HN3627
Designer: Valerie Annand
Height: 8in., 20cm.
Issued: 1996
Price: $288 £180 (R.R.P.)

ENIGMA HN3110
Designer: R. Jefferson
Height: 12¾in., 32cm.
Issued: 1987-1995
Price: $232 £145

ENTRANCED HN3186
Designer: E. J. Griffiths
Height: 7¼in., 18.5cm.
Issued: 1988-1989
Price: $216 £135

ERMINE COAT HN1981
Designer: L. Harradine
Height: 6¾in., 17.2cm.
Issued: 1945-1967
Price: $390 £245

EMMA HN3208

ENGLAND HN3627

ENCHANTING
EVENING
HN3108

ENCHANTMENT HN2178

ERMINE COAT HN1981

ESTELLE HN1566

ROYAL DOULTON FIGURES

ERMINE MUFF HN54
Designer: C. J. Noke
Height: 8½in., 21.6cm.
Issued: 1916-1938
Price: $2320 £1450

ERMINE MUFF HN332
Designer: C. J. Noke
Height: 8½in., 21.6cm.
Issued: 1918-1938
            Colour variation
Price: $1920 £1200

ERMINE MUFF HN671
Designer: C. J. Noke
Height: 8½in., 21.6cm.
Issued: 1924-1938
            Colour variation
Price: $960 £600

ERMINIE M40
Designer: Unknown
Height: 4in., 10.1cm.
Issued: 1933-1945
Price: $760 £475

ESMERALDA HN2168
Designer: P. Davies
Height: 5½in., 14cm.
Issued: 1956-1959
Price: $440 £275

ESTELLE HN1566
Designer: L. Harradine
Height: 8in., 20.3cm.
Issued: 1933-1940
Price: $1040 £650

ESTELLE HN1802
Designer: L. Harradine
Height: 8in., 20.3cm.
Issued: 1937-1949
            Colour variation
Price: $880 £550

ETE HN3067
Designer: R. Jefferson
Height: 11½in., 29cm.
Issued: 1989 in a limited
            edition of 300
Price: $1040 £650

EUGENE HN1520
Designer: L. Harradine
Height: 5¾in., 14.6cm.
Issued: 1932-1938
Price: $1560 £975

EUGENE HN1521
Designer: L. Harradine
Height: 5in., 12.7cm.
Issued: 1932-1938
            Colour variation
Price: $1560 £975

EUROPA AND THE BULL HN95
Designer: H. Tittensor
Height: 9¾in., 24.7cm.
Issued: 1918-1938
Price: $5200 £3250

ESMERALDA HN2168

ERMINE MUFF HN54

EUGENE HN1521

ENIGMA HN3110

EUROPA AND THE BULL HN2828

**EUROPA AND THE BULL
HN2828**
Designer: R. Jefferson
Height: 10½in., 26.5cm.
Issued: 1985 in a limited
edition of 300
Price: $2000 £1250

EVE HN2466
Designer: P. Davies
Height: 9¼in., 23.5cm.
Issued: 1984 in a limited
edition of 750
Price: $1200 £750

EVELYN HN1622
Designer: L. Harradine
Height: 6¼in., 15.9cm.
Issued: 1934-1940
Price: $1040 £650

EVELYN HN1637
Designer: L. Harradine
Height: 6in., 15.2cm.
Issued: 1934-1938
Colour variation
Price: $1040 £650

EVENTIDE HN2814
Designer: W. K. Harper
Height: 7¾in., 19.7cm.
Issued: 1977-
Price: $280 £175

F

FAGIN HN534
Designer: L. Harradine
Height: 4in., 10.1cm.
Issued: 1922-1932
Price: $88 £55

FAGIN HN3752 (Resin)
Designer: Arthur Dobson
Height: 8½in., 21.5cm.
Issued: 1995-1996
Price: $120 £75 (R.R.P.)

FAGIN M49
Designer: L. Harradine
Height: 4in., 10.1cm.
Issued: 1932-1983
Price: $72 £45

FAIR LADY HN2835
Designer: P. Davies
Height: 7¼in., 18.4cm.
Issued: 1977-1996
Colour variation
Price: $200 £125

FAIR LADY HN2832
Designer: P. Davies
Height: 7¼in., 18.4cm.
Issued: 1977-1996
Colour variation
Price: $200 £125

FAGIN HN3752

EVENTIDE HN2814

EVE HN2466

FAIR LADY HN2193
Designer: P. Davies
Height: 7¼in., 18.4cm.
Issued: 1963-1996
Price: $200 £125

FAIR LADY HN3216
Designer: P. Davies
Height: 3¾in., 9.5cm.
Issued: 1988-1995
Price: $104 £65

FAIR MAIDEN HN2211
Designer: P. Davies
Height: 5¼in., 13.3cm.
Issued: 1967-1994
Price: $120 £75

FAIR MAIDEN HN2434
Designer: P. Davies
Height: 5¼in., 13.3cm.
Issued: 1983-1994
         Colour variation
Price: $120 £75

FAIRY (Style one) HN1324
Designer: L. Harradine
Height: 6½in., 16.5cm.
Issued: 1929-1938
Price: $1520 £950

FAIRY (Style two) HN1374
Designer: L. Harradine
Height: 4in., 10.1cm.
Issued: 1930-1938
Price: $1600 £1000

FAIRY (Style two) HN1380
Designer: L. Harradine
Height: 4in., 10.1cm.
Issued: 1930-1938
         Colour variation
Price: $1600 £1000

FAIRY (Style two) HN1532
Designer: L. Harradine
Height: 4in., 10.1cm.
Issued: 1932-1938
Price: $1600 £1000

FAIRY (Style three) HN1375
Designer: L. Harradine
Height: 3in., 7.6cm.
Issued: 1930-1938
Price: $1200 £750

FAIRY (Style three) HN1395
Designer: L. Harradine
Height: 3in., 7.6cm.
Issued: 1930-1938
         Colour variation
Price: $1200 £750

FAIRY (Style three) HN1533
Designer: L. Harradine
Height: 3in., 7.6cm.
Issued: 1932-1938
Price: $1200 £750

FAIR MAIDEN HN2434

FAIR MAIDEN HN2211

FAIR LADY HN2193

FAIRY (Style three) HN1395

FAIRY (Style two) HN1380

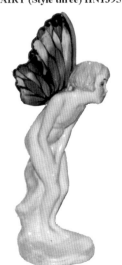

FAIRY (Style one) HN1324

FAIRY (Style two) HN1532

ROYAL DOULTON FIGURES

FAIRY (Style four) HN1376
Designer: L. Harradine
Height: 2½in., 6.3cm.
Issued: 1930-1938
Price: $880 £550

FAIRY (Style four) HN1536
Designer: L. Harradine
Height: 2½in., 6.3cm.
Issued: 1932-1938
Price: $880 £550

FAIRY (Style five) HN1378
Designer: L. Harradine
Height: 2½in., 6.3cm.
Issued: 1930-1938
Price: $800 £500

FAIRY (Style five) HN1396
Designer: L. Harradine
Height: 2½in., 6.3cm.
Issued: 1930-1938
Price: $800 £500

FAIRY (Style five) HN1535
Designer: L. Harradine
Height: 2½in., 6.3cm.
Issued: 1932-1938
        Colour variation
Price: $800 £500

FAIRY (Style six) HN1379
Designer: L. Harradine
Height: 2½in., 6.3cm.
Issued: 1930-1938
Price: $880 £550

FAIRY (Style six) HN1394
Designer: L. Harradine
Height: 2½in., 6.3cm.
Issued: 1930-1938
        Colour variation
Price: $1040 £650

FAIRY (Style six) HN1534
Designer: L. Harradine
Height: 2½in., 6.3cm.
Issued: 1932-1938
Price: $880 £550

FAIRY (Style seven) HN1393
Designer: L. Harradine
Height: 2½in., 6.3cm.
Issued: 1930-1938
Price: $880 £550

FAIRY SPELL HN2979
Designer: A. Hughes
Height: 5¼in., 13cm.
Issued: 1983-1986
Price: $232 £145

FAITH HN3082
Designer: E. J. Griffiths
Height: 8½in., 21.5cm.
Issued: 1986 in a limited
        edition of 9500
Price: $312 £195

FAIRY (Style six) HN1394

FAIRY (Style six) HN1379

FAIRY (Style five) HN1378

FAIRY SPELL HN2979

FAITH HN3082

FAITHFUL FRIEND
HN3696

FAITHFUL FRIEND HN3696
Designer: Nada Pedley
Height: 6in., 15cm.
Issued: 1995-1997
Price: $120 £75 (R.R.P.)

FALSTAFF (Style one) HN571
Designer: C. J. Noke
Height: 7in., 17.8cm.
Issued: 1923-1938
Price: $1200 £750

FALSTAFF (Style one) HN575
Designer: C. J. Noke
Height: 7in., 17.8cm.
Issued: 1923-1938
Price: $1200 £750

FALSTAFF (Style one) HN608
Designer: C. J. Noke
Height: 7in., 17.8cm.
Issued: 1924-1938
        Colour variation
Price: $1200 £750

FALSTAFF (Style one) HN609
Designer: C. J. Noke
Height: 7in., 17.8cm.
Issued: 1924-1938
        Colour variation
Price: $640 £400

FALSTAFF HN619
Designer: C. J. Noke
Height: 7in., 17.8cm.
Issued: 1924-1938
        Colour variation
Price: $640 £400

FALSTAFF (Style one) HN638
Designer: C. J. Noke
Height: 7in., 17.8cm.
Issued: 1924-1938
        Colour variation
Price: $1200 £750

FALSTAFF (Style one) HN1216
Designer: C. J. Noke
Height: 7in., 17.8cm.
Issued: 1926-1949
        Colour variation
Price: $1040 £650

FALSTAFF (Style one) HN1606
Designer: C. J. Noke
Height: 7in., 17.8cm.
Issued: 1933-1949
        Colour variation
Price: $880 £550

FALSTAFF (Style two) HN618
Designer: C. J. Noke
Height: 7in., 17.8cm.
Issued: 1924-1938
Price: $640 £400

FALSTAFF (Style two) HN2054
Designer: C. J. Noke
Height: 7in., 17.8cm.
Issued: 1950-1992
        Colour variation
Price: $264 £165

ROYAL DOULTON FIGURES

FALSTAFF HN3236
Designer: C. J. Noke
Height: 4in., 10cm.
Issued: 1989-1992
Price: $160 £100

FAMILY HN2730 (White)
Designer: E. Griffiths
Height: 12in., 30.5cm.
Issued: 1981
Price: $168 £105 (R.R.P.)

FAMILY HN2721 (Black)
Designer: E. Griffiths
Height: 12in., 30.5cm.
Issued: 1981-1992
Price: $200 £125

FAMILY ALBUM HN2321
Designer: M. Nicoll
Height: 6¼in., 15.9cm.
Issued: 1966-1973
Price: $470 £295

FANTASY HN3296
Designer: A. Hughes
Height: 12½in., 31.7cm.
Issued: 1990-1992
Price: $360 £225

FARAWAY HN2133
Designer: P. Davies
Height: 2½in., 6.3cm.
Issued: 1958-1962
Price: $472 £295

FARMER HN3195
Designer: A. Hughes
Height: 9in., 23cm.
Issued: 1988-1991
Price: $312 £195

FARMER'S BOY HN2520
Designer: W. M. Chance
Height: 8½in., 21.6cm.
Issued: 1938-1960
Price: $2000 £1250

FARMER'S WIFE HN2069
Designer: L. Harradine
Height: 9in., 22.9cm.
Issued: 1951-1955
Price: $760 £475

FARMER'S WIFE HN3164
Designer: A. Hughes
Height: 8¾in., 22cm.
Issued: 1988-1991
Price: $295 £185

FAT BOY (Style one) HN530
Designer: L. Harradine
Height: 3½in., 8.9cm.
Issued: 1922-1932
Price: $96 £60

FAT BOY (Style two) HN555
Designer: L. Harradine
Height: 7in., 17.8cm.
Issued: 1923-1939
Price: $520 £325

FAMILY ALBUM HN2321

FALSTAFF (Style one) HN1606

FARMER'S BOY HN2520

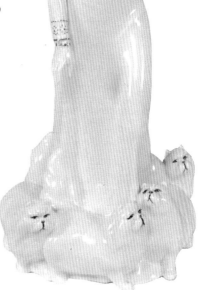

FALSTAFF (Style two) HN2054

FANTASY HN3296

177

ROYAL DOULTON FIGURES

FAT BOY (Style two) HN1893
Designer: L. Harradine
Height: 7in., 17.8cm.
Issued: 1938-1952
            Colour variation
Price: $440 £275

FAT BOY (Style three) HN2096
Designer: L. Harradine
Height: 7¼in., 18.4cm.
Issued: 1952-1967
Price: $440 £275

FAT BOY M44
Designer: L. Harradine
Height: 4¼in., 10.8cm.
Issued: 1932-1982
Price: $80 £50

**FATHER CHRISTMAS
HN3399**
Designer: Robert Tabbenor
Height: 9in., 23cm.
Issued: 1992
Price: $240 £150 (R.R.P.)

FAVOURITE HN2249
Designer: M. Nicoll
Height: 7¾in., 19.7cm.
Issued: 1960-1990
Price: $280 £175

FEBRUARY HN2703
Designer: P. Davies
Height: 7¾in., 19.7cm.
Issued: 1987 Only
Price: $232 £145

FEEDING TIME HN3373
Designer: Nada Pedley
Height: 7¼in., 18.5cm.
Issued: 1991 in a limited
            edition of 9500-
            1994
Price: $264 £165

FIDDLER HN2171
Designer: M. Nicoll
Height: 8¾in., 22.2cm.
Issued: 1956-1962
Price: $1200 £750

**FIELD MARSHAL
MONTGOMERY HN3405**
Designer: Robert Tabbenor
Height: 11¾in., 30cm.
Issued: 1994 in a limited
            edition of 1944
Price: $880 £550 (R.R.P.)

FIGHTER ELEPHANT HN2640
Designer: Charles Noke
Height: 12in., 30.5cm.
Issued: 1952-1992
Price: $1520 £950

FIONA (Style one) HN1924
Designer: L. Harradine
Height: 5¾in., 14.6cm.
Issued: 1940-1949
Price: $1200 £750

FAT BOY (Style two) HN555

FATHER CHRISTMAS
HN3399

FIELD MARSHAL
MONTGOMERY HN3405

FAVOURITE HN2249

FIDDLER HN2171

FAT BOY M44

FEBRUARY HN2703

FIONA (Style one) HN1925
Designer: L. Harradine
Height: 5¾in., 14.6cm.
Issued: 1940-1949
Colour variation
Price: $1200 £750

FIONA (Style one) HN1933
Designer: L. Harradine
Height: 5¾in., 14.6cm.
Issued: 1940-1949
Colour variation
Price: $1200 £750

FIONA (Style two) HN2694
Designer: P. Davies
Height: 7½in., 19.1cm.
Issued: 1974-1980
Price: $264 £165

FIONA HN3252
Designer: D. Tootle
Height: 7in., 17.8cm.
Issued: 1989-1992
Price: $280 £175

FIRST BORN HN3468
Designer: Adrian Hughes
Height: 6in., 15cm.
Issued: 1997
Price: $128 £80 (R.R.P.)

FIRST DANCE HN2803
Designer: P. Davies
Height: 7¼in., 18.4cm.
Issued: 1977-1992
Price: $264 £165

FIRST LOVE (White) HN2747
Designer: D. Tootle
Height: 13in., 33cm.
Issued: 1987-1997
Price: $152 £95 (R.R.P.)

FIRST OUTING HN3377
Designer: Nada Pedley
Height: 7½in., 19.5cm.
Issued: 1991 in a limited
edition of 9500-1994
Price: $264 £165

FIRST PERFORMANCE HN3605
Designer: Nada Pedley
Height: 6¼in., 16cm.
Issued: 1994
Price: $104 £65 (R.R.P.)

FIRST PRIZE HN3911
Designer: Nada Pedley
Height: 5in., 13cm.
Issued: 1997
Price: $104 £65 (R.R.P.)

FIRST RECITAL HN3652
Designer: Nada Pedley
Height: 4¼in., 11cm.
Issued: 1994-1996
Price: $104 £65

FIRST STEPS HN2242
Designer: P. Davies
Height: 6½in., 16.5cm.
Issued: 1959-1965
Price: $560 £350

FIONA HN1924

FIONA HN3252

FIRST PERFORMANCE HN3605

FIRST DANCE HN2803

FIRST OUTING HN3377

FIRST RECITAL HN3652

ROYAL DOULTON FIGURES

FIRST STEPS HN3282
Designer: Robert Tabbenor
Height: 10in., 25.5cm.
Issued: 1991
Price: $120 £75 (R.R.P.)

FIRST STEPS HN3361
Designer: V. Annand
Height: 5in., 12.7cm.
Issued: 1992-1996
Price: $176 £110

FIRST VIOLIN HN3704
In a limited edition of 1500
Designer: Valerie Annand
Height: 9in., 23cm.
Issued: 1996
Price: $400 £250

FIRST WALTZ HN2862
Designer: P. Davies
Height: 7¼in., 18.4cm.
Issued: 1979-1983
Price: $264 £165

FISHERWOMEN HN80
Designer: Unknown
Height: Unknown
Issued: 1917-1938
Price: $2400 £1500

FISHERWOMEN HN349
Designer: Unknown
Height: Unknown
Issued: 1919-1938
Colour variation
Price: $2400 £1500

FISHERWOMEN HN359
Designer: Unknown
Height: Unknown
Issued: 1919-1938
Colour variation
Price: $2400 £1500

FISHERWOMEN HN631
Designer: Unknown
Height: Unknown
Issued: 1924-1938
Colour variation
Price: $2400 £1500

FITZHERBERT, MRS HN2007
Designer: P. Davies
Height: 9¼in., 23.5cm.
Issued: 1948-1953
Price: $600 £375

FLEUR HN2368
Designer: J. Bromley
Height: 7¼in., 18.4cm.
Issued: 1968-1995
Price: $232 £145

FLEUR (Red) HN2369
Designer: J. Bromley
Height: 7¾in., 19.5cm.
Issued: 1983-1986
Colour variation
Price: $232 £145

FIRST STEPS HN2242

FIRST STEPS HN3361

FIRST WALTZ HN2862

FIRST STEPS HN3282

FLEUR HN2368

FLIRTATION HN3071

FLEURETTE HN1587
Designer: L. Harradine
Height: 6½in., 16.5cm.
Issued: 1933-1949
Price: $600 £375

FLIRTATION HN3071
Designer: A. Hughes
Height: 10in., 25.5cm.
Issued: 1987-1995
Price: $264 £165

FLORA HN2349
Designer: M. Nicoll
Height: 7¾in., 19.7cm.
Issued: 1966-1973
Price: $312 £195

FLORENCE HN2745
Designer: D. Tootle
Height: 8in., 20cm.
Issued: 1988-1992
Price: $232 £145

FLORENCE NIGHTINGALE HN3144
Designer: P. Parsons
Height: 8¼in., 21cm.
Issued: 1988 in a limited edition of 500
Price: $880 £550

FLOUNCED SKIRT HN57A
Designer: E. W. Light
Height: 9¾in., 24.7cm.
Issued: 1916-1938
Price: $1840 £1150

FLOUNCED SKIRT HN66
Designer: E. W. Light
Height: 9¾in., 24.7cm.
Issued: 1916-1938
   Colour variation
Price: $2000 £1250

FLOUNCED SKIRT HN77
Designer: E. W. Light
Height: 9¾in., 24.7cm.
Issued: 1917-1938
   Colour variation
Price: $1840 £1150

FLOUNCED SKIRT HN78
Designer: E. W. Light
Height: 9¾in., 24.7cm.
Issued: 1917-1938
   Colour variation
Price: $1840 £1150

FLOUNCED SKIRT HN333
Designer: E. W. Light
Height: 9¾in., 24.7cm.
Issued: 1918-1938
   Colour variation
Price: $1840 £1150

FLOWER ARRANGING HN3040
Designer: P. Parsons
Height: 8¾in., 22cm.
Issued: 1988 in a limited edition of 750
Price: $880 £550

FLEURETTE HN1587

FLORA HN2349

FLOWER ARRANGING
HN3040

FLOWERGIRL HN3602
Designer: Nada Pedley
Height: 4¼in., 10.5cm.
Issued: 1993-1996
Price: $72 £45

FLOWER OF LOVE HN2460
Designer: John Bromley
Height: 7½in., 19cm.
Issued: 1991-1997
Price: $152 £95

FLOWER SELLER HN789
Designer: L. Harradine
Height: 8¾in., 22.2cm.
Issued: 1926-1938
Price: $1040 £650

FLOWER SELLER'S CHILDREN HN525
Designer: L. Harradine
Height: 8¾in., 21cm.
Issued: 1921-1949
Price: $720 £450

FLOWER SELLER'S CHILDREN HN551
Designer: L. Harradine
Height: 8¼in., 21cm.
Issued: 1922-1949
Colour variation
Price: $720 £450

FLOWER SELLER'S CHILDREN HN1206
Designer: L. Harradine
Height: 8¼in., 21cm.
Issued: 1926-1949
Colour variation
Price: $952 $595

FLOWER SELLER'S CHILDREN HN1342
Designer: L. Harradine
Height: 8in., 20.3cm.
Issued: 1929-1993
Colour variation
Price: $632 £395

FLOWER SELLER'S CHILDREN HN1406
Designer: L. Harradine
Height: 8¼in., 21cm.
Issued: 1930-1938
Colour variation
Price: $1520 £950

FLOWERS FOR MOTHER HN3454
Designer: Pauline Parsons
Height: 5¾in., 14.5cm.
Issued: 1994-1997
Price: $88 £55

FLOWERS FOR YOU HN3889
Designer: Nada Pedley
Height: 5½in., 14.5cm.
Issued: 1997
Price: $80 £50 (R.R.P.)

FLOWERGIRL HN3602

FLOWER OF LOVE HN2460

FLOWER SELLER HN789

FLOWERS FOR MOTHER HN3454

FLOWER SELLER'S CHILDREN HN1342

FLUTE HN2483
Designer: P. Davies
Height: 6in., 15.2cm.
Issued: 1973 in a limited
             edition of 750
Price: $960 £600

FOAMING QUART HN2162
Designer: P. Davies
Height: 6in., 15.2cm.
Issued: 1955-1992
Price: $264 £165

FOLLY HN1335
Designer: L. Harradine
Height: 9in., 22.9cm.
Issued: 1929-1938
Price: $2960 £1850

FOLLY HN1750
Designer: L. Harradine
Height: 9½in., 24.1cm.
Issued: 1936-1949
             Colour variation
Price: $2960 £1850

FOND FAREWELL HN3815
Designer: Alan Maslankowski
Height: 8in., 20cm.
Issued: 1997
Price: $216 £135 (R.R.P.)

FOR YOU HN3754
Designer: Tim Potts
Height: 8¼in., 21cm.
Issued: 1996
Price: $128 £80 (R.R.P.)

FOR YOU (Pink) HN3863
Designer: Tim Potts
Height: 8in., 20.5cm.
Issued: 1997
Price: $128 £80 (R.R.P.)

FOREVER YOURS HN3949
Designer: Alan Maslankowski
Height: 3¾in, 9.5cm.
Issued: 1998
Price: $64 £40 (R.R.P.)

FORGET-ME-NOT HN1812
Designer: L. Harradine
Height: 6in., 15.2cm.
Issued: 1937-1949
Price: $760 £475

FORGET-ME-NOT HN1813
Designer: L. Harradine
Height: 6in., 15.2cm.
Issued: 1937-1949
             Colour variation
Price: $760 £475

FORGET-ME-NOT HN3388
Designer: A. Maslankowski
Height: 6in., 15cm.
Issued: 1991
Price: $64 £40 (R.R.P.)

FLUTE HN2483

FOLLY HN1335

FOND FAREWELL
HN3815

FOR YOU HN3754

FOAMING QUART HN2162

183

ROYAL DOULTON FIGURES

FORGET-ME-NOTS HN3700
Designer: V. Annand
Height: 9in., 22.5cm.
Issued: 1995
Price: $224 £140 (R.R.P.)

FORTUNE TELLER HN2159
Designer: L. Harradine
Height: 6½in., 16.5cm.
Issued: 1955-1967
Price: $520 £325

FORTY WINKS HN1974
Designer: H. Fenton
Height: 6¾in., 17cm.
Issued: 1945-1973
Price: $312 £195

FOUR O'CLOCK HN1760
Designer: L. Harradine
Height: 6in., 15.2cm.
Issued: 1936-1949
Price: $1040 £650

FOX HN2634
Designer: Unknown
Height: 10½in., 26.7cm.
Issued: 1952-1992
Price: $1040 £650

FRAGRANCE HN2334
Designer: P. Davies
Height: 7¼in., 18.4cm.
Issued: 1966-1995
Price: $200 £125

FRAGRANCE HN3220
Designer: P. Davies
Height: 3½in., 9cm.
Issued: 1988-1992
Price: $135 £85

FRAGRANCE HN3311
Designer: Peggy Davies
Height: 7¼in., 19cm.
Issued: 1991 only. (Michael
         Doulton Events)
Price: $232 £145

**FRANCES DUNCOMBE
HN3009**
Designer: Peter Gee
Height: 9¾in., 24.7cm.
Issued: 1991 in a limited
         edition of 5000-1994
Price: $520 £325

FRANCINE HN2422
Designer: J. Bromley
Height: 5in., 12.7cm.
Issued: 1972-1980
Price: $192 £120

FRANGÇON HN1720
Designer: L. Harradine
Height: 7½in., 19.1cm.
Issued: 1935-1949
Price: $1400 £875

FRANGÇON HN1721
Designer: L. Harradine
Height: 7¼in., 18.4cm.
Issued: 1935-1949
         Colour variation
Price: $1400 £875

FORGET-ME-NOT HN3388

FORGET-ME-NOT
HN1813

FORGET-ME-NOTS HN3700

FORTUNE TELLER HN2159

FORTY WINKS HN1974

FRANCES DUNCOMBE
HN3009

ROYAL DOULTON FIGURES

FREE AS THE WIND HN3139
Designer: P. Parsons
Height: 9½in., 24cm.
Issued: 1989-1995
Price: $264 £165

FREE SPIRIT (White) HN3157
Designer: A. Hughes
Height: 10½in., 26.5cm.
Issued: 1987-1992
Price: $200 £125

FREE SPIRIT (Black) HN3159
Designer: A. Hughes
Height: 10½in., 26.5cm.
Issued: 1987-1992
Price: $200 £125

FREE SPIRIT HN3728
Designer: A. Maslankowski
Height: 7½in., 19cm.
Issued: 1995
Price: $128 £80

FREEDOM HN3528
Designer: R. Jefferson
Height: 8½in., 22cm.
Issued: 1983-1986
Price: $72 £45

FRENCH HORN HN2795
Designer: P. Davies
Height: 6in., 15.2cm.
Issued: 1976 in a limited
edition of 750
Price: $880 £550

FRENCH PEASANT HN2075
Designer: L. Harradine
Height: 9¼in., 23.5cm.
Issued: 1951-1955
Price: $760 £475

FRIAR TUCK HN2143
Designer: P. Davies
Height: 7½in., 19.1cm.
Issued: 1954-1965
Price: $680 £425

FRIENDSHIP HN3543
(Dog & Cat)
Designer: John Ablitt
Height: 8¼in., 21cm.
Issued: 1990-1992
Price: $136 £85

FRIENDSHIP HN3491
Designer: Alan Maslankowski
Height: 6in., 15cm.
Issued: 1994
Price: $64 £40 (R.R.P.)

FRODO HN2912
Designer: H. Sales
Height: 4½in., 11.4cm.
Issued: 1979-1984
Price: $200 £125

FRUIT GATHERING HN449
Designer: L. Harradine
Height: 7¾in., 19.7cm.
Issued: 1921-1938
Price: $2160 £1350

FRUIT GATHERING HN476
Designer: L. Harradine
Height: 7¾in., 19.7cm.
Issued: 1921-1938
Colour variation
Price: $2080 £1300

FRAGRANCE HN3220

FRAGRANCE HN3311

FRAGRANCE HN2334

FREE SPIRIT HN3728

FRENCH HORN HN2795

FREE AS THE WIND HN3139

FRODO HN2912

185

FRUIT GATHERING HN503
Designer: L. Harradine
Height: 7¾in., 19.7in.,
Issued: 1921-1938
           Colour variation
Price: $2000 £1250

FRUIT GATHERING HN561
Designer: L. Harradine
Height: 7¾in., 19.7cm.
Issued: 1923-1938
           Colour variation
Price: $2160 £1350

FRUIT GATHERING HN562
Designer: L. Harradine
Height: 7¾in., 19.7cm.
Issued: 1923-1938
           Colour variation
Price: $2000 £1250

FRUIT GATHERING HN707
Designer: L. Harradine
Height: 7¼in., 18.4cm.
Issued: 1925-1938
           Colour variation
Price: $2000 £1250

FRUIT GATHERING HN706
Designer: L. Harradine
Height: 7¼in., 19cm.
Issued: 1925-1938
           Colour variation
Price: $2160 £1350

G

GAFFER HN2053
Designer: L. Harradine
Height: 7¾in., 19.7cm.
Issued: 1950-1959
Price: $472 £295

GAIETY HN3140
Designer: P. Parsons
Height: 10¼in., 26cm.
Issued: 1988-1990
Price: $280 £175

GAIL HN2937
Designer: P. Gee
Height: 7½in., 19cm.
Issued: 1986-1997
Price: $232 £145

GAIL HN3321
Designer: Peter Gee
Height: 3¾in., 9.5cm.
Issued: 1992-1997
Price: $104 £65

GAINSBOROUGH HAT HN46
Designer: H. Tittensor
Height: 8¾in., 22.2cm.
Issued: 1915-1938
Price: $2400 £1500

FRIAR TUCK HN2143

FRIENDSHIP HN3491

GAIL HN3321

GAIL HN2937

GAFFER HN2053

ROYAL DOULTON FIGURES

GAINSBOROUGH HAT HN46A
Designer: H. Tittensor
Height: 8¾in., 22.2cm.
Issued: 1915-1938
Colour variation
Price: $2640 £1650

GAINSBOROUGH HAT HN47
Designer: H. Tittensor
Height: 8¾in., 22.2cm.
Issued: 1915-1938
Colour variation
Price: $2640 £1650

GAINSBOROUGH HAT HN329
Designer: H. Tittensor
Height: 8¾in., 22.2cm.
Issued: 1918-1938
Colour variation
Price: $2640 £1650

GAINSBOROUGH HAT HN352
Designer: H. Tittensor
Height: 8¾in., 22.2cm.
Issued: 1919-1938
Colour variation
Price: $2640 £1650

GAINSBOROUGH HAT HN383
Designer: H. Tittensor
Height: 8¾in., 22.2cm.
Issued: 1920-1938
Colour variation
Price: $2640 £1650

GAINSBOROUGH HAT HN453
Designer: H. Tittensor
Height: 8¾in., 22.2cm.
Issued: 1921-1938
Colour variation
Price: $2640 £1650

GAINSBOROUGH HAT HN675
Designer: H. Tittensor
Height: 8¾in., 22.2cm.
Issued: 1924-1938
Colour variation
Price: $2000 £1250

GAINSBOROUGH HAT HN705
Designer: H. Tittensor
Height: 9in., 22.9cm.
Issued: 1925-1938
Colour variation
Price: $2000 £1250

GALADRIEL HN2915
Designer: H. Sales
Height: 5½in., 14cm.
Issued: 1979-1984
Price: $200 £125

GAMEKEEPER HN2879
Designer: E. Griffiths
Height: 7in., 17.8cm.
Issued: 1984-1992
Price: $264 £165

GALADRIEL HN2915

GAMEKEEPER HN2879

FRUIT GATHERING HN707   GAINSBOROUGH HAT HN705

ROYAL DOULTON FIGURES

GANDALF HN2911
Designer: H. Sales
Height: 7in., 17.8cm.
Issued: 1979-1984
Price: $264 £165

GARDENER HN3161
Designer: A. Hughes
Height: 8¼in., 21cm.
Issued: 1989-1991
Price: $312 £195

GARDENING TIME HN3401
Designer: Robert Tabbenor
Height: 5in., 12.5cm.
Issued: 1992-1994
Price: $232 £145

GAY MORNING HN2135
Designer: P. Davies
Height: 7in., 17.8cm.
Issued: 1954-1967
Price: $312 £195

GEISHA (Style one) HN354
Designer: H. Tittensor
Height: 10¾in., 27.3cm.
Issued: 1919-1938
Price: $3600 £2250

GEISHA (Style one) HN376
Designer: H. Tittensor
Height: 10¾in., 27.3cm.
Issued: 1920-1936
            Colour variation
Price: $3600 £2250

GEISHA (Style one) HN387
Designer: H. Tittensor
Height: 10¾in., 27cm.
Issued: 1920-1936
            Colour variation
Price: $3600 £2250

GEISHA (Style one) HN634
Designer: H. Tittensor
Height: 10¾in., 27.3cm.
Issued: 1924-1936
            Colour variation
Price: $3600 £2250

GEISHA (Style one) HN741
Designer: H. Tittensor
Height: 10¾in., 27.3cm.
Issued: 1925-1938
            Colour variation
Price: $4000 £2500

GEISHA (Style one) HN779
Designer: H. Tittensor
Height: 10¾in., 27.3cm.
Issued: 1926-1936
            Colour variation
Price: $4000 £2500

GEISHA (Style one) HN1321
Designer: H. Tittensor
Height: 10¾in., 27.3cm.
Issued: 1929-1936
            Colour variation
Price: $4000 £2500

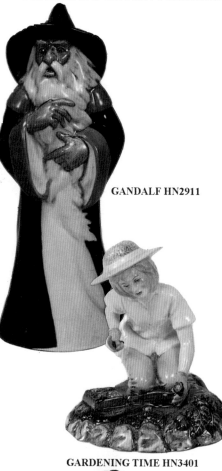

GANDALF HN2911

GARDENING TIME HN3401

GEISHA (Style two) HN1234

GEISHA (Style one) HN1322
Designer: H. Tittensor
Height: 10¾in., 27.3cm.
Issued: 1928-1936
            Colour variation
Price: $4000 £2500

GEISHA (Style two) HN1223
Designer: C. J. Noke
Height: 6¾in., 17.2cm.
Issued: 1927-1938
Price: $1200 £750

GEISHA (Style two) HN1234
Designer: C. J. Noke
Height: 6¾in., 17.2cm.
Issued: 1927-1938
            Colour variation
Price: $1200 £750

GEISHA (Style two) HN1292
Designer: C. J. Noke
Height: 6¾in., 17.2cm.
Issued: 1928-1938
            Colour variation
Price: $1200 £750

GEISHA (Style two) HN1310
Designer: C. J Noke
Height: 6¾in., 17.2cm.
Issued: 1929-1938
            Colour variation
Price: $1200 £750

GEISHA (Flambé) HN3229
(R.D.I.C.C)
Designer: P. Parsons
Height: 9½in., 24cm.
Issued: 1989 Only
Price: $360 £225

GEMMA HN3661
Designer: Nada Pedley
Height: 8in., 20cm.
Issued: 1995
Price: $152 £95

GENEVIEVE HN1962
Designer: L. Harradine
Height: 7in., 17.8cm.
Issued: 1941-1975
Price: $360 £225

GENIE HN2989
Designer: R. Tabbenor
Height: 9¾in., 24.5cm.
Issued: 1983-1990
Price: $280 £175

GENIE (Flambé) HN2999
Designer: R. Tabbenor
Height: 9¾in., 24.5cm.
Issued: 1989-1995
Price: $360 £225

GENTLEMAN FROM
WILLIAMSBURG HN2227
Designer: P. Davies
Height: 6¼in., 15.9cm.
Issued: 1960-1983
Price: $264 £165

ROYAL DOULTON FIGURES

GEISHA (Style two) HN1223

GENIE (Flambé) HN2999

GEMMA HN3661

GENIE HN2989

GENEVIEVE HN1962

GEISHA (Flambé) HN3229

GENTLEMAN FROM
WILLIAMSBURG HN2227

GENTLEWOMAN HN1632
Designer: L. Harradine
Height: 7½in., 19.1cm.
Issued: 1934-1949
Price: $760 £475

GEOFFREY BOYCOTT HN3890
Designer: Robert Tabbenor
Height: 9½in., 24cm.
Issued: 1996 in a limited editon of 8114
Price: $200 £125

GEORGE WASHINGTON AT PRAYER HN2861
Designer: L. Ispanky
Height: 12½in. 31.7cm.
Issued: 1977 in a limited edition of 750
Price: $2000 £1250

GEORGIANA HN2093
Designer: P. Davies
Height: 8¼in., 21cm.
Issued: 1952-1955
Price: $1520 £950

GEORGINA HN2377
Designer: P. Davies
Height: 5¾in., 14.6cm.
Issued: 1981-1986
Price: $264 £165

GERALDINE HN2348
Designer: P. Davies
Height: 7¼in., 18.4cm.
Issued: 1972-1976
Price: $232 £145

GIFT OF FREEDOM HN3442
Designer: Peter Gee
Height: 9¾in., 25cm.
Issued: 1993
Price: $112 £70 (R.R.P.)

GIFT OF LIFE HN3524
Designer: Russell Willis
Height: 8¼in., 21cm.
Issued: 1982-1995
Price: $840 £525

GIFT OF LOVE HN3427
Designer: Nada Pedley
Height: 7½in., 19cm.
Issued: 1993
Price: $130 £80 (R.R.P.)

GILLIAN HN1670
Designer: L. Harradine
Height: 7¾in., 19.7cm.
Issued: 1934-1949
Price: $840 £525

GILLIAN HN1670A
Designer: L. Harradine
Height: 7¾in., 19.7cm.
Issued: Unknown Colour variation
Price: $840 £525

GILLIAN HN3042
Designer: P. Parsons
Height: 8¼in., 21cm.
Issued: 1984-1990
Price: $264 £165

GEORGINA HN2377

GIFT OF LOVE HN3427

GERALDINE HN2348

GIMLI HN2922

GIFT OF FREEDOM HN3442

GILLIAN HN3742
Designer:	Unknown
Height:	7¾in., 19.5cm.
Issued:	1995
Price:	$200 £125

GIMLI HN2922
Designer:	H. Sales
Height:	5½in., 14cm.
Issued:	1980-1984
Price:	$232 £145

GIRL EVACUEE HN3023
Designer:	A. Hughes
Height:	8in., 20.3cm.
Issued:	1989 in a limited edition of 9500
Price:	$680 £425

GIRL WITH YELLOW FROCK HN588
Designer:	Unknown
Height:	6¼in., 15.9cm.
Issued:	1923-1938
Price:	$1600 £1000

GISELLE HN2139
Designer:	P. Davies
Height:	6in., 15.2cm.
Issued:	1954-1969
Price:	$470 £295

GISELLE, THE FOREST GLADE HN2140
Designer:	P. Davies
Height:	7¼in., 17.7cm.
Issued:	1954-1965
Price:	$520 £325

GLADYS HN1740
Designer:	L. Harradine
Height:	5¼in., 13.3cm.
Issued:	1935-1949
Price:	$920 £575

GLADYS HN1741
Designer:	L. Harradine
Height:	5in., 12.7cm.
Issued:	1935-1938 Colour variation
Price:	$920 £575

GLEANER HN1302
Designer:	Unknown
Height:	14½in., 36.8cm.
Issued:	1928-1938
Price:	$2400 £1500

GLORIA HN1488
Designer:	L. Harradine
Height:	7¼in., 18.4cm.
Issued:	1932-1938
Price:	$2160 £1350

GLORIA HN1700
Designer:	L. Harradine
Height:	7in., 17.8cm.
Issued:	1935-1938 Colour variation
Price:	$2160 £1350

GISELLE HN2139

GLEANER HN1302

GLORIA HN1700

GIRL WITH YELLOW FROCK HN588

GIRL EVACUEE HN3023

ROYAL DOULTON FIGURES

GLORIA HN3200
Designer: A. Hughes
Height: 9in., 23cm.
Issued: 1989
Price: $265 £165

GNOME HN319
Designer: H. Tittensor
Height: 6¼in., 15.9cm.
Issued: 1918-1938
Price: $1200 £750

GNOME HN380
Designer: H. Tittensor
Height: 6¼in., 15.9cm.
Issued: 1920-1938
  Colour variation
Price: $1200 £750

GNOME HN381
Designer: H. Tittensor
Height: 6¼in., 15.9cm.
Issued: 1920-1938
  Colour variation
Price: $1200 £750

GOD BLESS YOU HN3400
Designer: Robert Tabbenor
Height: 8in., 20cm.
Issued: 1992
Price: $48 £30 (R.R.P.)

GOING HOME HN3527
Designer: Adrian Hughes
Height: 6¼in., 16cm.
Issued: 1982
Price: $80 £50 (R.R.P.)

GOLDEN DAYS HN2274
Designer: P. Davies
Height: 3¾in., 9.5cm.
Issued: 1964-1973
Price: $264 £165

GOLFER HN2992
Designer: R. Tabbenor
Height: 9½in., 24cm.
Issued: 1988-1991
Price: $264 £165

GOLLUM HN2913
Designer: H. Sales
Height: 3¼in., 8.3cm.
Issued: 1979-1984
Price: $232 £145

GOLLYWOG HN1979
Designer: L. Harradine
Height: 5¼in., 13.3cm.
Issued: 1945-1959
Price: $680 £425

GOLLYWOG HN2040
Designer: L. Harradine
Height: 5¼in., 13.3cm.
Issued: 1949-1959
  Colour variation
Price: $520 £325

GOOD CATCH HN2258
Designer: M. Nicholl
Height: 7¼in., 18.4cm.
Issued: 1966-1986
Price: $280 £175

GOOD COMPANION HN3608
Designer: Nada Pedley
Height: 8¼in., 21cm.
Issued: 1994
Price: $152 £95 (R.R.P.)

GOOD DAY SIR HN2896
Designer: W. K. Harper
Height: 8½in., 21.5cm.
Issued: 1986-1989
Price: $264 £165

GOOD FRIENDS HN2783
Designer: W. K. Harper
Height: 9in., 23cm.
Issued: 1985-
Price: $232 £145

GOOD KING WENCESLAS HN2118
Designer: P. Davies
Height: 8½in., 21.6cm.
Issued: 1953-1976
Price: $440 £275

GOOD KING WENCESLAS HN3262
Designer: P. Davies
Height: 4½in., 11cm.
Issued: 1989-1992
Price: $176 £110

GOOD MORNING HN2671
Designer: M. Nicoll
Height: 8in., 20.3cm.
Issued: 1974-1976
Price: $240 £150

GOOD PALS HN3132
Designer: P. Parsons
Height: 6¼in., 15.5cm.
Issued: 1987-1992
Price: $200 £125

GOODY TWO SHOES HN1889
Designer: L. Harradine
Height: 4¾in., 12cm.
Issued: 1938-1949
Price: $312 £195

GOODY TWO SHOES HN1905
Designer: L. Harradine
Height: 4¾in., 12cm.
Issued: 1939-1949
  Colour variation
Price: $312 £195

GOODY TWO SHOES HN2037
Designer: L. Harradine
Height: 5in., 12.7cm.
Issued: 1949-1989
  Colour variation
Price: $192 £120

GOD BLESS YOU HN3400

GOOD MORNING HN2671

GOLLUM HN2913

GOOD FRIENDS HN2783

GOODY TWO SHOES HN2037

ROYAL DOULTON FIGURES

GOODY TWO SHOES M80
Designer: L. Harradine
Height: 4in., 10.1cm.
Issued: 1939-1949
Price: $840 £525

GOODY TWO SHOES M81
Designer: L. Harradine
Height: 4in., 10.1cm.
Issued: 1939-1949
Colour variation
Price: $840 £525

GOOSEGIRL HN425
Designer: L. Harradine
Height: 8in., 20.3cm.
Issued: 1921-1936
Price: $3600 £2250

GOOSEGIRL HN436
Designer: L. Harradine
Height: 8in., 20.3cm.
Issued: 1921-1936
Colour variation
Price: $3200 £2000

GOOSEGIRL HN437
Designer: L. Harradine
Height: 8in., 20.3cm.
Issued: 1921-1936
Price: $3200 £2000

GOOSEGIRL HN448
Designer: L. Harradine
Height: 8in., 20.3cm.
Issued: 1921-1936
Colour variation
Price: $3600 £2250

GOOSEGIRL HN559
Designer: L. Harradine
Height: 8in., 20.3cm.
Issued: 1923-1936
Colour variation
Price: $3200 £2000

GOOSEGIRL HN560
Designer: L. Harradine
Height: 8in., 20.3cm.
Issued: 1923-1936
Colour variation
Price: $3600 £2250

GOOSEGIRL HN2419
Designer: J. Bromley
Height: 8in., 20.3cm.
Issued: 1990 in a limited
edition of 12500
Price: $312 £195

GOOSEGIRL HN3936
Designer: Alan Maslankowski
Height: 11in., 28cm.
Issued: 1997
Price: $136 £85 (R.R.P.)

GOSSIPS HN1426
Designer: L. Harradine
Height: 5¾in., 14.6cm.
Issued: 1930-1949
Price: $880 £550

GOOD PALS HN3132

GOOD COMPANION HN3608

GOOD DAY SIR HN2896

GOOSEGIRL HN3936

GOOSEGIRL HN2419

GOOD CATCH HN2258

GOSSIPS HN1429
Designer: L. Harradine
Height: 5¾in., 14.6cm.
Issued: 1930-1949
Colour variation
Price: $840 £525

GOSSIPS HN2025
Designer: L. Harradine
Height: 5½in., 14cm.
Issued: 1949-1967
Colour variation
Price: $520 £325

GRACE HN2318
Designer: M. Nicoll
Height: 7¾in., 19.7cm.
Issued: 1966-1980
Price: $265 £165

GRACE HN3699
Designer: Nada Pedley
Height: 8in., 20cm.
Issued: 1996
Price: $128 £80 (R.R.P.)

GRACE DARLING HN3089
Designer: E. J. Griffiths
Height: 9in., 22.5cm.
Issued: 1987 in a limited
edition of 900
Price: $440 £275

GRACEFUL HN3540
(Panthers)
Designer: John Ablitt
Height: 4½in., 11cm.
Issued: 1989-1992
Price: $240 £150

GRADUATE (The Female)
HN3016
Designer: P. Parsons
Height: 8¾in., 22cm.
Issued: 1984
Price: $472 £295

GRADUATE (The Male)
HN3017
Designer: P. Parsons
Height: 9¼in., 23.5cm.
Issued: 1984-
Price: $472 £295

GRADUATE, THE HN3959
Designer: Alan Maslankowski
Height: 11½in., 29.5cm.
Issued: 1998
Price: $136 £85

GRADUATION, THE HN3942
Designer: Alan Maslankowski
Height: 11½in., 29cm.
Issued: 1997
Price: $136 £85 (R.R.P.)

GRAND MANNER HN2723
Designer: W. K. Harper
Height: 7¾in., 19.7cm.
Issued: 1975-1982
Price: $265 £165

GRACE HN2318

GRACE HN3699

GRACE DARLING HN3089

GRADUATE (The Female)
HN3016

GRANDMA HN2052
Designer: L. Harradine
Height: 6¾in., 17.2cm.
Issued: 1950-1959
Price: $472 £295

GRANDMA HN2052A
Designer: L. Harradine
Height: 6¾in., 17.2cm.
Issued: 1950-1959
      Colour variation
Price; $472 £295

GRANDPA'S STORY HN3456
Designer: Pauline Parsons
Height: 6in., 15.5cm.
Issued: 1994
Price: $240 £150

GRANNY HN1804
Designer: L. Harradine
Height: 7in., 17.8cm.
Issued: 1937-1949
Price: $2400 £1500

GRANNY HN1832
Designer: L. Harradine
Height: 6¾in., 17.1cm.
Issued: 1937-1949
      Colour variation
Price: $2000 £1250

GRANNY'S HERITAGE HN1873
Designer: L. Harradine
Height: 6¾in., 17.1cm.
Issued: 1938-1949
Price: $960 £600

GRANNY'S HERITAGE HN1874
Designer: L. Harradine
Height: 6¼in., 15.9cm.
Issued: 1938-1949
      Colour variation
Price: $960 £600

GRANNY'S HERITAGE HN2031
Designer: L. Harradine
Height: 6¾in., 17.1cm.
Issued: 1949-1969
      Colour variation
Price: $760 £475

GRANNY'S SHAWL HN1642
Designer: L. Harradine
Height: 5¾in., 14.6cm.
Issued: 1934-1949
Price: $480 £300

GRANNY'S SHAWL HN1647
Designer: L. Harradine
Height: 5¾in., 14.6cm.
Issued: 1934-1949
      Colour variation
Price: $480 £300

GRANDMA HN2052

GRADUATE (The Male) HN3017

GRADUATION HN3942

GRAND MANNER HN2723

GRANDPA'S STORY HN3456

GRETA HN1485
Designer: L. Harradine
Height: 5½in., 14cm.
Issued: 1931-1953
Price: $480 £300

GRETCHEN HN1397
Designer: L. Harradine
Height: 7¾in., 19.7cm.
Issued: 1930-1938
Price: $880 £550

GRETCHEN HN1562
Designer: L. Harradine
Height: 7¾in., 19.7cm.
Issued: 1933-1938
          Colour variation
Price: $1000 £625

GRIEF HN595
Designer: Unknown
Height: 2in., 5.1cm.
Issued: 1924-1938
Price: $960 $600

GRISELDA HN1993
Designer: L. Harradine
Height: 5¾in., 14.6cm.
Issued: 1947-1953
Price: $632 £395

GRIZEL HN1629
Designer: L. Harradine
Height: 6¾in., 17.2cm.
Issued: 1934-1938
Price: $1520 £950

GROSSMITH'S TSANG IHANG HN582
Designer: Unknown
Height: 11½in., 29.2cm.
Issued: 1923-?
Price: $880 £550

GROUCHO MARX HN2777
Designer: W. K. Harper
Height: 9½in., 24.1cm.
Issued: 1991 in a limited
          edition of 9500-1996
Price: $360 £225

GUARDSMAN HN2784
Designer: William K. Harper
Height: 9¾in., 24.5cm.
Issued: 1992-1995
Price: $232 £145

GULLIVER HN3750 (Resin)
Designer: David Biggs
Height: 8½in., 21.5cm.
Issued: 1995-1996
Price: $120 £75

GUY FAWKES HN98
Designer: C. J. Noke
Height: 10½in., 26.7cm.
Issued: 1918-1949
Price: $1760 £1100

GRETCHEN HN1397

GROUCHO MARX HN2777

GROSSMITH'S TSANG IHANG HN582

GUARDSMAN HN2784

GULLIVER HN3750

GUY FAWKES HN98

GUY FAWKES HN347
Designer: C. J. Noke
Height: 10½in., 26.7cm.
Issued: 1919-1938
           Colour variation
Price: $1520 £950

GUY FAWKES HN445
Designer: C. J. Noke
Height: 10½in., 26.7cm.
Issued: 1921-1938
           Colour variation
Price: $1200 £750

GUY FAWKES HN3271
Designer: C. J. Noke
Height: 4¼in., 11cm.
Issued: 1989
Price: $176 £110

GWENDOLEN HN1494
Designer: L. Harradine
Height: 6in., 15.2cm.
Issued: 1932-1940
Price: $1160 £725

GWENDOLEN HN1503
Designer: L. Harradine
Height: 6in., 15.2cm.
Issued: 1932-1949
Price: $1160 £725

GWENDOLEN HN1570
Designer: L. Harradine
Height: 6in., 15.2cm.
Issued: 1933-1949
           Colour variation
Price: $1160 £725

GWYNNETH HN1980
Designer: L. Harradine
Height: 7in., 17.8cm.
Issued: 1934-1952
Price: $440 £275

GYPSY DANCE (Style one) HN2157
Designer: P. Davies
Height: 7in., 17.8cm.
Issued: 1955-1957
Price: $680 £400

GYPSY DANCE (Style two) HN2230
Designer: P. Davies
Height: 7in., 17.8cm.
Issued: 1959-1971
Price: $390 £245

GYPSY WOMAN WITH CHILD HN1301
Designer: Unknown
Height: 14¼in., 36.2cm.
Issued: 1928-1938
Price: $2400 £1500

GWENDOLEN HN1503

GWENDOLEN HN1494

GYPSY DANCE (Style one) HN2157

GYPSY DANCE (Style two) HN2230

GWYNNETH HN1980

197

H

HANNAH HN3369
Designer: Nada Pedley
Height: 8¼in., 21cm.
Issued: 1991-1996
Price: $264 £165

HANNAH HN3649
Designer: Nada Pedley
Height: 4in., 10cm.
Issued: 1994
Price: $104 £65 (R.R.P.)

HANNAH HN3655
Designer: Nada Pedley
Height: 8¼in., 21cm.
Issued: 1995 Only
Price: $232 £145

HAPPY ANNIVERSARY HN3097
Designer: P. Parsons
Height: 6½in., 16.5cm.
Issued: 1987-1993
Price: $264 £165

HAPPY ANNIVERSARY HN3254
Designer: D. Tootle
Height: 12in., 30.5cm.
Issued: 1989
Price: $168 £105 (R.R.P.)

HAPPY BIRTHDAY HN3095
Designer: P. Parsons
Height: 7½in., 19.5cm.
Issued: 1987-1994
Price: $232 £145

HAPPY BIRTHDAY HN3660
Designer: Nada Pedley
Height: 8in., 20cm.
Issued: 1995
Price: $184 £115 (R.R.P.)

HAPPY BIRTHDAY HN3829
Designer: D.V. Tootle
Height: 7½in., 19cm.
Issued: 1997
Price: $80 £50

"HAPPY JOY BABY BOY…" HN1541
Designer: Unknown
Height: 6¼in., 15.9cm.
Issued: 1933-1949
Price: $560 £350

HARLEQUIN HN2186
Designer: P. Davies
Height: 7¼in., 18.4cm.
Issued: 1957-1969
Price: $312 £195

HARLEQUIN HN2737
Designer: D. Tootle
Height: 12½in., 31cm.
Issued: 1982-
Price: $2000 £1250 (R.R.P.)

HANNAH HN3369

"HAPPY JOY BABY BOY…" HN1541

HANNAH HN3649

HAPPY BIRTHDAY HN3095

HAPPY ANNIVERSARY HN3254

HAPPY BIRTHDAY HN3660

HARLEQUIN HN2186

ROYAL DOULTON FIGURES

HARLEQUIN HN3287
U.S.A. edition.
Commissioned by Harrods
Issued: 1993 Only
Price: $2000 £1250

HARLEQUINADE HN585
Designer: L. Harradine
Height: 6½in., 16.5cm.
Issued: 1923-1938
Price: $1040 £650

HARLEQUINADE HN1401
Designer: L. Harradine
Height: 8½in., 21.6cm.
Issued: 1930-1938
Price: $2400 £1500

HARLEQUINADE HN635
Designer: L. Harradine
Height: 6½in., 16.5cm.
Issued: 1924-1938
           Colour variation
Price: $880 £550

HARLEQUINADE HN711
Designer: L. Harradine
Height: 6½in., 16.5cm.
Issued: 1925-1938
           Colour variation
Price: $880 £550

HARLEQUINADE HN780
Designer: L. Harradine
Height: 6½in., 16.5cm.
Issues: 1926-1939
           Colour variation
Price: $880 £550

HARLEQUINADE MASKED HN768
Designer: L. Harradine
Height: 6½in., 16.5cm.
Issued: 1925-1938
Price: $2960 £1850

HARLEQUINADE MASKED HN1304
Designer: L. Harradine
Height: 6½in., 16.5m.
Issued: 1928-1938
           Colour variation
Price: $2800 £1750

HARLEQUINADE MASKED HN769
Designer: L. Harradine
Height: 6½in., 16.5cm.
Issued: 1925-1938
           Colour variation
Price: $2800 £1750

HARLEQUINADE MASKED HN1274
Designer: L. Harradine
Height: 6½in., 16.5cm.
Issued: 1928-1938
           Colour variation
Price: $2800 £1750

HARMONY HN2824
Designer: R. Jefferson
Height: 8in., 20.3cm.
Issued: 1978-1984
Price: $264 £165

HARLEQUINADE HN1401

HARLEQUINADE MASKED HN769

HARLEQUINADE HN585

HARLEQUINADE MASKED HN1304

HARLEQUIN HN2737

HARLEQUIN HN3287

HARMONY HN2824

HARP HN2482
Designer: P. Davies
Height: 8¾in., 22.2cm.
Issued: 1973 in a limited
edition of 750
Price: $1360 £850

HARRIET HN3177
Designer: D. Tootle
Height: 7¼in., 18.5cm.
Issued: 1988-1991
Price: $264 £165

HARRIET (Green) HN3794
Designer: Alan Maslankowski
Height: 9¼in., 23.5cm.
Issued: 1996-1997
Price: $200 £125

HARRIET (Ivory/Gold) HN3797
Designer: Alan Maslankowski
Height: 7¼in., 23.5cm.
Issued: 1996-1997
Price: $200 £125

HARVESTIME HN3084
Designer: E. J. Griffiths
Height: 8in., 20cm.
Issued: 1988-1990
Price: $232 £145

HAZEL HN1796
Designer: Leslie Harradine
Height: 5¼in., 13cm.
Issued: 1936-1949
Price: $520 £325

HAZEL HN1797
Designer: L. Harradine
Height: 5¼in., 13.3cm.
Issued: 1936-1949
Colour variation
Price: $585 £365

HAZEL HN3167
Designer: P. Davies
Height: 8in., 20cm.
Issued: 1988-1991
Price: $232 £145

HE LOVES ME HN2046
Designer: L. Harradine
Height: 5½in., 14cm.
Issued: 1949-1962
Price: $280 £175

HEART TO HEART HN2276
Designer: P. Davies
Height: 5½in., 14cm.
Issued: 1961-1971
Price: $560 £350

HEATHER HN2956
Designer: P. Parsons
Height: 6in., 15cm.
Issued: 1982-
Price: $136 £85 (R.R.P.)

HEATHER HN2956

HE LOVES ME
HN2046

HEIDI HN2975

HARRIET
HN3794

HARP HN2482

HELLO DADDY HN3651

ROYAL DOULTON FIGURES

HEIDI HN2975
Designer: A. Hughes
Height: 4½in., 11.5cm.
Issued: 1983-1986
Price: $264 £165

HELEN HN1508
Designer: L. Harradine
Height: 8in., 20.3cm.
Issued: 1932-1938
Price: $1112 £695

HELEN HN1509
Designer: L. Harradine
Height: 8in., 20.3cm.
Issued: 1932-1938
   Colour variation
Price: $1112 £695

HELEN HN1572
Designer: L. Harradine
Height: 8in., 20.3cm.
Issued: 1933-1938
   Colour variation
Price: $1112 £695

HELEN HN2994
Designer: R. Tabbenor
Height: 5in., 12.5cm.
Issued: 1985-1987
Price: $176 £110

HELEN HN3601
Designer: Nada Pedley
Height: 8in., 20cm.
Issued: 1993
Price: $160 £100 (R.R.P.)

HELEN (Red) HN3886
Designer: Nada Pedley
Height: 8¼in., 21cm.
Issued: 1997
Price: $216 £135 (R.R.P.)

HELEN OF TROY HN2387
Designer: P. Davies
Height: 9¼in., 23.4cm.
Issued: 1981 as a limited
   edition of 750
Price: $1125 £750

HELLO DADDY HN3651
Designer: Nada Pedley
Height: 5¾in., 14.5cm.
Issued: 1994
Price: $104 £65 (R.R.P.)

HELMSMAN HN2499
Designer: M. Nicoll
Height: 9in., 22.9cm.
Issued: 1974-1986
Price: $360 £225

HENLEY HN3367
Designer: Valerie Annand
Height: 8in., 20cm.
Issued: 1993 in a limited
   edition of 5000
Price: $360 £225 (R.R.P.)

HELEN HN1572

HELEN HN3601

HENLEY HN3367

HELEN HN2994

HELEN HN1509

HELMSMAN HN2499

HELEN OF TROY HN2387

ROYAL DOULTON FIGURES

HENRIETTA MARIA HN2005
Designer: P. Davies
Height: 9½in., 24.1cm.
Issued: 1948-1953
Price: $680 £425

HENRY V AT AGINCOURT HN3947
Designer: Alan Maslankowski
Height: 20in., 51cm.
Issued: 1997
Price: $15920 £9950
(R.R.P.)

HENRY VIII (Style one) HN370
Designer: C. J. Noke
Height: Unknown
Issued: 1920- 1938
Price: $1600 £1000

HENRY VIII (Style one) HN673
Designer: C. J. Noke
Height: Unknown
Issued: 1924-1938
Colour variation
Price: $1600 £1000

HENRY VIII (Style two) HN1792
Designer: C. J. Noke
Height: 11½in., 29.2cm.
Issued: 1933 in a limited
edition of 200
Price: $4160 £2600

HENRY VIII HN3350
Designer: Pauline Parsons
Height: 9½in., 24.1cm.
Issued: 1991 in a limited
edition of 1991
Price: $1200 £750

HENRY VIII HN3458
In a imited edition of 9500
Designer: Pauline Parsons
Height: 9¼in., 23.5cm.
Issued: 1994
Price: $560 £350

HENRY IRVING AS CARDI-NAL WOLSEY HN344
Designer: C. J. Noke
Height: 13¼in., 33.7cm.
Issued: 1919-1949
Price: $2400 £1500

HENRY LYTTON AS JACK POINT HN610
Designer: C. J. Noke
Height: 6½in., 16.5cm.
Issued: 1924-1949
Price: $720 £450

HER LADYSHIP HN1977
Designer: L. Harradine
Height: 7¼in., 18.4cm.
Issued: 1945-1959
Price: $440 £275

HER LADYSHIP
HN1977

HENRIETTA MARIA HN2005

HENRY VIII HN3350

HENRY VIII (Style two)
HN1792

ROYAL DOULTON FIGURES

HER MAJESTY QUEEN ELIZ-
ABETH II HN2878
Designer: E. J. Griffiths
Height: 10½in., 27cm.
Issued: 1983 in a limited
            edition of 2500
Price: $520 £325

HM QUEEN ELIZABETH II &
DUKE OF EDINBURGH ,
GOLDEN WEDDING HN3836
In a limited edition of 750
Designer: Pauline Parsons
Height: 9¼in., 23.5cm.
Issued: 1997
Price: $632 £395 (R.R.P.)

H.M. QUEEN ELIZABETH
THE QUEEN MOTHER
HN3944
Designer: Alan Maslankowski
Height: 10½in., 26.5cm.
Issued: 1997 in a limited
            edition of 5000
Price: $472 £295 (R.R.P.)

HER MAJESTY QUEEN
ELIZABETH, THE QUEEN
MOTHER HN2882
Designer: E. J. Griffiths
Height: 11¼in., 29.8cm.
Issued: 1980 in a limited
            edition of 1500
Price: $1040 £650

"HERE A LITTLE CHILD I
STAND" HN1546
Designer: Unknown
Height: 6¼in., 15.9cm.
Issued: 1933-1949
Price: $600 £375

HERMINIA HN1644
Designer: L. Harradine
Height: 6½in., 16.5cm.
Issued: 1934-1938
Price: $1200 £750

HERMINIA HN1646
Designer: L. Harradine
Height: 6½in., 16.5cm.
Issued: 1934-1938
            Colour variation
Price: $1200 £750

HERMINIA HN1704
Designer: L. Harradine
Height: 6¾in., 17.2cm.
Issued: 1935-1938
            Colour variation
Price: $1200 £750

"HERE A LITTLE CHILD I
STAND" HN1546

H.M. QUEEN ELIZABETH
THE QUEEN MOTHER
HN3944

HER MAJESTY QUEEN ELIZ-
ABETH II HN2878

HERMIONE HN2058
Designer: P. Davies
Height: 7¾in., 19.7cm.
Issued: 1950-1952
Price: $1520 £950

HIBERNIA HN2932
Designer: S. Keenan
Height: 9in., 23cm.
Issued: 1983 in a limited
            edition of 950
Price: $560 £350

HIGHWAYMAN HN527
Designer: L. Harradine
Height: 6½in., 16.5cm.
Issued: 1921-1949
Price: $680 £425

HIGHWAYMAN HN592
Designer: L. Harradine
Height: 6½in., 16.5cm.
Issued: 1924-1949
Price: $680 £425

HIGHWAYMAN HN1257
Designer: L. Harradine
Height: 6½in., 16.5cm.
Issued: 1927-1949
Price: $680 £425

HILARY HN2335
Designer: P. Davies
Height: 7¼in., 18.4cm.
Issued: 1967-1980
Price: $264 £165

HINGED PARASOL HN1578
Designer: L. Harradine
Height: 6½in., 16.5cm.
Issued: 1933-1949
Price: $880 £550

HINGED PARASOL HN1579
Designer: L. Harradine
Height: 6½in., 16.5cm.
Issued: 1933-1949
            Colour variation
Price: $880 £550

HIS ROYAL HIGHNESS
PRINCE PHILIP DUKE OF
EDINBURGH HN2386
Designer: P. Davies
Height: 8¼in., 21cm.
Issued: 1981 in a limited
            edition of 1500
Price: $390 £245

HIVER HN3069
Designer: R. Jefferson
Height: 11½in., 29cm.
Issued: 1988 in a limited
            edition of 300
Price: $1200 £750

HOLD TIGHT HN3298
Designer: Adrian Hughes
Height: 8½in., 21.5cm.
Issued: 1990-1993
Price: $392 £245

ROYAL DOULTON FIGURES

HILARY HN2335

HINGED PARASOL HN1578

HOLD TIGHT HN3298

HIS ROYAL HIGHNESS
PRINCE PHILIP DUKE OF ED-
INBURGH HN2386

HOLLY HN3647
Designer: Nada Pedley
Height: 8in., 20cm.
Issued: 1994
Price: $168 £105 (R.R.P.)

HOME AGAIN HN2167
Designer: P. Davies
Height: 3¼in., 8.3cm.
Issued: 1956-1995
Price: $152 £95

HOME AT LAST HN3697
Designer: Nada Pedley
Height: 5¾in., 14.5cm.
Issued: 1995
Price: $112 £70 (R.R.P.)

HOMECOMING HN3295
Designer: A. Hughes
Height: 7in., 17.8cm.
Issued: 1990 in a limited
edition of 9500
Price: $440 £275

HOMECOMING HN3532
Designer: R. Willis
Height: 14¾in., 37.5cm.
Issued: 1987
Price: $632 £395 (R.R.P

HOMETIME HN3685
Designer: Nada Pedley
Height: 6in., 15cm.
Issued: 1995-1997
Price: $120 £75

HONEY HN1909
Designer: L. Harradine
Height: 7in., 17.8cm.
Issued: 1939-1949
Price: $520 £325

HONEY HN1910
Designer: L. Harradine
Height: 6¾in., 17.2cm.
Issued: 1939-1949
Colour variation
Price: $520 £325

HONEY HN1963
Designer: L. Harradine
Height: 6¾in., 17.2cm.
Issued: 1941-1949
Colour variation
Price: $520 £325

HOPE HN3061
Designer: E. J. Griffiths
Height: 8¾in., 21.5cm.
Issued: 1984 in a limited
edition of 9500
Price: $392 £245

HORNPIPE HN2161
Designer: M. Nicoll
Height: 9¼in., 23.5cm.
Issued: 1955-1962
Price: $840 £525

ROYAL DOULTON FIGURES

HOMECOMING HN3295

HOME AT LAST HN3697

HOLLY HN3647

HOME AGAIN HN2167

HOMECOMING HN3532

HOMETIME HN3685

HOPE HN3061

HOSTESS OF WILLIAMS-BURG HN2209
Designer: P. Davies
Height: 7¼in., 18.4cm.
Issued: 1960-1983
Price: $264 £165

HUCKLEBERRY FINN HN2927
Designer: D. Lyttleton
Height: 7in., 17.5cm.
Issued: 1982-1985
Price: $232 £145

HUNTING SQUIRE HN1409
Designer: Unknown
Height: 9¼in., 24.7cm.
Issued: 1930-1938
Price: $3600 £2250

HUNTS LADY HN1201
Designer: L. Harradine
Height: 8¼in., 21cm.
Issued: 1926-1938
Price: $2400 £1500

HUNTSMAN (Style one) HN1226
Designer: L. Harradine
Height: 8¾in., 22.2cm.
Issued: 1927-1938
Price: $2000 £1250

HUNTSMAN (Style two) HN1815
Designer: Unknown
Height: 9½in., 24.1cm.
Issued: 1937-1949
Price: $3200 £2000
Also called John Peel

HUNTSMAN (Style three) HN2492
Designer: M. Nicoll
Height: 7½in., 19.1cm.
Issued: 1974-1978
Price: $360 £225

HURDY GURDY HN2796
Designer: P. Davies
Height: 6in., 15.2cm.
Issued: 1975 in a limited edition of 750
Price: $880 £550

I

IAN BOTHAM (Resin)
Designer: Unknown
Height: 10in., 25.4cm.
Issued: 1996-1997
Price: $158 £99

IBRAHIM HN2095
Designer: C. J. Noke
Height: 7¾in., 19.7cm.
Issued: 1952-1955
Price: $680 £425
Also called Emir

IDLE HOURS HN3115
Designer: A. Maslankowski
Height: 12¼in., 31cm.
Issued: 1987-1989
Price: $312 £195

HURDY GURDY HN2796

HOSTESS OF WILLIAMS-BURG HN2209

HUCKLEBERRY FINN HN2927

HUNTSMAN (Style three) HN2492

I'M NEARLY READY HN2976
Designer: A. Hughes
Height: 7½in., 19cm.
Issued: 1984-1986
Price: $230 £145

IN GRANDMA'S DAYS HN339
Designer: C. J. Noke
Height: 8¾in., 22.2cm.
Issued: 1919-1938
Price: $2000 £1250

IN GRANDMA'S DAYS HN340
Designer: C. J. Noke
Height: 8¾in., 22.2cm.
Issued: 1919-1938
   Colour variation
Price: $2000 £1250

IN GRANDMA'S DAYS HN362
Designer: Charles Noke
Height: 9½in., 24cm.
Issued: 1919-1938
Price: $1840 £1150

IN GRANDMA'S DAYS HN388
Designer: C. J. Noke
Height: 8¾in., 22.2cm.
Issued: 1920-1938
   Colour variation
Price: $2400 £1500

IN GRANDMA'S DAYS HN442
Designer: C. J. Noke
Height: 8¾in., 22.2cm.
Issued: 1921-1938
   Colour variation
Price: $2400 £1500
Also called Lilac Shawl and Poke
Bonnet

IN THE STOCKS (Style one)
HN1474
Designer: L. Harradine
Height: 5in., 12.7cm.
Issued: 1931-1938
Price: $2000 £1250

IN THE STOCKS (Style one)
HN1475
Designer: L. Harradine
Height: 5¼in., 13.3cm.
Issued: 1931-1938
   Colour variation
Price: $2000 £1250

IN THE STOCKS (Style two)
HN2163
Designer: M. Nicoll
Height: 5¾in., 14.6cm.
Issued: 1955-1959
Price: $880 £550

INDIAN BRAVE HN2376
Designer: P. Davies
Height: 16in., 40.6cm.
Issued: 1967 in a limited
   edition of 500
Price: $3200 £2000

IDLE HOURS HN3115

HUNTSMAN (Style one)
HN1226

IN THE STOCKS (Style one)
HN1474

IN THE STOCKS (Style one)
HN1475

IN THE STOCKS (Style two)
HN2163

INDIAN BRAVE HN2376

ROYAL DOULTON FIGURES

INDIAN MAIDEN HN3117
Designer: A. Maslankowski
Height: 12in., 30.5cm.
Issued: 1988-1990
Price: $264 £165

**INDIAN TEMPLE DANCER
HN2830**
Designer: P. Davies
Height: 9¼in., 23.5cm.
Issued: 1977 in a limited
             edition of 750
Price: $680 £425

INNOCENCE HN2842
Designer: E. J. Griffiths
Height: 7½in., 19.1cm.
Issued: 1979-1983
Price: $264 £165

INNOCENCE HN3226
Designer: P. Parsons
Height: 7¾in., 19.7cm.
Issued: 1988 in a limited
             edition of 9500-
             1989
Price: $200 £125

INNOCENCE HN3730
Designer: Alan Maslankowski
Height: 3½in., 9cm.
Issued: 1996
Price: $56 £35 (R.R.P.)

INVITATION HN2170
Designer: P. Davies
Height: 5½in., 14cm.
Issued: 1956-1975
Price: $230 £145

IONA HN1346
Designer: L. Harradine
Height: 7½in., 19.1cm.
Issued: 1929-1938
Price: $3200 £2000

IRELAND HN3628
Designer: Valerie Annand
Height: 7¾in., 19.5cm.
Issued: 1996
Price: $288 £180 (R.R.P.)

IRENE HN1621
Designer: L. Harradine
Height: 6½in., 16.5cm.
Issued: 1934-1951
Price: $520 £325

IRENE HN1697
Designer: L. Harradine
Height: 7in., 17.8cm.
Issued: 1935-1949
             Colour variation
Price: $640 £400

IRENE HN1952
Designer: L. Harradine
Height: 6¾in., 17.2cm.
Issued: 1940-1950
             Colour variation
Price: $720 £450

IRELAND HN3628

INVITATION HN2170

INNOCENCE HN3730

INDIAN TEMPLE DANCER
HN2830

IONA HN1346

208

IRISH COLLEEN HN766
Designer: L. Harradine
Height: 6½in., 16.5cm.
Issued: 1925-1938
Price: $2800 £1750

IRISH COLLEEN HN767
Designer: L. Harradine
Height: 6½in., 16.5cm.
Issued: 1925-1938
Price: $2800 £1750

IRISHMAN HN1307
Designer: H. Fenton
Height: 6¾in., 17.2cm.
Issued: 1928-1938
Price: $2800 £1750

ISABEL HN3716
Designer: Valerie Annand
Height: 8½in., 21cm.
Issued: 1997
Price: $128 £80 (R.R.P.)

ISABELLA, COUNTESS OF SEFTON HN3010
Designer: P. Gee
Height: 9¾in., 24.7cm.
Issued: 1991 in a limited
edition of 5000-1994
Price: $520 £325

ISADORA HN2938
Designer: P. Gee
Height: 8in., 20cm.
Issued: 1986
Price: $310 £195

IT WON'T HURT HN2963
Designer: P. Parsons
Height: 7½in., 19cm.
Issued: 1982-1986
Price: $232 £145

IVY HN1768
Designer: L. Harradine
Height: 4¾in., 12cm.
Issued: 1936-1979
Price: $165 £110

IVY HN1769
Designer: L. Harradine
Height: 4¾in., 12cm.
Issued: 1936-1938
Colour variation
Price: $360 £225

J

JACK HN2060
Designer: L. Harradine
Height: 5½in., 14cm.
Issued: 1950-1971
Price: $230 £145

JACK POINT HN85
Designer: C. J. Noke
Height: 16¼in., 41.2cm.
Issued: 1918-1938
Price: $3200 £2000

ISABELLA, COUNTESS OF
SEFTON HN3010

IRISH COLLEEN HN766

INNOCENCE HN2842

ISADORA HN2938

IT WON'T HURT HN2963

ROYAL DOULTON FIGURES

JACK POINT HN91
Designer: C. J. Noke
Height: 16¼in., 41.2cm.
Issued: 1918-1938
Colour variation
Price: $2800 £1750

JACK POINT HN99
Designer: C. J. Noke
Height: 16¼in., 41.2cm.
Issued: 1918-1938
Colour variation
Price: $2560 £1600

JACK POINT HN2080
Designer: C. J. Noke
Height: 16in., 40.6cm.
Issued: 1952-
Colour variation
Price: $2800 £1750
(R.R.P.)

JACK POINT HN3920
In a limited edition of 250
Designer: C. J. Noke
Height: 17in., 43cm.
Issued: 1996
Colour variation
Price: $4400 £2750
(R.R.P.)

JACQUELINE HN2000
Designer: L. Harradine
Height: 7¼in., 18.4cm.
Issued: 1947-1951
Price: $680 £425

JACQUELINE HN2333
Designer: P. Davies
Height: 7½in., 19cm.
Issued: 1983-
Price: $264 £165

JACQUELINE HN2001
Designer: L. Harradine
Height: 7¼in., 18.4cm.
Issued: 1947-1951
Colour variation
Price: $680 £425

JACQUELINE HN3689
Designer: Nada Pedley
Height: 8in., 20.5cm.
Issued: 1995 Only
Price: $200 £125

JAMES HN3013
Designer: P. Parsons
Height: 6in., 15cm.
Issued: 1983-1987
Price: $520 £325

JAMES I HN3822
Designer: D. Tootle
Height: 9in., 22.8cm.
Issued: 1997 in a limite
edition of 1500
Price: $792 £495

JANE HN2014
Designer: L. Harradine
Height: 6¼in., 15.9cm.
Issued: 1948-1951
Price: $1200 £750

JACK POINT HN2080

JACK POINT HN3920

JANE HN3260

JACQUELINE HN2000

JACQUELINE HN2333

JANE HN2806
Designer: P. Davies
Height: 8in., 20cm.
Issued: 1983-1986
Price: $264 £165

JANE HN3260
Designer: D. V. Tootle
Height: 7¾in., 19.5cm.
Issued: 1990-1993
Price: $230 £145

JANE EYRE HN3842
In a limited edition of 3500
Designer: Pauline Parsons
Height: 8¼in., 21cm.
Issued: 1998
Price: $320 £200

**JANE, LADY DOULTON
HN3711**
Designer: Valerie Annand
Height: 7in., 17.75cm.
Issued: 1997 only
Price: $240 £150

JANE SEYMOUR HN3349
Designer: P. Parsons
Height: 9in., 22.9cm.
Issued: 1991 in a limited
edition of 9500
Price: $424 £265 (R.R.P.)

JANET (Style one) HN1537
Designer: L. Harradine
Height: 6¼in., 15.9cm.
Issued: 1932-1995
Price: $176 £110

JANET (Style one) HN1538
Designer: L. Harradine
Height: 6¼in., 15.9cm.
Issued: 1932-1949
Colour variation
Price: $520 £325

JANET (Style one) HN1652
Designer: L. Harradine
Height: 6½in., 16.5cm.
Issued: 1934-1949
Colour variation
Price: $632 £395

JANET (Style one) HN1737
Designer: L. Harradine
Height: 6¼in., 15.9cm.
Issued: 1935-1949
Colour variation
Price: $520 £325

JANET (Style two) HN1916
Designer: L. Harradine
Height: 5¼in., 13.3cm.,
Issued: 1939-1949
Price: $360 £225

JANET (Style two) HN1964
Designer: L. Harradine
Height: 5in., 12.7cm.
Issued: 1941-1949
Colour variation
Price: $472 £295

JANET M69
Designer: L. Harradine
Height: 4in., 10.1cm.
Issued: 1936-1949
Price: $632 £395

ROYAL DOULTON FIGURES

JANET M75
Designer: L. Harradine
Height: 4in., 10.1cm.
Issued: 1936-1949
Colour variation
Price: $632 £395

JANICE HN2022
Designer: P. Davies
Height: 7¼in., 18.4cm.
Issued: 1949-1955
Price: $560 £350

JANICE HN2165
Designer: P. Davies
Height: 7¼in., 18.4cm.
Issued: 1955-1965
Colour variation
Price: $632 £395

JANICE HN3624
Designer: Valerie Annand
Height: 7½in., 19.1cm.
Issued: 1994 special
Commission
Price: $240 £150 (R.R.P.)

JANINE HN2461
Designer: J. Bromley
Height: 7½in., 19.1cm.
Issued: 1971-1995
Price: $200 £125

JANUARY HN2697
Designer: P. Davies
Height: 7¾in., 19.7cm.
Issued: 1987 Only
Price: $232 £145

JANUARY HN3330
Designer: P. Davies
Height: 7½in., 19cm.
Issued: 1990 Only
U.S.A. only
Price: $165 £110

JANUARY HN3341
Designer: P. Davies
Height: 7½in., 19cm.
Issued: 1991 Only
Canada only
Price: $232 £145

JAPANESE FAN HN399
Designer: H. Tittensor
Height: 4¾in., 12.1cm.
Issued: 1920-1938
Price: $2320 £1450

JAPANESE FAN HN405
Designer: H. Tittensor
Height: 4¾in., 12.1cm.
Issued: 1920-1938
Colour variation
Price: $2320 £1450

JAPANESE FAN HN439
Designer: H. Tittensor
Height: 4½in., 12.1cm.
Issued: 1921-1938
Colour variation
Price: $2320 £1450

JANE HN2806

JANE SEYMOUR
HN3349

JANET (Style one)
HN1537

JANINE HN2461

JANUARY HN3330

JANUARY HN3341

211

JAPANESE FAN HN440
Designer: H. Tittensor
Height: 4¾in., 12.1cm.
Issued: 1921-1938
Colour variation
Price: $2320 £1450

JASMINE HN1862
Designer: L. Harradine
Height: 7¼in., 18.4cm.
Issued: 1938-1949
Price: $1040 £650

JASMINE HN1863
Designer: L. Harradine
Height: 7½in., 19.1cm.
Issued: 1938-1949
Colour variation
Price: $1040 £650

JASMINE HN1876
Designer: L. Harradine
Height: 7½in., 19.1cm.
Issued: 1938-1949
Colour variation
Price: $720 £450

JASMINE HN3832
Designer: Pauline Parson
Height: 7½in., 19cm.
Issued: 1996 in a limited
edition of 2000
Price: $360 £225

JASMINE HN3832
Designer: Pauline Parsons
Height: 7½in., 19cm.
Issued: 1997
Price: $240 £150

JEAN HN1877
Designer: L. Harradine
Height: 7½in., 19.1cm.
Issued: 1938-1949
Price: $560 £350

JEAN HN1878
Designer: L. Harradine
Height: 7½in., 19.1cm.
Issued: 1938-1949
Colour variation
Price: $560 £350

JEAN HN2032
Designer: L. Harradine
Height: 7½in., 19.1cm.
Issued: 1949-1959
Colour variation
Price: $520 £325

JEAN HN2710
Designer: P. Davies
Height: 5¾in., 14.5cm.
Issued: 1983-1986
Price: $280 £175

JEMMA HN3168
Designer: P. Davies
Height: 8½in., 21cm.
Issued: 1988-1991
Price: $232 £145

JENNIFER HN1484
Designer: L. Harradine
Height: 6½in., 16.5cm.
Issued: 1931-1949
Price: $472 £295

JASMINE HN1862

JEAN HN2032

JEAN HN1877

JENNIFER HN2392

JENNIFER HN2392
Designer: P. Davies
Height: 7in., 17.5cm.
Issued: 1982-1992
Price: $232 £145

JENNIFER HN3447
Figure of The Year
Designer: Peter Gee
Height: 7¾in., 19.5cm.
Issued: 1994 Only
Price: $280 £175

JERSEY MILKMAID HN2057
Designer: L. Harradine
Height: 6½in., 16.5cm.
Issued: 1950-1959
Price: $360 £225
Also called The Milkmaid

JESSICA HN3169
Designer: P. Davies
Height: 7in., 18cm.
Issued: 1988-1995
Price: $200 £125

JESSICA HN3497
Designer: P. Davies
Height: 7in., 17.8cm.
Issued: 1993
Colour variation
U.S.A. only
Price: $176 £110 (R.R.P.)

JESSICA HN3850
Figure of The Year
Designer: Nada Pedley
Height: 8in., 20cm.
Issued: 1997 Only
Price: $200 £125

JESTER (Style one) HN45
Designer: C. J. Noke
Height: 9½in., 24.1cm.
Issued: 1915-1938
Price: $2400 £1500

JESTER (Style one) HN71
Designer: C. J. Noke
Height: 9½in., 24.1cm.
Issued: 1917-1938
Colour variation
Price: $2400 £1500

JESTER (Style one) HN71A
Designer: C. J. Noke
Height: 9½in., 24.1cm.
Issued: 1917-1938
Colour variation
Price: $2400 £1500

JESTER (Style one) HN320
Designer: C. J. Noke
Height: 10in., 25.4cm.
Issued: 1918-1938
Colour variation
Price: $2400 £1500

ROYAL DOULTON FIGURES

JESTER (Style one) HN367
Designer: C. J. Noke
Height: 10in., 25.4cm.
Issued: 1920-1938
            Colour variation
Price: $2400 £1500

JESTER (Style one) HN412
Designer: C. J. Noke
Height: 10in., 25.4cm.
Issued: 1920-1938
            Colour variation
Price: $2800 £1750

JESTER (Style one) HN426
Designer: C. J. Noke
Height: 10in., 25.4cm.
Issued: 1921-1938
            Colour variation
Price: $2400 £1500

JESTER (Style one) HN446
Designer: C. J. Noke
Height: 10in., 25.4cm.
Issued: 1921-1938
            Colour variation
Price: $2400 £1500

JESTER (Style one) HN552
Designer: C. J. Noke
Height: 10in., 25.4cm.
Issued: 1922-1938
            Colour variation
Price: $2400 £1500

JESTER (Style one) HN616
Designer: C. J. Noke
Height: 10in., 25.4cm.
Issued: 1924-1938
            Colour variation
Price: $2800 £1750

JESTER (Style one) HN627
Designer: C. J. Noke
Height: 10in., 25.4cm.
Issued: 1924-1938
            Colour variation
Price: $2400 £1500

JESTER (Style one) HN1295
Designer: C. J. Noke
Height: 10in., 25.4cm.
Issued: 1928-1949
            Colour variation
Price: $880 £550

JESTER (Style one) HN1702
Designer: C. J. Noke
Height: 10in., 25.4cm.
Issued: 1935-1949
            Colour variation
Price: $720 £450

JESTER (Style one) HN2016
Designer: C. J. Noke
Height: 10in., 25.4cm.
Issued: 1949-1997
            Colour variation
Price: $312 £195

JESSICA HN3497

JESSICA HN3850

JESSICA HN3169

JESTER (Style one) HN1295

JESTER (Style one) HN71

JESTER (Style one) HN2016

ROYAL DOULTON FIGURES

JESTER (Style two) HN45A
Designer: C. J. Noke
Height: 10¼in., 26cm.
Issued: 1915-1938
Price: $2400 £1500

JESTER (Style two) HN45B
Designer: C. J. Noke
Height: 10¼in., 26cm.
Issued: 1915-1938
             Colour variation
Price: $2400 £1500

JESTER (Style two) HN55
Designer: C. J. Noke
Height: 10¼in., 26cm.
Issued: 1916-1938
             Colour variation
Price: $2400 £1500

JESTER (Style two) HN308
Designer: C. J. Noke
Height: 10¼in., 26cm.
Issued: 1918-1938
             Colour variation
Price: $3200 £2000

JESTER (Style two) HN630
Designer: C.J. Noke
Height: 10¼in., 26cm.
Issued: 1924-1938
             Colour variation
Price: $2400 £1500

JESTER (Style two) HN1333
Designer: C.J. Noke
Height: 10¼in., 26cm.
Issued: 1929-1949
             Colour variation
Price: $2000 £1250

JESTER HN3335
Designer: C. J. Noke
Height: 4in., 10cm.
             (Miniature)
Issued: 1990 only.
Price: $176 £110

JESUS HN3487
Designer: Alan Maslankowski
Height: 2½in., 6.5cm.
Issued: 1993-1995
             Decorated
             U.S.A. Only
Price: $152 £95

JESUS HN3484
Designer: Alan Maslankowski
Height: 2½in., 6.5cm.
Issued: 1993-1995
             White - U.S.A. only
Price: $152 £95

JILL HN2061
Designer: L. Harradine
Height: 5½in., 14cm.
Issued: 1950-1971
Price: $230 £145

JOAN HN1422
Designer: L. Harradine
Height: 5½in., 14cm.
Issued: 1930-1949
Price: $440 £275

JESUS HN3487

JESTER (Style two) HN45B

JESTER (Style two) HN45A

JOKER HN2252

JOAN OF ARC HN3681

JOAN HN2023

214

ROYAL DOULTON FIGURES

JOAN HN2023
Designer: L. Harradine
Height: 5¾in., 14.6cm.
Issued: 1949-1959
            Colour variation
Price: $390 £245

JOAN HN3217
Designer: P. Davies
Height: 7½in., 19cm.
Issued: 1988 in a limited
            edition of 2000
Price: $264 £165

JOAN OF ARC HN3681
Designer: Pauline Parsons
Height: 10in., 25.5cm.
Issued: 1996
Price: $400 £250

JOANNE HN2373
Designer: J. Bromley
Height: 5¼in., 13cm.
Issued: 1982-1988
Price: $295 £185

JOANNE HN3422
Designer: Nada Pedley
Height: 7½in., 19cm.
Issued: 1993
Price: $184 £115 (R.R.P.)

JOHN PEEL HN1408
Designer: Unknown
Height: 8¾in., 22.2cm.
Issued: 1930-1937
Price: $3600 £2250
Also called Huntsman

JOKER HN3196
Designer: A. Hughes
Height: 9¾in.., 23.5cm.
Issued: 1988-1990
Price: $264 £165

JOKER HN2252
Designer: M. Nicoll
Height: 8½in., 21.6cm.
Issued: 1990-1992
Price: $264 £165

JOLLY SAILOR HN2172
Designer: M. Nicoll
Height: 6½in., 16.5cm.
Issued: 1956-1965
Price: $790 £495

JOSEPH HN3486
Designer: Alan Maslankowski
Height: 5¾in., 14.6cm.
Issued: 1993-1995
            U.S.A. only
Price: $232 £145

JOSEPH (White) HN3438
Designer: Alan Maslankowski
Height: 5¾in., 14.6cm.
Issued: 1993-1995
            U.S.A. only
Price: $232 £145

JOVIAL MONK HN2144
Designer: P. Davies
Height: 7¾in., 19.7cm.
Issued: 1954-1976
Price: $360 £225

JOANNE HN3422

JOANNE HN2373

JOSEPH (White) HN3438

JOHN PEEL HN1408

JOSEPH HN3486

JOVIAL MONK HN2144

ROYAL DOULTON FIGURES

JOY HN3184
Designer: D. Tootle
Height: 6¾in., 17cm.
Issued: 1988-1990
Price: $232 £145

JUDGE HN2443
Designer: M. Nicoll
Height: 6½in., 16.5cm.
Issued: 1972-1976
Matte
Price: $264 £165

JUDGE HN2443A
Designer: M. Nicoll
Height: 6½in., 16.5cm.
Issued: 1976
Gloss
Price: $264 £165

JUDGE AND JURY HN1264
Designer: J. G. Hughes
Height: 6in., 15.2cm.
Issued: 1927-1938
Price: $2400 £1500

JUDITH HN2089
Designer: L. Harradine
Height: 7in., 17.8cm.
Issued: 1952-1959
Price: $470 £295

JUDITH HN2278
Designer: M. Nicoll
Height: 6¾in., 17cm.
Issued: 1987-1989
Price: $312 £195

JULIA HN2705
Designer: P. Davies
Height: 7½in., 19.1cm.
Issued: 1975-1990
Price: $232 £145

JULIA HN2706
Designer: P. Davies
Height: 7½in., 19.1cm.
Issued: 1985-1993
Colour variation
Price: $232 £145

JULIE HN2995
Designer: R. Tabbenor
Height: 5in., 12.5cm.
Issued: 1985-1995
Price: $80 £50

JULIE HN3407
Designer: R. Tabbenor
Height: 5in., 12.7cm.
Issued: 1993
Colour variation
U.S.A.
Price: $96 £60 (R.R.P.)

JULIE HN3878
Designer: Nada Pedley
Height: 8in., 20cm.
Issued: 1997
Price: $128 £80 (R.R.P.)

JUDGE AND JURY HN1264

JUDITH HN2278

JULIA HN2705

JUDGE HN2443

JULIET (Amex) HN2968
Designer: Pauline Parsons
Height: 7in., 17.5cm.
Issued: 1983-1984
Price: $360 £225

JULIET HN3453
In a limited edition of 5000
Designer: Pauline Parsons
Height: 6in., 15cm.
Issued: 1994
Price: $360 £225

JULY HN2794
Designer: P. Davies
Height: 7¾in., 19.7cm.
Issued: 1987 only
Price: $200 £125

JULY HN3324
Designer: P. Davies
Height: 7½in., 19.1cm.
Issued: U.S.A. & 1990 only
Price: $176 £110

JULY HN3347
Designer: P. Davies
Height: 7½in., 19.1cm.
Issued: Canada 1991 only
Price: $200 £125

JUNE HN1690
Designer: L. Harradine
Height: 7¼in., 18.4cm.
Issued: 1935-1949
Price: $680 £425

JUNE HN1691
Designer: L. Harradine
Height: 7¼in., 18.4cm.
Issued: 1935-1949
Colour variation
Price: $680 £425

JUNE HN1947
Designer: L. Harradine
Height: 7¼in., 18.4cm.
Issued: 1940-1949
Colour variation
Price: $720 £450

JUNE HN2027
Designer: L. Harradine
Height: 7¼in., 18.4cm.
Issued: 1949-1952
Colour variation
Price: $720 £450

JUNE M65
Designer: L. Harradine
Height: 4½in., 10.8cm.
Issued: 1935-1949
Price: $720 £450

JUNE M71
Designer: L. Harradine
Height: 4¼in., 10.8cm.
Issued: 1936-1949
Colour variation
Price: $720 £450

ROYAL DOULTON FIGURES

JUNE HN2790
Designer: P. Davies
Height;   7¾in., 19.7cm.
Issued: 1987 only
Price: $200 £125

JUNE HN2991
Designer: R. Tabbenor
Height: 9in., 22.5cm.
Issued: 1988-1994
Price: $264 £165

JUNE HN3323
Designer: P. Davies
Height: 7½in., 19.1cm.
Issued: 1991 U.S.A. only
Price: $200 £125

JUNE HN3346
Designer: P. Davies
Height: 7½in., 19.1cm.
Issued: 1991 Canada only
Price: $200 £125

**JUNO AND THE PEACOCK
HN2827**
Designer: R. Jefferson
Height: 11in., 27.9cm.
Issued: 1984 in a limited
            edition of 300
Price: $2000 £1250

JUST FOR YOU HN3355
Designer: Pauline Parsons
Height: 8¼in., 21cm.
Issued: 1992
Price: $185 £115 (R.R.P.)

JUST ONE MORE HN2980
Designer: A. Hughes
Height: 7in., 17.5cm.
Issued: 1984-1986
Price: $232 £145

K

KAREN HN1994
Designer: L. Harradine
Height: 8in., 20.3cm.
Issued: 1947-1955
Price: $632 £395

KAREN HN2388
Designer: P. Davies
Height: 8in., 20cm.
Issued: 1982-1995
Price: $296 £185

KAREN HN3270
Designer: Peggy Davies
Height: 3¾in., 9.5cm.
Issued: 1990-1995
Price: $120 £75

KATE HN2789
Designer: P. Davies
Height: 7½in., 19.1cm.
Issued: 1978-1987
Price: $232 £145

JULY HN3324

JULY HN3347

JUNO AND THE PEACOCK
HN2827

KAREN HN2388

JUST FOR YOU HN3355

KATE HANNIGAN HN3088
Designer: E. J. Griffiths
Height: 9in., 27.5cm.
Issued: 1987
Price: $440 £275

KATE HARDCASTLE HN1919
Designer: L. Harradine
Height: 8¼in., 21cm.
Issued: 1939-1949
Colour variation
Price: $880 £550

KATE HARDCASTLE HN2028
Designer: L. Harradine
Height: 7¾in., 19.7cm.
Issued: 1949-1952
Colour variation
Price: $720 £450

KATE HARDCASTLE HN1734
Designer: L. Harradine
Height: 8¼in., 21cm.
Issued: 1935-1949
Colour variation
Price: $800 £500

KATE HARDCASTLE HN1861
Designer: L. Harradine
Height: 8in., 20.3cm.
Issued: 1938-1949
Colour variation
Price: $880 £550

KATE HARDCASTLE HN 1718
Designer: L. Harradine
Height: 8in., 20.3cm.
Issued: 1935-1949
Price: $800 £500

KATE HARDCASTLE HN1719
Designer: L. Harradine
Height: 8in., 20.3cm.
Issued: 1935-1949
Colour variation
Price: $720 £450

KATHARINE HN61
Designer: C. J. Noke
Height: 5¾in., 14.6cm.
Issued: 1916-1938
Price: $2000 £1250

KATHARINE HN74
Designer: C. J. Noke
Height: 5¾in., 14.6cm.
Issued: 1917-1938
Colour variation
Price: $2400 £1500

KATHARINE HN341
Designer: C. J. Noke
Height: 5¾in., 14.6cm.
Issued: 1919-1938
Colour variation
Price: $1920 £1200

KATE HARDCASTLE
HN1861

**KATHLEEN
HN1279**

KATHLEEN
HN1252

KATE HARDCASTLE HN 1718

KATHARINE HN471
Designer: C. J. Noke
Height: 5¾in., 14.6cm.
Issued: 1921-1938
Colour variation
Price: $1840 £1150

KATHARINE HN615
Designer: C. J. Noke
Height: 5¾in., 14.6cm.
Issued: 1924-1938
Colour variation
Price: $1920 £1200

KATHARINE HN793
Designer: C. J. Noke
Height: 5¾in., 14.6cm.
Issued: 1926-1938
Colour variation
Price: $2000 £1250

KATHERINE (LADY DOULTON) HN3708
Designer: Valerie Annand
Height: 9in,. 23cm.
Issued: 1996 only
Price: $264 £165

KATHLEEN HN1252
Designer: L. Harradine
Height: 7¾in., 19.7cm.
Issued: 1927-1938
Colour variation
Price: $760 £475

KATHLEEN HN1253
Designer: L. Harradine
Height: 7½in., 19.1cm.
Issued: 1927-1938
Colour variation
Price: $760 £475

KATHLEEN HN1275
Designer: L. Harradine
Height: 7½in., 19.1cm.
Issued: 1928-1938
Colour variation
Price: $760 £475

KATHLEEN HN1279
Designer: L. Harradine
Height: 7¾in., 19.7cm.
Issued: 1928-1938
Colour variation
Price: $760 £475

KATHLEEN HN1291
Designer: L. Harradine
Height: 7½in., 19.1cm.
Issued: 1928-1938
Colour variation
Price: $760 £475

KATHLEEN HN1357
Designer: L. Harradine
Height: 7½in., 19.1cm.
Issued: 1929-1938
Colour variation
Price: $760 £475

ROYAL DOULTON FIGURES

KATHLEEN HN1512
Designer: L. Harradine
Height: 7½in., 19.1cm.
Issued: 1932-1938
            Colour variation
Price: $920 £575

KATHLEEN HN2933
Designer: S. Keenan
Height: 6½in., 16.5cm.
Issued: 1984-1987
Price: $312 £195

KATHLEEN HN3100
Designer: S. Keenan
Height: 6½in., 16.5cm.
Issued: 1986 only
Price: $290 £195

KATHLEEN HN3609
Designer: Nada Pedley
Height: 8¼in., 21cm.
Issued: 1994
Price: $128 £80 (R.R.P.)

KATHRYN HN3413
Designer: P. Davies
Height: 7½in., 19.1cm.
Issued: 1991-1992
Price: $230 £145

KATHRYN HN4040
Designer: Valerie Annand
Height: 8½in., 21.5cm.
Issued: 1997
Price: $128 £80 (R.R.P.)

KATHY HN2346
Designer: P. Davies
Height: 4¾in., 12cm.
Issued: 1981-1987
Price: $232 £145

KATHY HN3305
Designer: Peggy Davies
Height: 7in., 17.5cm.
Issued: 1990-1996
Price: $200 £125

KATIE HN3360
Designer: Valerie Annand
Height: 8¼in., 21cm.
Issued: 1992-1997
Price: $264 £165

KATRINA HN2327
Designer: P. Davies
Height: 7½in., 19.1cm.
Issued: 1965-1969
Price: $440 £275

KAY HN3340
U.S.A. edition
Designer: P. Davies
Height: 7¼in., 18.4cm.
Issued: 1991-1996
Price: $200 £125

KATHLEEN HN3100

KATHRYN HN3413

KATIE HN3360

KATHY HN3305

KATHLEEN HN3609)

KATHY HN2346

KAY HN3340

219

ROYAL DOULTON FIGURES

KELLY HN2478
Designer: P. Davies
Height: 7½in., 19cm.
Issued: 1985-1992
Price: $200 £125

KERRY HN3036
Designer: A. Hughes
Height: 5¼in., 13.5cm.
Issued: 1986-1992
Price: $120 £75

KERRY HN3461
Designer: A. Hughes
Height: 5¼in., 13.3cm.
Issued: 1993
    Colour variation
    U.S.A. only
Issued: $100 £65 (R.R.P.)

KIMBERLEY HN3379
Designer: Tim Potts
Height: 8½in., 21.5cm.
Issued: 1992-1997
Price: $136 £85

KIMBERLEY HN3382
Designer: T. Potts
Height: 8½in., 21.6cm.
Issued: 1993
    Colour variation
    U.S.A. only
Price: $200 £125 (R.R.P.)

KING CHARLES HN404
Designer: C. J. Noke and
    H. Tittensor
Height: 16¾in., 42.5cm.
Issued: 1920-1951
Price: $2320 £1450

KING CHARLES HN2084
Designer: C. J. Noke
Height: 16in., 40.6cm.
Issued: 1952-1992
Price: $2000 £1250

KING CHARLES I HN3459
Designer: C. J. Noke and
    H. Tittensor
Height: 16¾in., 42.5cm.
Issued: 1992 in a limited
    edition of 350
Price: $2400 £1500

KIRSTY HN2381
Designer: P. Davies
Height: 7½in., 19.1cm.
Issued: 1971-1996
Price: $232 £145

KIRSTY HN3213
Designer: P. Davies
Height: 3¾in., 9.5cm.
Issued: 1989-1997
Price: $120 £75

KIMBERLEY HN3379

KELLY HN2478

KERRY HN3461

KIMBERLEY HN3382

KING CHARLES HN2084

KING CHARLES I HN3459

KIRSTY HN3480
U.S.A. edition
Designer: P. Davies
Height: 3¾in., 9.5cm.
Issued: 1993-
Price: $200 £125 (R.R.P.)

KIRSTY HN3743
Designer: Peggy Davies
Height: 3¾in., 9.5cm.
Issued: 1996
Price: $62 £39

KISS (Boy), THE HN4065
Designer: Alan Maslankowski
Height: 6¼in., 16cm.
Issued: 1998
Price: $48 £30 (R.R.P.)

KISS (Girl), THE HN4065
Designer: Alan Maslankowski
Height: 6in., 15.5cm.
Issued: 1998
Price: $48 £30 (R.R.P.)

KITTY HN1367
Designer: Unknown
Height: 4in., 10.1cm.
Issued: 1930-1938
Price: $975 £650

KITTY HN3876
Designer: Nada Pedley
Height: 4½in., 11.5cm.
Issued: 1997
Price: $80 £50 (R.R.P.)

KO-KO (Style one) HN1266
Designer: L. Harradine
Height: 5in., 12.7cm.
Issued: 1928-1949
Price: $840 £525

KO-KO (Style one) HN1286
Designer: L. Harradine
Height: 5in., 12.7cm.
Issued: 1938-1949
            Colour variation
Price: $840 £525

KO-KO (Style two) HN2898
Designer: W. K. Harper
Height: 11½in., 29.2cm.
Issued: 1980-1986
Price: $630 £395

KURDISH DANCER HN2867
Designer: P. Davies
Height: 8¼in., 21cm.
Issued: 1979 in a limited
            edition of 750
Price: $630 £395

L

L'AMBITIEUSE HN3359
Designer: V. Annand
Height: 8¼in., 20.9cm.
Issued: 1991 in a limited
            edition of 5000
Price: $360 £225

KIRSTY HN3480

KIRSTY HN3213

KIRSTY HN2381

KITTY HN3876

KO-KO (Style one) HN1286

KO-KO (Style two) HN2898

LA LOGE HN3472
Designer: V. Annand
Height: 8½in., 21.5cm.
Issued: 1993 in a limited
edition of 7500
Price: $360 £225

LA SYLPHIDE HN2138
Designer: P. Davies
Height: 7in., 17.8cm.
Issued: 1956-1965
Price: $520 £325

LADY AND BLACKAMOOR
(Style one) HN374
Designer: H. Tittensor
Height: Unknown
Issued: 1920-1938
Price: $3600 £2250

LADY AND BLACKAMOOR
(Style two) HN375
Designer: H. Tittensor
Height: Unknown
Issued: 1920-1938
Price: $3600 £2250

LADY AND BLACKAMOOR
(Style two) HN377
Designer: H. Tittensor
Height: Unknown
Issued: 1920-1938
Colour variation
Price: $3600 £2250

LADY AND BLACKAMOOR
(Style two) HN470
Designer: H. Tittensor
Height: Unknown
Issued: 1921-1938
Colour variation
Price: $3600 $2250

LADY AND THE UNICORN
HN2825
Designer: R. Jefferson
Height: 8¾in., 22.2cm.
Issued: 1982 in a limited
edition of 300
Price: $2000 £1250

LADY ANNE HN83
Designer: E. W. Light
Height: Unknown
Issued: 1918-1938
Price: $3200 £2000

LADY ANNE HN87
Designer: E. W. Light
Height: Unknown
Issued: 1918-1938
Colour variation
Price: $3200 £2000

LADY ANNE HN93
Designer: E. W. Light
Height: Unknown
Issued: 1918-1938
Colour variation
Price: $3200 £2000

KURDISH DANCER HN2867

L'AMBITIEUSE HN3359

LADY AND THE UNICORN
HN2825

LADY ANNE NEVILL HN200
Designer: P. Davies
Height: 9¾in., 24.7cm.
Issued: 1948-1953
Price: $840 £525

LADY APRIL HN1958
Designer: L. Harradine
Height: 7in., 17.8cm.
Issued: 1940-1959
Price: $470 £295

LADY APRIL HN1965
Designer: L. Harradine
Height: 7in., 17.8cm.
Issued: 1941-1949
Colour variation
Price: $880 £550

LADY BETTY HN1967
Designer: L. Harradine
Height: 6½in., 16.5cm.
Issued: 1941-1951
Price: $680 £425

LADY CHARMIAN HN1948
Designer: L. Harradine
Height: 8in., 20.3cm.
Issued: 1940-1973
Price: $360 £225

LADY CHARMIAN HN1949
Designer: L. Harradine
Height: 8in., 20.3cm.
Issued: 1940-1975
Colour variation
Price: $360 £225

LADY CLARE HN1465
Designer: L. Harradine
Height: 7¾in., 19.7cm.
Issued: 1931-1938
Price: $792 £495

LADY CLOWN HN717
Designer: L. Harradine
Height: 7½in., 19.1cm.
Issued: 1925-1938
Price: $4000 £2500

LADY CLOWN HN718
Designer: L. Harradine
Height: 7½in., 19.1cm.
Issued: 1925-1938
Colour variation
Price: $4400 £2750

LADY CLOWN HN738
Designer: L. Harradine
Height: 7½in., 19.1cm.
Issued: 1925-1938
Colour variation
Price: $4400 £2750

LADY CLOWN HN770
Designer: L. Harradine
Height: 7½in., 19.1cm.
Issued: 1925-1938
Colour variation
Price: $4400 £2750

LA SYLPHIDE
HN2138

LADY CHARMIAN HN1949

LA LOGE HN3472

LADY ANNE NEVILL HN2006

ROYAL DOULTON FIGURES

LADY CLOWN HN1263
Designer: L. Harradine
Height: 7¼in., 18.4cm.
Issued: 1927-1938
Colour variation
Price: $4000 £2500
Also called CLOWNETTE

LADY DIANA SPENCER HN2885
Designer: E. Griffiths
Height: 7¾in., 19.6cm.
Issued: 1982 as a limited edition of 1500
Price: $720 £450

LADY EATON HN3623
Designer: Valerie Annand
Height: 7½in., 19.1cm.
Issued: 1994 In a limited edition of 2500 Canada only
Price: $400 £250 (R.R.P.)

LADY FAYRE HN1265
Designer: L. Harradine
Height: 5¼in., 13.3cm.
Issued: 1928-1938
Price: $720 £450

LADY FAYRE HN1557
Designer: L. Harradine
Height: 5¾in., 14.6cm.
Issued: 1933-1938
Colour variation
Price: $840 £525

LADY FROM WILLIAMS-BURG HN2228
Designer: P. Davies
Height: 6in., 15.2cm.
Issued: 1960-1983
Price: $264 £165

LADY JANE GREY HN3680
In a limited edition of 5000
Designer: Pauline Parsons
Height: 8¼in., 21cm.
Issued: 1996
Price: $400 £250

LADY JESTER (Style one) HN1221
Designer: L. Harradine
Height: 7in., 17.8cm.
Issued: 1927-1938
Price: $2400 £1500

LADY JESTER (Style one) HN 1222
Designer: L. Harradine
Height: 7in., 17.8cm.
Issued: 1927-1938
Colour variation
Price: $2400 £1500

LADY CLOWN HN717

LADY CLOWN HN1263

LADY FROM WILLIAMS-BURG HN2228

LADY JESTER (Style one) HN1332
Designer: L. Harradine
Height: 7in., 17.8cm.
Issued: 1929-1938
Colour variation
Price: $2400 £1500

LADY JESTER (Style two) HN1284
Designer: L. Harradine
Height: 4¼in., 10.8cm.
Issued: 1928-1938
Price: $2400 £1500

LADY JESTER (Style two) HN1285
Designer: L. Harradine
Height: 4¼in., 10.8cm.
Issued: 1928-1938
Colour variation
Price: $2400 £1500

LADY OF THE ELIZA-BETHAN PERIOD (Style one) HN40
Designer: E. W. Light
Height: 9½in., 24.1cm.
Issued: 1914-1938
Price: $2400 £1500

LADY OF THE ELIZA-BETHAN PERIOD (Style one) HN40A
Designer: E. W. Light
Height: 9½in., 24.1cm.
Issued: 1914-1938
Price: $2400 £1500

LADY OF THE ELIZA-BETHAN PERIOD (Style one) HN73
Designer: E. W. Light
Height: 9½in., 24.1cm.
Issued: 1917-1938
Colour variation
Price: $2400 £1500

LADY OF THE ELIZA-BETHAN PERIOD (Style one) HN411
Designer: E. W. Light
Height: 9¾in., 24.7cm.
Issued: 1920-1938
Colour variation
Price: $2000 £1250

LADY OF THE ELIZA-BETHAN PERIOD (Style two) HN309
Designer: E. W. Light
Height: 9½in., 24.1cm.
Issued: 1918-1938
Price: $2640 £1650

LADY OF THE FAN HN48
Designer: E. W. Light
Height: 9½in. 24.1cm.
Issued: 1916-1938
Price: $2640 £1650

LADY OF THE FAN HN52
Designer: E. W. Light
Height: 9½in., 24.1cm.
Issued: 1916-1938
             Colour variation
Price: $2640 £1650

LADY OF THE FAN HN335
Designer: E. W. Light
Height: 9½in., 24.1cm.
Issued: 1919-1938
             Colour variation
Price: $2400 £1500

LADY OF THE FAN HN509
Designer: E. W. Light
Height: 9½in., 24.1cm.
Issued: 1921-1938
             Colour variation
Price: $2640 £1650

LADY OF THE FAN HN53A
Designer: E. W. Light
Height: 9in., 22.9cm.
Issued: 1916-1938
             Colour variation
Price: $2640 £1650

LADY OF THE FAN HN53
Designer: E. W. Light
Height: 9½in., 24.1cm.
Issued: 1916-1938
             Colour variation
Price: $2640 £1650

**LADY OF THE GEORGIAN
PERIOD HN41**
Designer: E. W. Light
Height: 10¼in., 26cm.
Issued: 1914-1938
Price: $2000 £1250

**LADY OF THE GEORGIAN
PERIOD HN331**
Designer: E. W. Light
Height: 10¼in., 26cm.
Issued: 1918-1938
             Colour variation
Price: $2000 £1250

**LADY OF THE GEORGIAN
PERIOD HN444**
Designer: E. W. Light
Height: 10¼in., 26cm.
Issued: 1921-1938
             Colour variation
Price: $2400 £1500

**LADY OF THE GEORGIAN
PERIOD HN690**
Designer: E. W. Light
Height: 10¼in., 26cm.
Issued: 1925-1938
Price: $2400 £1500

**LADY OF THE GEORGIAN
PERIOD HN702**
Designer: E. W. Light
Height: 10¼in., 26cm.
Issued: 1925-1938
Price: $2400 £1500

LADY JESTER
HN1285

LADY OF THE GEORGIAN
PERIOD HN331

LADY DIANA SPENCER
HN 2885

LADY OF THE FAN HN52

LADY JESTER (Style one)
HN1221

LADY OF THE FAN HN335

225

**LADY OF THE SNOWS
HN1780**
Designer: R. Garbe
Height: Unknown
Issued: 1933-?
Price: $3600 £2250

**LADY OF THE SNOWS
HN1830**
Designer: R. Garbe
Height: Unknown
Issued: 1937-1949
Price: $3600 £2250

**LADY OF THE TIME OF
HENRY VI HN43**
Designer: E. W. Light
Height: 9¼in., 23.5cm.
Issued: 1914-1938
Price: $2000 £1250

LADY PAMELA HN2718
Designer: D. V. Tootle
Height: 8in., 20.3cm.
Issued: 1974-1980
Price: $264 £165

**LADY WITH ERMINE MUFF
HN82**
Designer: E. W. Light
Height: 6¾in., 17.2cm.
Issued: 1918-1938
Price: $2800 £1750
Also known as 'The Afternoon
Call'

LADY WITH ROSE HN48A
Designer: E. W. Light
Height: 9½in., 24.1cm,
Issued: 1916-1936
Price: $2160 £1350

LADY WITH ROSE HN52A
Designer: E. W. Light
Height: 9½in., 24.1cm.
Issued: 1916-1936
        Colour variation
Price: $2160 £1350

LADY WITH ROSE HN68
Designer: E. W. Light
Height: 9½in., 24.1cm.
Issued: 1916-1938
        Colour variation
Price: $2160 £1350

LADY WITH ROSE HN304
Designer: E. W. Light
Height: 9½in., 24.1cm.
Issued: 1918-1936
        Colour variation
Price: $2160 £1350

LADY WITH ROSE HN336
Designer: E. W. Light
Height: 9½in., 24.1cm.
Issued: 1919-1936
        Colour variation
Price: $2160 £1350

LADY PAMELA HN2718

LADYBIRD HN1638

LADY WITH ROSE HN515
Designer: E. W. Light
Height: 9½in., 24.1cm.
Issued: 1921-1936
        Colour variation
Price: $2160 £1350

LADY WITH ROSE HN517
Designer: E. W. Light
Height: 9½in., 24.1cm.
Issued: 1921-1936
        Colour variation
Price: $2160 £1350

LADY WITH ROSE HN584
Designer: E. W. Light
Height: 9½in., 24.1cm.
Issued: 1923-1936
        Colour variation
Price: $2160 £1350

LADY WITH ROSE HN624
Designer: E. W. Light
Height: 9½in., 24.1cm.
Issued: 1924-1936
        Colour variation
Price: $2160 £1350

LADY WITH SHAWL HN447
Designer: L. Harradine
Height: 13¼in., 33.7cm.
Issued: 1921-1936
Price: $2400 £1500

LADY WITH SHAWL HN458
Designer: L. Harradine
Height: 13¼in., 33.7cm.
Issued: 1921-1936
        Colour variation
Price: $2800 £1750

LADY WITH SHAWL HN626
Designer: L. Harradine
Height: 13¼in., 33.7cm.
Issued: 1924-1936
        Colour variation
Price: $2800 £1750

LADY WITH SHAWL HN678
Designer: L. Harradine
Height: 13¼in., 33.7cm.
Issued: 1924-1936
        Colour variation
Price: $2800 £1750

LADY WITH SHAWL HN679
Designer: L. Harradine
Height: 13¼in., 33.7cm.
Issued: 1924-1936
Price: $2800 £1750

**LADY WITHOUT BOUQUET
HN393**
Designer: G. Lambert
Height: 9in., 22.9cm.
Issued: 1920-1936
Price: $3600 £2250

LADY WITHOUT BOUQUET
HN394
Designer: G. Lambert
Height: 9in., 22.9cm.
Issued: 1920-1936
            Colour variation
Price: $3600 £2250

LADY WORSLEY HN3318
Designer: Peter Gee
Height: 9½in., 24cm.
Issued: 1991 in a limited
            edition of 5000-1995
Price: $520 £325

LADYBIRD HN1638
Designer: L. Harradine
Height: 7¾in., 19.7cm.
Issued: 1934-1949
Price: $2320 £1450

LADYBIRD HN1640
Designer: L. Harradine
Height: 7¾in., 19.7cm.
Issued: 1934-1938
            Colour variation
Price: $2640 £1650

LAIRD HN2361
Designer: M. Nicoll
Height: 8in., 20.3cm.
Issued: 1969-
Price: $208 £130 (R.R.P.)

LALLA ROOKH HN2910
Designer: S. Keenan
Height: 9in., 22.8cm.
Issued: 1981 in a limited
            edition of 950
Price: $560 £350

LAMBETH WALK HN1880
Designer: L. Harradine
Height: 10in., 25.4cm.
Issued: 1938-1949
Price: $2320 £1450

LAMBETH WALK HN1881
Designer: L. Harradine
Height: 10in., 25.4cm.
Issued: 1938-1949
            Colour variation
Price: $2320 £1450

LAMBING TIME HN1890
Designer: L. Harradine
Height: 9¼in., 23.5cm.
Issued: 1938-1981
Price: $264 £165

LAMBING TIME HN3855
Designer: Tim Potts
Height: 8in., 20cm.
Issued: 1996
Price: $128 £80 (R.R.P.)

LAMP SELLER HN3278
(Flambé)
Designer: R. Tabbenor
Height: 9in., 22.9cm.
Issued: 1990-1995
Price: $440 £275

LALLA ROOKH HN2910

LAIRD HN2361

LAMBING TIME HN3855

LAMBETH WALK HN1880

LAMP SELLER HN3278

227

LANCELOT & GUINEVERE HN3112
Designer: Robert Jefferson
Height: 12in., 30.5cm.
Issued: 1996-1997 in a limited edition of 150
Price: $3120 £1950 (R.R.P.)

LAND OF NOD HN56
Designer: H. Tittensor
Height: 9½in., 24.1cm.
Issued: 1916-1938
Price: $2800 £1750

LAND OF NOD HN56A
Designer: H. Tittensor
Height: 9½in., 24.1cm.
Issued: 1916-1938
Price: $2800 £1750

LAND OF NOD HN56B
Designer: H. Tittensor
Height: 9½in., 24.1cm.
Issued: 1916-1938
             Colour variation
Price: $2800 £1750

LAST WALTZ HN2315
Designer: P.Davies
Height: 7¾in., 19.7cm.
Issued: 1967-1993
Price: $232 £145

LAURA HN2960
Designer: P. Parsons
Height: 7¼in., 18cm.
Issued: 1982-1994
Price: $232 £145

LAURA HN3136
Designer: P. Parsons
Height: 7¼in., 18.4cm.
Issued: 1988-1989
Price: $310 £195

LAURA HN3760
Designer: Nada Pedley
Height: 8in., 20cm.
Issued: 1996
Price: $128 £80

LAURIANNE HN2719
Designer: D. V. Tootle
Height: 6¼in., 15.9cm.
Issued: 1974-1978
Price: $256 £160

LAUREN HN3872
(Roadshow Figure)
Designer: Nada Pedley
Height: 8in., 20.3cm.
Issued: 1997
Price: £128 £80

LAVENDER WOMAN HN22
Designer: P. Stabler
Height: 8¼in., 21cm.
Issued: 1913-1938
Price: $2800 £1750

LAVENDER WOMAN HN23
Designer: P. Stabler
Height: 8¼in., 21cm.
Issued: 1913-1938
             Colour variation
Price: $3200 £2000

LAST WALTZ HN2315

LAURIANNE HN2719

LAURA HN3760

LAVENDER WOMAN HN23A
Designer: P. Stabler
Height: 8¼in., 21cm.
Issued: 1913-1938
             Colour variation
Price: $3200 £2000

LAVENDER WOMAN HN342
Designer: P. Stabler
Height: 8¼in., 21cm.
Issued: 1919-1938
             Colour variation
Price: $2800 £1750

LAVENDER WOMAN HN569
Designer: P. Stabler
Height: 8¼in., 21cm.
Issued: 1924-1938
             Colour variation
Price: $2800 £1750

LAVENDER WOMAN HN744
Designer: P. Stabler
Height: 8¼in., 21cm.
Issued: 1925-1938
             Colour variation
Price: $2800 £1750

LAVINIA HN1955
Designer: L. Harradine
Height: 5in., 12.7cm.
Issued: 1940-1978
Price: $192 £120

LAWYER HN3041
Designer: P. Parsons
Height: 9in., 23cm.
Issued: 1985-1995
Price: $232 £145

LE BAL HN3702 (R.D.I.C.C.)
Designer: Valerie Annand
Height: 8½in., 22.5cm.
Issued: 1995-1996 in a limited edition of 5000
Price: $312 £195

LEADING LADY HN2269
Designer: P. Davies
Height: 7¾in., 19.7cm.
Issued: 1965-1976
Price: $265 £165

THE LEAP HN3522
Designer: Adrian Hughes
Height: 8¾in., 22cm.
Issued: 1982
Price: $128 £80 (R.R.P.)

LEDA AND THE SWAN HN2826
Designer: R. Jefferson
Height: 9¾in., 25cm.
Issued: 1983 in a limited edition of 300
Price: $2000 £1250

ROYAL DOULTON FIGURES

LEGOLAS HN2917
Designer: H. Sales
Height: 6¼in., 15.9cm.
Issued: 1980-1984
Price: $200 £125

LEISURE HOUR HN2055
Designer: P. Davies
Height: 7in., 17.8cm.
Issued: 1950-1965
Price: $680 £425

**LEOPARD ON THE ROCK
HN2638**
Designer: Charles Noke
Height: 9in., 22.9cm.
Issued: 1952-1981
Price: $1200 £750

LES PARAPLUIES HN3473
In a limited edition of 7500
Designer: Valerie Annand
Height: 8⅓in., 21cm.
Issued: 1993
Price: $360 £225

LESLEY HN2410
Designer: M. Nicoll
Height: 8in., 20cm.
Issued: 1986-1990
Price: $264 £165

LET'S PLAY HN3397
Designer: Alan Maslankowski
Height: 4in., 10cm.
Issued: 1992-1996
Price: $96 £60

LIBERTY HN3201
Designer: A. Hughes
Height: 9½in., 23.5cm.
Issued: 1989-1990
Price: $280 £175

LIDO LADY HN1220
Designer: L. Harradine
Height: 6¾in., 17.2cm.
Issued: 1927-1936
Price: $2000 £1250

LIDO LADY HN1229
Designer: L. Harradine
Height: 6¾in., 17.2cm.
Issued: 1927-1938
Colour variation
Price: $2000 £1250

LIFEBOAT MAN HN2764
Designer: W. K. Harper
Height: 9½in., 24cm.
Issued: 1987-1991
Price: $280 £175

LIFEGUARD HN2781
Designer: William K. Harper
Height: 9½in., 24cm.
Issued: 1992-1995
Price: $232 £145

LAWYER HN3041

LET'S PLAY HN3397

LES PARAPLUIES HN3473

LEGOLAS HN2917

LIFEGUARD
HN2781

LIDO LADY HN1229

LEDA AND THE SWAN HN2826

ROYAL DOULTON FIGURES

LIGHTS OUT HN2262
Designer: P. Davies
Height: 5in., 12.7cm.
Issued: 1965-1969
Price: $296 £185

LILAC SHAWL HN44
Designer: C. J. Noke
Height: 8¾in., 22.2cm.
Issued: 1915-1938
Price: $1600 £1000

LILAC SHAWL HN44A
Designer: C. J. Noke
Height: 8¾in., 22.2cm.
Issued: 1915-1938
           Colour variation
Price: $1600 £1000
Also called In Grandma's Days
and Poke Bonnet

LILAC TIME HN2137
Designer: P. Davies
Height: 7¼in., 18.4cm.
Issued: 1954-1969
Price: $360 £225

LILLIAN IN SUMMER HN3003
Designer: Peter Gee
Height: 8½in., 20.5cm.
Issued: 1985 Danbury Mint
           commission
Price: $360 £225

LILLIE LANGTRY HN3820
In a limited edition of 5000
Designer: Douglas Tootle
Height: 8½in., 21.5cm.
Issued: 1996
Price: $312 £195

LILY HN1798
Designer: L. Harradine
Height: 5in., 12.7cm.
Issued: 1936-1971
Price: $200 £125

LILY HN1799
Designer: L. Harradine
Height: 5in., 12.7cm.
Issued: 1936-1949
           Colour variation
Price: $440 £275

LILY HN3902
Designer: Peggy Davies
Height: 7½in., 19.5cm.
Issued: 1997 (Mid Year)
Price: $206 £129 (R.R.P.)

LINDA HN2106
Designer: L. Harradine
Height: 4¾in., 12cm.
Issued: 1953-1976
Price: $230 £145

LINDA HN2758
Designer: E. Griffiths
Height: 7¾in., 19.5cm.
Issued: 1984-1988
Price: $265 £165

LINDA HN2758

LINDA HN3374

LILAC TIME HN2137

"LITTLE CHILD SO RARE
AND SWEET" (Style two)
HN1542

LITTLE BO-PEEP HN3030

LISA HN2394

LINDA HN3374
Designer: Nada Pedley
Height: 8¼in., 21cm.
Issued: 1991-1995
Price: $200 £125

LINDSAY HN3645
Designer: Nada Pedley
Height: 8in., 20cm.
Issued: 1996
Price: $152 £95 (R.R.P.)

LION ON ROCK HN2641
Designer: Charles Noke
Height: 10½in., 26.7cm.
Issued: 1952-1992
Price: $1520 £950

LISA HN2310
Designer: P. Davies
Height: 7¼in., 18.4cm.
Issued: 1969-1982
Price: $232 £145

LISA HN2394
Designer: P. Davies
Height: 7¾in., 19.7cm.
Issued: 1983-1990
Price: $200 £125

LISA HN3265
Designer: P. Davies
Height: 7¾in., 19.7cm.
Issued: 1989-1995
Price: $176 £110

LISE HN3474
In a limited edition of 7500
Designer: Valerie Annand
Height: 8¼in., 21cm.
Issued: 1993
Price: $360 £225

LISETTE HN1523
Designer: L. Harradine
Height: 5¼in., 13.3cm.
Issued: 1932-1936
Price: $1200 £750

LISETTE HN1524
Designer: L. Harradine
Height: 5¼in., 13.3cm.
Issued: 1932-1936
           Colour variation
Price: $1200 £750

LISETTE HN1684
Designer: L. Harradine
Height: 6½in., 16.5cm.
Issued: 1935-1938
           Colour variation
Price: $1200 £750

LITTLE BALLERINA HN3395
Designer: Alan Maslankowski
Height: 6in., 15cm.
Issued: 1992
Price: $65 £40 (R.R.P.)

ROYAL DOULTON FIGURES

LITTLE BALLERINA HN3431
Designer: A. Maslankowski
Height: 6in., 15cm.
Issued: 1993 in a limited
edition of 2000
Colour variation
U.S.A. only
Price: $152 £95

LITTLE BO-PEEP HN3030
Designer: A. Hughes
Height: 8in., 20cm.
Issued: 1984-1987
Price: $232 £145

LITTLE BOY BLUE HN2062
Designer: L. Harradine
Height: 5½in., 14cm.
Issued: 1950-1973
Price: $264 £165

LITTLE BOY BLUE HN2062
Designer: L. Harradine
Height: 5½in., 14cm.
Issued: 1950-1973
Colour variation
Price: $264 £165

LITTLE BOY BLUE HN3035
Designer: A. Hughes
Height: 7¾in., 19.7cm.
Issued: 1984-1987
Price: $200 £125

**"LITTLE CHILD SO RARE
AND SWEET"** (Style one)
HN1540
Designer: Unknown
Height: 5in., 12.7cm.
Issued: 1933-1949
Price: $600 £375

**"LITTLE CHILD SO RARE
AND SWEET"** (Style two)
HN1542
Designer: Unknown
Height: 5in., 12.7cm.
Issued: 1933-1949
Price: $600 £375

**LITTLE JACK HORNER
HN2063**
Designer: L. Harradine
Height: 4½in., 11.4cm.
Issued: 1950-1953
Price: $600 £375

**LITTLE JACK HORNER
HN3034**
Designer: A. Hughes
Height: 7in., 17.5cm.
Issued: 1984-1987
Price: $232 £145

**LITTLE LADY MAKE BE-
LIEVE HN1870**
Designer: L. Harradine
Height: 6¼in., 15.9cm.
Issued: 1938-1949
Price: $680 £425

LITTLE JACK HORNER
HN3034

LITTLE BOY BLUE HN3035

LITTLE BOY BLUE HN2062

LITTLE BALLERINA
HN3395

LINDSAY HN3645

LISETTE HN1523

LISA HN2310

LITTLE LAND, THE HN63
Designer: H. Tittensor
Height: 7½in., 19.1cm.
Issued: 1916-1936
Price: $3600 £2250

LITTLE LAND, THE HN67
Designer: H. Tittensor
Height: 7½in., 19.1cm.
Issued: 1916-1936
Price: $3200 £2000

LITTLE LORD FAUNTLEROY HN2972
Designer: A. Hughes
Height: 6¼in., 16cm.
Issued: 1982-1986
Price: $232 £145

LITTLE MISS MUFFET HN2727
Designer: W. K. Harper
Height: 6¼in., 16cm.
Issued: 1984-1987
Price: $200 £125

LITTLE MISTRESS HN1449
Designer: L. Harradine
Height: 5¾in., 14.6cm.
Issued: 1931-1949
Price: $520 £325

LITTLE MOTHER (Style one) HN389
Designer: H. Tittensor
Height: Unknown
Issued: 1920-1938
Price: $3200 £2000

LITTLE MOTHER (Style one) HN390
Designer: H. Tittensor
Height: Unknown
Issued: 1920-1938
              Colour variation
Price: $3200 £2000

LITTLE MOTHER (Style one) HN469
Designer: H. Tittensor
Height: Unknown
Issued: 1921-1938
              Colour variation
Price: $3200 £2000

LITTLE MOTHER (Style two) HN1418
Designer: L. Harradine
Height: 8in., 20.3cm.
Issued: 1930-1938
Price: $2000 £1250

LITTLE MOTHER (Style two) HN1641
Designer: L. Harradine
Height: 8in., 20.3cm.
Issued: 1934-1949
Price: $2400 £1500
Also called Young Widow

LITTLE LORD FAUNTLEROY HN2972

LONG JOHN SILVER HN2204

LIZANA HN1756

LOUISE HN2869

LOBSTER MAN HN2317

LITTLE NELL HN540
Designer: L. Harradine
Height: 4in., 10.1cm.
Issued: 1922-1932
Price: $96 £60

LITTLE NELL M51
Designer: L. Harradine
Height: 4¼in., 10.8cm.
Issued: 1932-1982
Price: $80 £50

LIZANA HN1756
Designer: L. Harradine
Height: 8½in., 21.6cm.
Issued: 1936-1949
Price: $1040 £650

LIZANA HN1761
Designer: L. Harradine
Height: 8½in., 21.6cm.
Issued: 1936-1938
Price: $1040 £650

LIZZIE HN2749
Designer: D. Tootle
Height: 8½in., 22cm.
Issued: 1988-1991
Price: $256 £160

LOBSTER MAN HN2317
Designer: M. Nicoll
Height: 7¼in., 18.4cm.
Issued: 1964-1995
Price: $232 £145

LOBSTER MAN HN2323
Designer: Mary Nicoll
Height: 7½in., 19cm.
Issued: 1987-1995
Price: $264 £165

LOBSTER MAN HN2327
Designer: M. Nicoll
Height: 7½in., 19cm.
Issued: 1987-1995
Price: $264 £165

LONDON CRY, STRAWBERRIES HN749
Designer: L. Harradine
Height: 6¾in., 17.2cm.
Issued: 1925-1936
Price: $1840 £1150

LONDON CRY, STRAWBERRIES HN772
Designer: L. Harradine
Height: 6¾in., 17.2cm.
Issued: 1925-1936
              Colour variation
Price: $1840 £1150

LONDON CRY, TURNIPS AND CARROTS HN752
Designer: L. Harradine
Height: 6¾in., 17.2cm.
Issued: 1925-1938
Price: $1840 £1150

ROYAL DOULTON FIGURES

LONDON CRY, TURNIPS AND CARROTS HN771
Designer: L. Harradine
Height: 6¾in., 17.2cm.
Issued: 1925-1938
Price: $1840 £1150

LONG JOHN SILVER HN2204
Designer: M. Nicoll
Height: 9in., 22.9cm.
Issued: 1957-1965
Price: $632 £395

LONG JOHN SILVER HN3719
(Resin)
Designer: Alan Maslankowski
Height: 8¾in., 22cm.
Issued: 1993-1996
Price: $120 £75

LORD NELSON, VICE ADMIRAL HN3489
Designer: Alan Maslankowski
Height: 12½in., 32cm.
Issued: 1993 in a limited edition of 950
Price: $1592 £995 (R.R.P.)

LORD OLIVIER AS RICHARD III HN2881
Designer: E. Griffiths
Height: 11¼in., 28.5cm.
Issued: 1985 in a limited edition of 750
Price: $760 £475

LORETTA HN2337
Designer: P. Davies
Height: 7¾in., 19.7cm.
Issued: 1966-1980
Price: $230 £145

LORI HN2801
Designer: P. Davies
Height: 5¾in., 14.6cm.
Issued: 1976-1987
Price: $232 £145

LORNA HN2311
Designer: P. Davies
Height: 8¼in., 21cm.
Issued: 1965-1985
Price: $264 £165

LORRAINE HN3118
Designer: A. Maslankowski
Height: 8in., 20cm.
Issued: 1988-1995
Price: $232 £145

LOUISE HN2869
Designer: P. Davies
Height: 6in., 15.2cm.
Issued: 1980-1986
Price: $280 £175

LOUISE HN3207
Designer: Adrian Hughes
Height: 7½in., 19cm.
Issued: 1990-1996
Price: $280 £175

LORRAINE HN3118

OUISE HN3207

LORNA HN2311

LORD OLIVIER AS RICHARD III HN2881

LORD NELSON, VICE ADMIRAL HN3489

LORETTA HN2337

ROYAL DOULTON FIGURES

LOUISE HN3888
Designer: Nada Pedley
Height: 8in., 20.5cm.
Issued: 1997
Price: $152 £95 (R.R.P.)

LOVE LETTER HN2149
Designer: P. Davies
Height: 5½in., 14cm.
Issued: 1958-1976
Price: $520 £325

LOVE LETTER, THE HN3105
Designer: R. Jefferson
Height: 12in., 30.5cm.
Issued: 1986-1988
Price: $232 £145

LOVERS HN2762 (White)
Designer: D. Tootle
Height: 12in., 30.5cm.
Issued: 1981-1997
Price: $176 £110

LOVERS HN2763 (Black)
Designer: D. Tootle
Height: 12in., 30.5cm.
Issued: 1981-1992
Price: $200 £125

LOVING THOUGHTS
Designer: Alan Maslankowski
Height: 6in., 15.5cm.
Issued: 1997
Price: $64 £40 (R.R.P.)

LOVING YOU HN3389
Designer: Alan Maslankowski
Height: 6¼in., 16cm.
Issued: 1991
Price: $64 £40 (R.R.P.)

LOYAL FRIEND HN3358
Designer: Valerie Annand
Height: 8¼in., 21cm.
Issued: 1991-1995
Price: $312 £195

LUCREZIA BORGIA HN2342
Designer: P. Davies
Height: 8in., 20cm.
Issued: 1985 in a limited
edition of 750
Price: $1040 £650

LUCY HN2863
Designer: P. Davies
Height: 6in., 15.2cm.
Issued: 1980-1984
Price: $264 £165

LUCY HN3653
Designer: P. Davies
Height: Unknown
Issued: 1994 only
Price: $200 £125

LUCY HN3858
Designer: Tim Potts
Height: 8½in., 21.5cm.
Issued: 1997
Price: $152 £95 (R.R.P.)

LOVE LETTER HN2149

OVERS HN2762

LOVE LETTER,
THE HN3105

LOVING YOU HN3389

LUCREZIA BORGIA HN2342

ROYAL DOULTON FIGURES

LUCY ANN HN1502
Designer: L. Harradine
Height: 5¼in., 13.3cm.
Issued: 1932-1951
Price: $520 £325

LUCY ANN HN1565
Designer: L. Harradine
Height: 5¼in., 13.3cm.
Issued: 1933-1938
   Colour variation
Price: $520 £325

LUCY LOCKETT (Style one)
HN485
Designer: L. Harradine
Height: 6in., 15.2cm.
Issued: 1921-1949
Price: $1040 £650

LUCY LOCKETT (Style one)
HN524
Designer: L. Harradine
Height: 6in., 15.2cm.
Issued: 1921-1949
   Colour variation
Price: $880 £550

LUCY LOCKETT (Style two)
HN695
Designer: L. Harradine
Height: 6in., 15.2cm.
Issued: 1925-1949
Price: $880 £550

LUCY LOCKETT (Style two)
HN696
Designer: L. Harradine
Height: 6in., 15.2cm.
Issued: 1925-1949
   Colour variation
Price: $1040 £650

LUNCHTIME HN2485
Designer: M. Nicoll
Height: 8in., 20.3cm.
Issued: 1973-1981
Price: $360 £225

LUTE HN2431
Designer: P. Davies
Height: 6¼in., 15.9cm.
Issued: 1972 in a limited
   edition of 750
Price: $1040 £650

LYDIA HN1906
Designer: L. Harradine
Height: 4¼in., 10.8cm.
Issued: 1939-1949
Price: $560 £350

LYDIA HN1907
Designer: L. Harradine
Height: 4¾in., 12cm.
Issued: 1939-1949
Price: $560 £350

LUCY HN2863   LUCY ANN HN1502

LOYAL FRIEND HN3358

LUTE HN2431

LUCY HN3858   LUNCHTIME HN2485

235

LYDIA HN1908
Designer: L. Harradine
Height: 4¾in., 12cm.
Issued: 1939-1995
            Colour variation
Price: $152 £95

LYDIA HN1908

LYNNE HN2329
Designer: P. Davies
Height: 7in., 17.8cm.
Issued: 1971-1996
Price: $200 £125

LYNSEY HN3043
Designer: P. Parsons
Height: 4¾in., 12cm.
Issued: 1985-1995
Price: $72 £45

LYRIC HN2757
Designer: E. Griffiths
Height: 6¼in., 16cm.
Issued: 1983-1986
Price: $232 £145

M

**MADONNA OF THE SQUARE
HN10**
Designer: P. Stabler
Height: 7in., 17.8cm.
Issued: 1913-1938
Price: $1360 £850

**MADONNA OF THE SQUARE
HN10A**
Designer: P. Stabler
Height: 7in., 17.8cm.
Issued: 1913-1938
            Colour variation
Price: $1200 £750

**MADONNA OF THE SQUARE
HN11**
Designer: P. Stabler
Height: 7in., 17.8cm.
Issued: 1913-1938
            Colour variation
Price: $1440 £900

**MADONNA OF THE SQUARE
HN14**
Designer: P. Stabler
Height: 7in., 17.8cm.
Issued: 1913-1938
            Colour variation
Price: $1040 £650

**MADONNA OF THE SQUARE
HN27**
Designer: P. Stabler
Height: 7in., 17.8cm.
Issued: 1913-1938
            Colour variation
Price: $1440 £900

LYNNE HN2329

LYNSEY HN3043

LYRIC HN2757

**MADONNA OF THE SQUARE
HN326**
Designer: P. Stabler
Height: 7in., 17.8cm.
Issued: 1918-1938
            Colour variation
Price: $975 £650

**MADONNA OF THE SQUARE
HN573**
Designer: P. Stabler
Height: 7in., 17.8cm.
Issued: 1913-1938
            Colour variation
Price: $1360 £850

**MADONNA OF THE SQUARE
HN576**
Designer: P. Stabler
Height: 7in., 17.8cm.
Issued: 1923-1938
            Colour variation
Price: $1200 £750

**MADONNA OF THE SQUARE
HN594**
esigner: P. Stabler
Height: 7in., 17.8cm.
Issued: 1924-1938
            Colour variation
Price: $1360 £850

**MADONNA OF THE SQUARE
HN613**
Designer: P. Stabler
Height: 7in., 17.8cm.
Issued: 1924-1938
            Colour variation
Price: $1040 £650

**MADONNA OF THE SQUARE
HN764**
Designer: P. Stabler
Height: 7in., 17.8cm.
Issued: 1925-1938
            Colour variation
Price: $1360 £850

**MADONNA OF THE SQUARE
HN1968**
Designer: P. Stabler
Height: 7in., 17.8cm.
Issued: 1941-1949
            Colour variation
Price: $800 £500

**MADONNA OF THE SQUARE
HN1969**
Designer: P. Stabler
Height: 7in., 17.8cm.
Issued: 1941-1949
            Colour variation
Price: $800 £500

**MADONNA OF THE SQUARE
HN2034**
Designer: P. Stabler
Height: 7in., 17.8cm.
            Colour variation
Issued: 1949-1951
Price: $800 £500

ROYAL DOULTON FIGURES

MAGIC DRAGON HN2977
Designer: A. Hughes
Height: 4¾in., 12cm.
Issued: 1983-1986
Price: $264 £165

MAGPIE RING HN2978
Designer: A. Hughes
Height: 8in., 20cm.
Issued: 1983-1986
Price: $265 £165

MAISIE HN1618
Designer: L. Harradine
Height: 6¼in., 15.9cm.
Issued: 1934-1949
Price: $680 £425

MAISIE HN1619
Designer: L. Harradine
Height: 6¼in., 15.9cm.
Issued: 1934-1949
           Colour variation
Price: $680 £425

**MAJOR, 3rd JERSEY
REGIMENT 1776 HN2752**
Designer: E. J. Griffiths
Height: 10in., 25.4cm.
Issued: 1975 in a limited
           edition of 350
Price: $880 £550

MAKE BELIEVE HN2225
Designer: M. Nicoll
Height: 5¾in., 14.6cm.
Issued: 1962-1988
Price: $150 £95

**MAKE BELIEVE (White)
HN2224**
Designer: M. Nicoll
Height: 5¾in., 14.6cm.
Issued: 1984-1988
           Colour variation
Price: $200 £125

MAKING FRIENDS HN3372
Designer: Nada Pedley
Height: 5½in., 14cm.
Issued: 1991 in a limited
           edition of 9500-1994
Price: $264 £165

MAM'SELLE HN658
Designer: L. Harradine
Height: 7in., 17.8cm.
Issued: 1924-1938
Price: $2320 £1450

MAM'SELLE HN659
Designer: L. Harradine
Height: 7in., 17.8cm.
Issued: 1924-1938
           Colour variation
Price: $2320 £1450

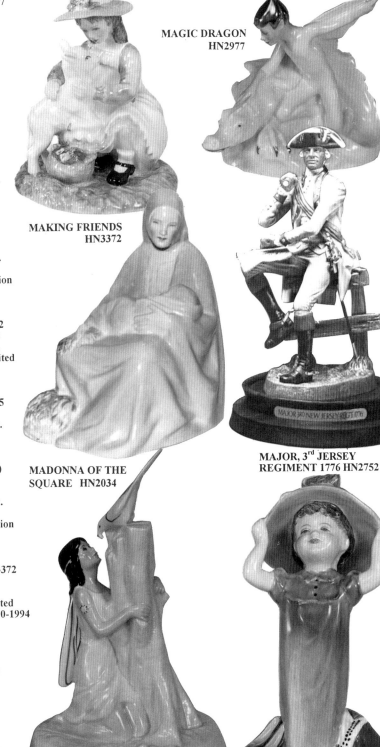

MAGIC DRAGON
HN2977

MAKING FRIENDS
HN3372

MADONNA OF THE
SQUARE   HN2034

MAJOR, 3rd JERSEY
REGIMENT 1776 HN2752

MAGPIE RING HN2978

MAKE BELIEVE HN2225

ROYAL DOULTON FIGURES

MAM'SELLE HN724
Designer: L. Harradine
Height: 7in., 17.8cm.
Issued: 1925-1938
Colour variation
Price: $2320 £1450

MAM'SELLE HN786
Designer: L. Harradine
Height: 7in., 17.8cm.
Issued: 1926-1938
Colour variation
Price: $2320 £1450

MAN IN TUDOR COSTUME HN563
Designer: Unknown
Height: 3¾in., 9.5cm.
Issued: 1923-1938
Price: $3200 £2000

MANDARIN (Style one) HN84
Designer: C. J. Noke
Height: 10¼in., 26cm.
Issued: 1918-1938
Price: $5600 £3500

MANDARIN (Style one) HN316
Designer: 10¼in., 26cm.
Issued: 1918-1938
Colour variation
Price: $4000 £2500

MANDARIN (Style one) HN318
Designer: C. J. Noke
Height: 10in., 25.4cm.
Issued: 1918-1938
Colour variation
Price: $4800 £3000

MANDARIN (Style one) HN382
Designer: C. J. Noke
Height: 10in., 25.4cm.
Issued: 1920-1938
Colour variation
Price: $4000 £2500

MANDARIN (Style one) HN611
Designer: C. J. Noke
Height: 10in., 25.4cm.
Issued: 1924-1938
Colour variation
Price: $4400 £2750

MANDARIN (Style one) HN746
Designer: C. J. Noke
Height: 10in., 25.4cm.
Issued: 1925-1938
Colour variation
Price: $3600 £2250

MANDARIN (Style one) HN787
Designer: C. J. Noke
Height: 10in., 25.4cm.
Issued: 1926-1938
Colour variation
Price: $5600 £3500

MAM'SELLE HN786

MAM'SELLE HN724

MANDARIN HN450

MANDY HN2476

MARCH HN2707

MARCH HN3332

MANDARIN (Style one) HN791
Designer: C. J. Noke
Height: 10in., 25.4cm.
Issued: 1926-1938
Colour variation
Price: $4400 £2750

MANDARIN (Style two) HN366
Designer: C. J. Noke
Height: 10in., 25.4cm.
Issued: 1920-1938
Price: $5600 £3500

MANDARIN (Style two) HN455
Designer: C. J. Noke
Height: 10in., 25.4cm.
Issued: 1921-1938
Price: $5600 £3500

MANDARIN (Style two) HN641
Designer: C. J. Noke
Height: 10in., 25.4cm.
Issued: 1924-1938
Colour variation
Price: $5600 £3500

MANDARIN (Style three) HN450
Designer: C. J. Noke
Height: Unknown
Issued: 1921-1938
Price: $5600 £3500

MANDARIN (Style three) HN460
Designer: C. J. Noke
Height: Unknown
Issued: 1921-1938
Colour variation
Price: $5600 £3500

MANDARIN (Style three) HN461
Designer: C. J. Noke
Height: Unknown
Issued: 1921-1938
Colour variation
Price: $5600 £3500

MANDARIN (Style three) HN601
Designer: C. J. Noke
Height: Unknown
Issued: 1924-1938
Colour variation
Price: $3200 £2000

MANDY HN2476
Designer: P. Davies
Height: 4½in., 11.5cm.
Issued: 1982-1992
Price: $136 £85

MANTILLA HN2712
Designer: E. J. Griffiths
Height: 11½in., 29.2cm.
Issued: 1974-1977
Price: $632 £395

ROYAL DOULTON FIGURES

MANTILLA HN3192
Designer: E. J. Griffiths
Height: 11½in., 29.2cm.
Issued: 1992 in a limited
edition of 1992 for
Expo 92
Price: $632 £395

MARCH HN2707
Designer: P. Davies
Height: 7¾in., 19.7cm.
Issued: 1987
Price: $232 £145

MARCH HN3332
Designer: P. Davies
Height: 7½in., 19cm.
Issued: 1991 U.S.A. only
Price: $165 £110

MARGARET HN1989
Designer: L. Harradine
Height: 7¼in., 18.4cm.
Issued: 1947-1959
Price: $472 £295

MARGARET HN2397
Designer: P. Davies
Height: 7½in., 19cm.
Issued: 1982-
Price: $128 £80 (R.R.P.)

MARGARET HN3496
Designer: P. Davies
Height: 7½in., 19.1cm.
Issued: 1993
Colour variation
U.S.A. only
Price: $264 £165 (R.R.P.)

MARGARET OF ANJOU
HN2012
Designer: P. Davies
Height: 9¼in., 23.5cm.
Issued: 1949-1953
Price: $880 £550

MARGARET TUDOR HN3838
In a limited edition of 5000
Designer: Pauline Parsons
Height: 8¼in., 21cm.
Issued: 1997-
Price: $400 £250

MARGERY HN1413
Designer: L. Harradine
Height: 11in., 27.9cm.
Issued: 1930-1949
Price: $520 £325

MARGOT HN1628
Designer: L. Harradine
Height: 5½in., 14cm.
Issued: 1934-1938
Price: $960 £600

MARGOT HN1636
Designer: L. Harradine
Height: 5¾in., 14.6cm.
Issued: 1934-1938
Colour variation
Price: $1040 £650

MARGARET HN2397

MARGARET
HN3496

MANTILLA HN3192

MARGARET OF ANJOU
HN2012

MARGERY HN1413

239

MARGOT HN1653
Designer: L. Harradine
Height: 5¾in., 14.6cm.
Issued: 1934-1938
Colour variation
Price: $1040 £650

MARGUERITE HN1928
Designer: L. Harradine
Height: 8in., 20.3cm.
Issued: 1940-1959
Price: $440 £275

MARGUERITE HN1929
Designer: L. Harradine
Height: 8in.,, 20.3cm.
Issued: 1940-1949
Colour variation
Price: $440 £275

MARGUERITE HN1930
Designer: L. Harradine
Height: 8in., 20.3cm.
Issued: 1940-1949
Colour variation
Price: $840 £525

MARGUERITE HN1946
Designer: L. Harradine
Height: 8in., 20.3cm.
Issued: 1940-1949
Colour variation
Price: $640 £400

MARIA HN3381
Designer: Tim Potts
Height: 8½in., 22cm.
Issued: 1994
Price: $128 £80 (R.R.P.)

MARIANNE HN2074
Designer: L. Harradine
Height: 7¼in., 18.4cm.
Issued: 1951-1953
Price: $920 £575

MARIE (Style one) HN401
Designer: L. Harradine
Height: 7in., 17.7cm.
Issued: 1920-1938
Price: $1600 £1000

MARIE (Style one) HN434
Designer: L. Harradine
Height: 7in., 17.7cm.
Issued: 1921-1938
Colour variation
Price: $1600 £1000

MARIE (Style one) HN502
Designer: L. Harradine
Height: 7in., 17.7cm.
Issued: 1921-1938
Colour variation
Price: $1600 £1000

MARIE (Style one) HN504
Designer: L. Harradine
Height: 7in., 17.7cm.
Issued: 1921-1938
Colour variation
Price: $1600 £1000

MARGUERITE HN1946

MARIANNE HN2074

MARIA HN3381

MARIE (Style two) HN1370

MARIE (Style one) HN505
Designer: L. Harradine
Height: 7in., 17.7cm.
Issued: 1921-1938
Colour variation
Price: $1600 £1000

MARIE (Style one) HN506
Designer: L. Harradine
Height: 7in., 17.7cm.
Issued: 1921-1938
Colour variation
Price: $1600 £1000

MARIE (Style two) HN1370
Designer: L. Harradine
Height: 4¾in., 12cm.
Issued: 1930-1988
Price: $140 £95

MARIE (Style two) HN1388
Designer: L. Harradine
Height: 4½in., 11.4cm.
Issued: 1930-1938
Colour variation
Price: $360 £225

MARIE (Style two) HN1417
Designer: L. Harradine
Height: 4¾in., 12cm.
Issued: 1930-1949
Colour variation
Price: $312 £195

MARIE (Style two) HN1489
Designer: L. Harradine
Height: 4½in., 11.4cm.
Issued: 1932-1949
Colour variation
Price: $360 £225

MARIE (Style two) HN1531
Designer: L. Harradine
Height: 4½in., 11.4cm.
Issued: 1932-1938
Colour variation
Price: $400 £250

MARIE (Style two) HN1635
Designer: L. Harradine
Height: 4¾in., 12cm.
Issued: 1934-1949
Colour variation
Price: $320 £200

MARIE (Style two) HN1655
Designer: L. Harradine
Height: 4½in., 11.4cm.
Issued: 1934-1938
Colour variation
Price: $480 £300

MARIE HN3357
Designer: P. Parsons
Height: 6in., 15.2cm.
Issued: 1992
Price: $200 £125

MARIETTA HN1341
Designer: L. Harradine
Height: 8in., 20.3cm.
Issued: 1929-1949
Price: $1040 £650

ROYAL DOULTON FIGURES

MARIETTA HN1446
Designer: L. Harradine
Height: 8in., 20.3cm.
Issued: 1931-1949
Colour variation
Price: $1200 £750

MARIETTA HN1699
Designer: L. Harradine
Height: 8in., 20.3cm.
Issued: 1935-1949
Price: $1360 £850

MARIGOLD HN1447
Designer: L. Harradine
Height: 6in., 15.2cm.
Issued: 1931-1949
Price: $560 £350

MARIGOLD HN1451
Designer: L. Harradine
Height: 6in., 15.2cm.
Issued: 1931-1938
Price: $720 £450

MARIGOLD HN1555
Designer: L. Harradine
Height: 6in., 15.2cm.
Issued: 1933-1949
Colour variation
Price: $632 £395

MARILYN HN3002
Designer: P. Gee
Height: 7¼in., 18.5cm.
Issued: 1986-1995
Price: $200 £125

MARION HN1582
Designer: L. Harradine
Height: 6½in., 16.5cm.
Issued: 1933-1938
Price: $1200 £750

MARION HN1583
Designer: L. Harradine
Height: 6½in., 16.5cm.
Issued: 1933-1938
Colour variation
Price: $1200 £750

MARIQUITA HN1837
Designer: L. Harradine
Height: 8in., 20.3cm.
Issued: 1938-1949
Price: $1760 £1100

MARJORIE HN2788
Designer: P. Davies
Height: 5¼in., 13.3cm.
Issued: 1980-1984
Price: $312 £195

MARKET DAY HN1991
Designer: L. Harradine
Height: 7¼in., 18.4cm.
Issued: 1975-1981
Price: $360 £225
Also called Country Lass

MARIE HN3357

MARILYN HN3002

MARIETTA HN1699

MARJORIE HN2788

MARIGOLD HN1447

MARKET DAY HN1991

MARIQUITA HN1837

ROYAL DOULTON FIGURES

**MARRIAGE OF ART AND I
DUSTRY HN2261**
Designer: P. Davies
Height: 19in., 48.3cm.
Issued: 1958 in a limited
edition of 12
Price: $4800 £3000

MARY HN2374
Designer: J. Bromley
Height: 7¾in., 19.5cm.
Issued: 1984-1986
Price: $264 £165

MARY HN3375
(Figure of the year 1992)
Designer: Nada Pedley
Height: 8½in., 21.5cm.
Issued: 1992
Price: $632 £395

MARY (White) HN3437
Designer: Alan Maslankowski
Height: 3¼in., 8cm.
Issued: 1993
U.S.A. only
Price: $200 £125 (R.R.P.)

MARY (Decorated) HN3485
Designer: Alan Maslankowski
Height: 3¼in., 8cm.
Issued: 1993-
U.S.A. only
Price: $200 £125 (R.R.P.)

MARY HN3903
Designer: Peggy Davies
Height: 7in., 18cm.
Issued: 1997
Price: $206 £129 (R.R.P.)

**MARY, COUNTESS HOWE
HN3007**
Designer: P. Gee
Height: 9¼in., 23.5cm.
Issued: 1990 in a limited
edition of 5000-1994
Price: $560 £350

**MARY HAD A LITTLE LAMB
HN2048**
Designer: P. Davies
Height: 3½in., 8.9cm.
Issued: 1949-1988
Price: $232 £145

MARY JANE HN1990
Designer: L. Harradine
Height: 7½in., 19.1cm.
Issued: 1947-1959
Price: $600 £375

MARY, MARY HN2044
Designer: L. Harradine
Height: 5in., 12.7cm.
Issued: 1949-1973
Price: $264 £165

**MARY
HN3485**

MARY HN3375

MARY (White) HN3437

**MARY, MARY
HN2044**

**MARY, COUNTESS
HOWE HN3007**

MARY JANE HN1990

**MARY QUEEN OF SCOTS
HN2931** (Ship's figurehead)
Designer: S. Keenan
Height: 9½in., 24cm.
Issued: 1983 in a limited
edition of 950
Price: $720 £450

**MARY QUEEN OF SCOTS
HN3142**
Designer: P. Parsons
Height: 9in., 22.5cm.
Issued: 1990 in a limited
edition of 5000
Price: $680 £425

MARY TUDOR HN3834
Designer: Pauline Parsons
Height: 6¼in., 16cm.
Issued: 1996
Price: $376 £235

MASK HN656
Designer: L. Harradine
Height: 6¾in., 17.2cm.
Issued: 1924-1938
Price: $2320 £1450

MASK HN657
Designer: L. Harradine
Height: 6¾in., 17.2cm.
Issued: 1924-1938
Colour variation
Price: $2320 £1450

MASK HN729
Designer: L. Harradine
Height: 6¾in., 17.2cm.
Issued: 1925-1938
Colour variation
Price: $2560 £1600

MASK HN733
Designer: L. Harradine
Height: 6¾in., 17.2cm.
Issued: 1925-1938
Colour variation
Price: $2320 £1450

MASK HN785
Designer: L. Harradine
Height: 6¾in., 17.2cm.
Issued: 1926-1938
Colour variation
Price: $2160 £1350

MASK HN1271
Designer: L. Harradine
Height: 6¾in., 17.2cm.
Issued: 1928-1938
Colour variation
Price: $2560 £1600

MASK SELLER HN1361
Designer: L. Harradine
Height: 8½in., 21.6cm.
Issued: 1929-1938
Price: $1200 £750

MASK SELLER HN2103
Designer: L. Harradine
Height: 8½in., 21.6cm.
Issued: 1953-1995
Colour variation
Price: $264 £165

MASQUE HN2554
Designer: D. V. Tootle
Height: 8½in., 21.6cm.
Issued: 1973-1982
Price: $312 £195

MASQUE HN2554A
Designer: D. V. Tootle
Height: 8½in., 21.6cm.
Issued: 1973-1982
Colour variation
Price: $260 £175

MASQUERADE (Style one, man) HN599
Designer: L. Harradine
Height: 6¾in., 17.2cm.
Issued: 1924-1949
Price: $760 £475

MASQUERADE (Style one, man) HN636
Designer: L. Harradine
Height: 6¾in., 17.2cm.
Issued: 1924-1938
Colour variation
Price: $720 £450

MASQUERADE (Style one, man) HN683
Designer: L. Harradine
Height: 7¼in., 18.4cm.
Issued: 1924-1938
Colour variation
Price: $720 $450

MASQUERADE (Style one, woman) HN600
Designer: L. Harradine
Height: 6¾in., 17.2cm.
Issued: 1924-1949
Price: $680 £425

MASQUERADE (Style one, woman) HN600A
Designer: L. Harradine
Height: 6in., 15.2cm.
Issued: 1924-1949
Colour variation
Price: $680 £425

MASQUERADE (Style one, woman) HN637
Designer: L. Harradine
Height: 6¾in., 17.2cm.
Issued: 1924-1938
Colour variation
Price: $800 £500

MASQUERADE (Style one, woman) HN674
Designer: L. Harradine
Height: 6¾in., 17.2cm.
Issued: 1924-1938
Colour variation
Price: $880 £550

MASK SELLER HN2103

MASK HN1271

MASQUE HN2554

MARY HAD A LITTLE LAMB HN2048

MASQUERADE (Style one, man) HN599

MARY QUEEN OF SCOTS HN3142

243

MASQUERADE (Style two) HN2251
Designer: P. Davies
Height: 8½in., 21.6cm.
Issued: 1960-1965
Price: $360 £225

MASQUERADE (Style two) HN2259
Designer: P. Davies
Height: 8½in., 21.6cm.
Issued: 1960-1965
Colour variation
Price: $360 £225

MASTER HN2325
Designer: P. Davies
Height: 6¼in., 15.9cm.
Issued: 1967-1992
Price: $264 £165

MASTER SWEEP HN2205
Designer: M. Nicoll
Height: 8½in., 21.6cm.
Issued: 1957-1962
Price: $720 £450

MATADOR AND BULL HN2324
Designer: P. Davies
Height: 16in., 40.6cm.
Issued: 1964-
Price: $16400 £10250
(R.R.P.)

MATILDA HN2011
Designer: P. Davies
Height: 9¼in., 23.5cm.
Issued: 1949-1953
Price: $680 £425

MAUREEN HN1770
Designer: L. Harradine
Height: 7½in., 19.1cm.
Issued: 1936-1959
Price: $520 £325

MAUREEN HN1771
Designer: L. Harradine
Height: 7½in., 19.1cm.
Issued: 1936-1949
Colour variation
Price: $792 £495

MAUREEN M84
Designer: L. Harradine
Height: 4in., 10.1cm.
Issued: 1939-1949
Price: $880 £550

MAUREEN M85
Designer: L. Harradine
Height: 4in., 10.1cm.
Issued: 1939-1949
Colour variation
Price: $880 £550

MAUREEN HN2481
Designer: P. Davies
Height: 7½in., 19cm.
Issued: 1987-1992
Price: $200 £125

MASQUERADE (Style one, woman) HN600

MASTER SWEEP HN2205

MATADOR AND BULL HN2324

MATILDA HN2011

MASTER HN2325

MAXINE HN3199
Designer: A. Hughes
Height: 9in., 23cm.
Issued: 1989-1990
Price: $264 £165

MAY HN2711
Designer: P. Davies
Height: 7¾in., 19.5cm.
Issued: 1987
Price: $200 £125

MAY HN2746
Designer: D. Tootle
Height: 8in., 20cm.
Issued: 1987-1992
Price: $264 £165

MAY HN3251
Designer: D. Tootle
Height: 8in., 20cm.
Issued: 1989 in a limited
            edition of 2000
Price: $280 £175

MAY HN3334
U.S.A. edition
Designer: R. Tabbenor
Height: 5¼in., 13.3cm.
Issued: 1990 only
Price: $152 £95

MAYOR HN2280
Designer: M. Nicoll
Height: 8¼in., 21cm.
Issued: 1963-1971
Price: $520 £325

MAYTIME HN2113
Designer: L. Harradine
Height: 7in., 17.8cm.
Issued: 1953-1967
Price: $392 £245

MEDITATION HN2330
Designer: P. Davies
Height: 5¾in., 14.6cm.
Issued: 1971-1983
Price: $360 £225

MEG HN2743
Designer: D. Tootle
Height: 8½in., 22cm.
Issued: 1988-1991
Price: $232 £145

MEGAN HN3306
Designer: Peggy Davies
Height: 7½in., 19cm.
Issued: 1991-1994
Price: $200 £125

MEGAN HN3887
Designer: Nada Pedley
Height: 8in., 20.5cm.
Issued: 1997
Price: $128 £80

MAY HN3334

MAY HN2711

MEDITATION HN2330

MAYTIME HN2113

MEGAN HN3306

MELANIE HN2271
Designer: P. Davies
Height: 7¾in., 19.7cm.
Issued: 1965-1980
Price: $264 £165

MELISSA HN2467
Designer: P. Davies
Height: 6¾in., 17.2cm.,
Issued: 1981-1994
Price: $232 £145

MELISSA HN3885
Designer: Nada Pedley
Height: 8¼in., 21cm.
Issued: 1997
Price: $184 £115 (R.R.P.)

MELODY HN2202
Designer: P. Davies
Height: 6¼in., 15.9cm.
Issued: 1957-1962
Price: $360 £225

MEMORIES HN1855
Designer: L. Harradine
Height: 6in., 15.2cm.
Issued: 1938-1949
Price: $760 £475

MEMORIES HN1856
Designer: L. Harradine
Height: 6in., 15.2cm.
Issued: 1938-1949
Colour variation
Price: $760 £475

MEMORIES HN1857
Designer: L. Harradine
Height: 6in., 15.2cm.
Issued: 1938-1949
Colour variation
Price: $760 £475

MEMORIES HN2030
Designer: L. Harradine
Height: 6in., 15.2cm.
Issued: 1949-1959
Colour variation
Price: $520 £325

MENDICANT HN1355
Designer: L. Harradine
Height: 8½in., 21cm.
Issued: 1929-1938
Price: $720 £450

MENDICANT HN1365
Designer: L. Harradine
Height: 8¼in., 21cm.
Issued: 1929-1969
Price: $360 £225

MEPHISTO HN722
Designer: L. Harradine
Height: 6½in., 16.5cm.
Issued: 1925-1938
Price: $2800 £1750

MELANIE HN2271

MELISSA HN2467

MEPHISTO HN723

MEPHISTO HN722

MENDICANT HN1365

MEPHISTO HN723
Designer: L. Harradine
Height: 6½in., 16.5cm.
Issued: 1925-1938
Colour variation
Price: $2800 £1750

MEPHISTOPHELES AND MARGUERITE HN755
Designer: C. J. Noke
Height: 7¾in., 19.7cm.
Issued: 1925-1949
Price: $2080 £1300

MEPHISTOPHELES AND MARGUERITE HN775
Designer: C. J. Noke
Height: 7¾in., 19.7cm.
Issued: 1925-1949
Colour variation
Price: $2080 £1300

MERIEL HN1931
Designer: L. Harradine
Height: 7¼in., 18.4cm.
Issued: 1940-1949
Price: $1520 £950

MERIEL HN1932
Designer: L. Harradine
Height: 7¼in., 18.4cm.
Issued: 1940-1949
Colour variation
Price: $1520 £950

MERMAID HN97
Designer: H. Tittensor
Height: 7in., 17.8cm.
Issued: 1918-1936
Price: $720 £450

MERMAID HN300
Designer: H. Tittensor
Height: 7in., 17.8cm.
Issued: 1918-1936
Price: $880 £550

MERRY CHRISTMAS HN3096
Designer: P. Parsons
Height: 8½in., 22cm.
Issued: 1987-1992
Price: $264 £165

MERYLL HN1917
Designer: L. Harradine
Height: 6¾in., 17.2cm.
Issued: 1939-1940
Price: $2560 £1600
Also called Toinette

MESSIAH, THE HN3952
Designer: Alan Maslankowski
Height: 11in., 28cm.
Issued: 1997
Price: $136 £85 (R.R.P.)

MEXICAN DANCER HN2866
Designer: P. Davies
Height: 8¼in., 21cm.
Issued: 1979 in a limited edition of 750
Price: $680 £425

MERMAID HN97

MERIEL HN1931

MERRY CHRISTMAS HN3096

MEXICAN DANCER HN2866

ROYAL DOULTON FIGURES

MICHELLE HN2234
Designer: P. Davies
Height: 7in., 17.8cm.
Issued: 1967-1993
Price: $216 £135

MICK THE MILLER DA214
In a limited edition of 7500
Designer: Graham Tongue
Height: 9½in., 24cm.
Issued: 1993
Price: $232 £145

MIDINETTE (Style one) HN1289
Designer: L. Harradine
Height: 9in., 22.9cm.
Issued: 1928-1938
Price: $2800 £1750

MIDINETTE (Style one)HN1306
Designer: L. Harradine
Height: 9in., 22.9cm.
Issue: 1928-1938
         Colour variation
Price: $2800 £1750

MIDINETTE (Style two) HN2090
Designer: L. Harradine
Height: 7¼in., 18.4cm.
Issued: 1952-1965
Price: $400 £250

MIDSUMMER NOON HN1899
Designer: L. Harradine
Height: 4¾in., 12cm.
Issued: 1939-1949
Price: $720 £450

MIDSUMMER NOON HN1900
Designer: L. Harradine
Height: 4¾in., 12cm.
Issued: 1939-1949
         Colour variation
Price: $952 £595

MIDSUMMER NOON HN2033
Designer: L. Harradine
Height: 4¾in., 12cm.
Issued: 1949-1955
         Colour variation
Price: $720 £450

MILADY HN1970
Designer: L. Harradine
Height: 6½in., 16.5cm.
Issued: 1941-1949
Price: $1200 £750

MILESTONE HN3297
Designer: Adrian Hughes
Height: 7¼in., 18.5cm.
Issued: 1990-1994
Price: $280 £175

MILKING TIME HN3
Designer: P. Stabler
Height: Unknown
Issued: 1913-1938
Price: $3200 £2000

MIDINETTE (Style one)
HN1289

MIDINETTE (Style two)
HN2090

MICHELLE HN2234

MILKING TIME HN306
Designer: P. Stabler
Height: 6in., 5.5cm.
Issued: 1913-1938
         Colour variation
Price: $3600 £2250

MILKMAID HN2057
Designer: L. Harradine
Height: 6½in., 16.5cm.
Issued: 1975-1982
Price: $360 £225
Also called The Jersey Milkmaid

MILLICENT HN1714
Designer: L. Harradine
Height: 8in., 20.3cm.
Issued: 1935-1949
Price: $1120 £700

MILLICENT HN1715
Designer: L. Harradine
Height: 8in., 20.3cm.
Issued: 1935-1949
         Colour variation
Price: $1520 £950

MILLICENT HN1860
Designer: L. Harradine
Height: 8in., 20.3cm.
Issued: 1938-1949
         Colour variation
Price: $1520 £950

MILLIE (Green) HN3945
Designer: Alan Maslankowski
Height: 8¾in., 22.5cm.
Issued: 1997 only
Price: $200 £125

MILLIE (Ivory/Gold) HN3946
Designer: Alan Maslankowski
Height: 8¾in., 22.5cm.
Issued: 1997 only
Price: $200 £125

MINUET HN2019
Designer: P. Davies
Height: 7¼in., 18.4cm.
Issued: 1949-1971
Price: $392 £245

MINUET HN2066
Designer: P. Davies
Height: 7¼in., 18.4cm.
Issued: 1950-1955
         Colour variation
Price: $640 £400

MIRABEL HN1743
Designer: L. Harradine
Height: 7¾in., 19.7cm.
Issued: 1935-1949
Price: $1200 £750

MIRABEL HN1744
Designer: L. Harradine
Height: 7¾in., 19.7cm.
Issued: 1935-1949
         Colour variation
Price: $1120 £700

ROYAL DOULTON FIGURES

MIRABEL M68
Designer: L. Harradine
Height: 4in., 10.1cm.
Issued: 1936-1949
Price: $800 £500

MIRABEL M74
Designer: L. Harradine
Height: 4in., 10.1cm.
Issued: 1936-1949
           Colour variation
Price: $800 £500

MIRANDA HN1818
Designer: L. Harradine
Height: 8½in., 21.6cm.
Issued: 1937-1949
Price: $1520 £950

MIRANDA HN1819
Designer: L. Harradine
Height: 8½in., 21.6cm.
Issued: 1937-1949
           Colour variation
Price: $1520 £950

MIRANDA HN3037
Designer: A. Hughes
Height: 8½in., 21cm.
Issued: 1987-1990
Price: $264 £165

MIRROR HN1852
Designer: L. Harradine
Height: 7½in., 18.4cm.
Issued: 1938-1949
Price: $2560 £1600

MIRROR HN1853
Designer: L. Harradine
Height: 7½in., 18.4cm.
Issued: 1938-1949
           Colour variation
Price: $3200 £2000

MISS DEMURE HN1402
Designer: L. Harradine
Height: 7½in., 19.1cm.
Issued: 1930-1975
Price: $312 £195

MISS DEMURE HN1440
Designer: L. Harradine
Height: 7in., 17.8cm.
Issued: 1930-1949
           Colour variation
Price: $520 £325

MISS DEMURE HN1463
Designer: L. Harradine
Height: 7in., 17.8cm.
Issued: 1931-1949
           Colour variation
Price: $520 £325

MISS DEMURE HN1499
Designer: L. Harradine
Height: 7in., 17.8cm.
Issued: 1932-1938
           Colour variation
Price: $720 £450

MINUET HN2019

MILESTONE HN3297

MILLIE (Green) HN3945

MILLICENT HN1715

MILKMAID HN2057

MIRANDA HN1818

ROYAL DOULTON FIGURES

MISS DEMURE HN1560
Designer: L. Harradine
Height: 7in., 17.7cm.
Issued: 1933-1949
Price: $560 £350

MISS FORTUNE HN1897
Designer: L. Harradine
Height: 6in., 15.2cm.
Issued: 1938-1949
Price: $920 £575

MISS FORTUNE HN1898
Designer: L. Harradine
Height: 5¾in., 14.6cm.
Issued: 1938-1949
Colour variation
Price: $960 £600

MISS MUFFET HN1936
Designer: L. Harradine
Height: 5½in., 13.3cm.
Issued: 1940-1967
Price: $280 £175

MISS MUFFET HN1937
Designer: L. Harradine
Height: 5½in., 13.3cm.
Issued: 1940-1952
Colour variation
Price: $400 £250

MISS 1926 HN1205
Designer: L. Harradine
Height: 7¼in., 18.4cm.
Issued: 1926-1938
Price: $3200 £2000

MISS 1926 HN1207
Designer: L. Harradine
Height: 7¼in., 18.4cm.
Issued: 1926-1938
Colour variation
Price: $3600 £2250

MISS WINSOME HN1665
Designer: L. Harradine
Height: 6¾in., 17.2cm.
Issued: 1934-1949
Price: $1040 £650

MISS WINSOME HN1666
Designer: L. Harradine
Height: 6¾in., 17.2cm.
Issued: 1934-1938
Colour variation
Price: $800 £500

M'LADY'S MAID HN1795
Designer: L Harradine
Height; 9in., 22.9cm.
Issued: 1936-1949
Price: $1760 £1100

M'LADY'S MAID HN1822
Designer: L. Harradine
Height: 9in., 22.9cm.
Issued: 1937-1949
Colour variation
Price: $2160 £1350

MISS 1926 HN1205

MISS DEMURE
HN1402

MISS DEMURE
HN1463

MOOR HN2082

M'LADY'S MAID HN1795

MODENA HN1845
Designer: L. Harradine
Height: 7¼in., 18.4cm.
Issued: 1938-1949
Price: $1760 £1100

MODENA HN1846
Designer: L. Harradine
Height: 7¼in., 18.4cm.
Issued: 1938-1949
Colour variation
Price: $1760 £1100

MODERN PIPER HN756
Designer: L. Harradine
Height: 8½in., 21.6cm.
Issued: 1925-1938
Price: $2800 £1750

MODESTY HN2744
Designer: D. Tootle
Height: 8¼in., 21cm.
Issued: 1988-1991
Price: $232 £145

MOIRA HN1347
Designer: L. Harradine
Height: 6½in., 16.5cm.
Issued: 1929-1938
Price: $3200 £2000

MOLLY MALONE HN1455
Designer: L. Harradine
Height: 7in., 17.8cm.
Issued: 1931-1938
Price: $2560 £1600

MONICA HN1458
Designer: L. Harradine
Height: 4in., 10.1cm.
Issued: 1931-1949
Price: $360 £225

MONICA HN1459
Designer: L. Harradine
Height: 4in., 10.1cm.
Issued: 1931-1949
Price: $360 £225

MONICA HN1467
Designer: L. Harradine
Height: 4in., 10.1cm.
Issued: 1931-1995
Colour variation
Price: $120 £75

MONICA M66
Designer: L. Harradine
Height: 3in., 7.6cm.
Issued: 1935-1949
Price: $560 £350

MONICA M72
Designer: L. Harradine
Height: 3in., 7.6cm.
Issued: 1936-1949
Colour variation
Price: $560 £350

ROYAL DOULTON FIGURES

MONICA HN3617
Designer: L. Harradine
Height: 4in., 10.1cm.
Issued: 1994
           Colour variation
Price: $120 £75

MONTE CARLO HN2332
Designer: P. Davies
Height: 8¼in., 20.9cm.
Issued: 1982 in a limited
           edition of 1500
Price: $440 £275

MOON DANCER HN3181
Designer: D. Tootle
Height: 11¾in., 30cm.
Issued: 1988-1990
Price: $264 £165

MOONLIGHT ROSE HN3483
Designer: P. Davies
Height: 6in., 15.2cm.
Issued: 1993-1995
Price: $152 £95

MOONLIGHT STROLL HN3884
Designer: Alan Maslankowski
Height: 7¾in., 19.5cm.
Issued: 1997
Price: $216 £135 (R.R.P.)

MOOR HN1308
Designer: C. J. Noke
Height: 16½in., 41.9cm.
Issued: 1929-1938
Price: $3200 £2000

MOOR HN1366
Designer: C. J. Noke
Height: 16½in., 41.9cm.
Issued: 1930-1949
           Colour variation
Price: $2160 £1350

MOOR HN1425
Designer: C. J. Noke
Height: 16½in,. 41.9cm.
Issued: 1930-1949
           Colour variation
Price: $2320 £1450

MOOR HN1657
Designer: C. J. Noke
Height: 16½in., 41.9cm.
Issued: 1934-1949
           Colour variation
Price: $2320 £1450

MOOR HN2082
Designer: C. J. Noke
Height: 16¼in., 41.2cm.
Issued: 1952-
           Colour variation
Price: $2400 £1500
           (R.R.P.)
Also called "An Arab"

MONICA HN1467

MONICA HN3617

MODERN PIPER HN756

MOONLIGHT ROSE HN3483

MOIRA HN1347

MONTE CARLO HN2332

MOLLY MALONE HN1455

MOORISH MINSTREL HN34
Designer: C. J. Noke
Height: 13½in., 34.3cm.
Issued: 1913-1938
Colour variation
Price: $2960 £1850

MOORISH MINSTREL HN364
Designer: C. J. Noke
Height: 13½in., 34.3cm.
Issued: 1920-1938
Colour variation
Price: $2640 £1650

MOORISH MINSTREL HN415
Designer: C. J. Noke
Height: 13½in., 34.3cm.
Issued: 1920-1938
Colour variation
Price: $3120 £1950

MOORISH MINSTREL HN797
Designer: C. J. Noke
Height: 13½in., 34.3cm.
Issued: 1926-1949
Colour variation
Price: $2400 £1500

MOORISH PIPER MINSTREL HN301
Designer: C. J. Noke
Height: 13½in., 34.3cm.
Issued: 1918-1938
Price: $2320 £1450

MOORISH PIPER MINSTREL HN328
Designer: C. J. Noke
Height: 13½in., 34.3cm.
Issued: 1918-1938
Colour variation
Price: $2560 £1600

MOORISH PIPER MINSTREL HN416
Designer: C. J. Noke
Height: 13½in., 34.3cm.
Issued: 1920-1938
Colour variation
Price: $2560 £1600

MORNING BREEZE HN3313
Designer: Peter Gee
Height: 8½in., 21.5cm.
Issued: 1990-1994
Price: $264 £165

MORNING GLORY HN3093
Designer: P. Parsons
Height: 12¾in., 32cm.
Issued: 1987-1989
Price: $232 £145

MORNING MA'AM HN2895
Designer: W. K. Harper
Height: 9in., 23cm.
Issued: 1986-1989
Price: $264 £165

MOORISH PIPER MINSTREL HN301

MORNING BREEZE HN3313

MORNING GLORY HN3093

MORNING MA'AM HN2895

MOTHER & CHILD HN3938

MORNING WALK HN3860
Designer: Tim Potts
Height: 8in., 20cm.
Issued: 1997
Price: $120 £75 (R.R.P.)

MOTHER AND BABY HN3235 (Blue)
Designer: Pauline Parsons
Height: 7½in., 19cm.
Issued: 1991
Price: $264 £165

MOTHER AND BABY HN3348 (Pink)
Designer: Pauline Parsons
Height: 7½in., 19cm.
Issued: 1991
Price: $264 £165

MOTHER AND BABY HN3353 (White)
Designer: Pauline Parsons
Height: 7½in., 19cm.
Issued: 1992
Price: $136 £85 (R.R.P.)

MOTHER & CHILD HN3938
Designer: Alan Maslankowski
Height: 11½in., 29cm.
Issued: 1997
Price: $136 £85 (R.R.P.)

MOTHER AND DAUGHTER HN2843 (Black)
Designer: E. Griffiths
Height: 8½in., 21.5cm.
Issued: 1981-1995
Price: $152 £95

MOTHER AND DAUGHTER HN2841 (White)
Designer: E. Griffiths
Height: 8½in., 21.5cm.
Issued: 1981-1997
Price: $176 £110

MOTHERHOOD HN28
Designer: P. Stabler
Height: 8in., 20.3cm.
Issued: 1913- 1938
Price: $3600 £2250

MOTHERHOOD HN30
Designer: P. Stabler
Height: 8in., 20.3cm.
Issued: 1913-1938
Colour variation
Price: $4000 £2500

MOTHERHOOD HN303
Designer: P. Stabler
Height: 8in., 20.3cm
Issued: 1918-1938
Colour variation
Price: $3840 £2400

ROYAL DOULTON FIGURES

MOTHERHOOD HN3463
Designer: Adrian Hughes
Height: 8¾in., 22cm.
Issued: 1995
Price: $240 £150 (R.R.P.)

MOTHERLY LOVE HN3545
Designer: Adrian Hughes
Height: 6in., 15cm.
Issued: 1990
Price: $136 £80 (R.R.P.)

MOTHER'S HELP HN2151
Designer: P. Davies
Height: 5in., 12.7cm.
Issued: 1962-1969
Price: $232 £145

MOTHER'S HELPER HN3650
Designer: Nada Pedley
Height: 4½in., 11.5cm.
Issued: 1994
Price: $80 £50 (R.R.P.)

MR MICAWBER (Style one)
HN532
Designer: L. Harradine
Height: 3½in., 8.9cm.
Issued: 1922-1932
Price: $88 £55

MR MICAWBER (Style two)
HN557
Designer: L. Harradine
Height: 7in., 17.8cm.
Issued: 1923-1939
Price: $520 £325

MR MICAWBER (Style two)
HN1895
Designer: L. Harradine
Height; 7in., 17.8cm.
Issued: 1938-1952
Colour variation
Price: $440 £275

MR MICAWBER (Style three)
HN2097
Designer: L. Harradine
Height: 7½in., 19.1cm.
Issued: 1952-1967
Price: $392 £245

MR MICAWBER M42
Designer: L. Harradine
Height: 4in., 10.1cm.
Issued: 1932-1982
Price: $80 £50

MR PICKWICK (Style one)
HN529
Designer: L. Harradine
Height: 3¾in., 9.5cm.
Issued: 1922-1932
Price: $88 £55

MR PICKWICK (Style two)
HN556
Designer: L. Harradine
Height: 7in., 17.8cm.
Issued: 1923-1939
Price: $392 £245

MOTHER AND BABY

MORNING
WALK HN3860

MOTHER'S HELPER HN3650

MR MICAWBER M42

MOTHER AND DAUGHTER
HN2841 (White)

MR PICKWICK (Style two)
HN556

MR PICKWICK (Style two)
HN1894
Designer: L. Harradine
Height: 7in., 17.8cm.
Issued: 1938-1952
             Colour variation
Price: $472 £295

MR PICKWICK (Style three)
HN2099
Designer: L. Harradine
Height: 7½in., 19.1cm.
Issued: 1952-1967
Price: $392 £245

MR PICKWICK M41
Designer: L. Harradine
Height: 4in., 10.1cm.
Issued: 1932-1982
             Colour variation
Price: $72 £45

MRS BARDELL M86
Designer: L. Harradine
Height: 4¼in., 10.1cm.
Issued: 1949-1982
Price: $72 £45

MRS FITZHERBERT HN2007
Designer: P. Davies
Height: 9¼in., 23.5cm.
Issued: 1948-1953
Price: $680 £425

MRS HUGH BONFOY HN3319
Designer: Peter Gee
Height: 9½in., 24cm.
Issued: 1992 in a limited
             edition of 5000-1995
Price: $520 £325

MRS SISLEY HN3475
In a limited edition of 7500
Designer: Valerie Annand
Height: 8½in., 21.5cm.
Issued: 1994-1997
Price: $360 £225

MUSICALE HN2756
Designer: E. Griffiths
Height: 9in., 23cm.
Issued: 1983-1986
Price: $264 £165

MY BEST FRIEND HN3011
Designer: Peter Gee
Height: 8in., 20cm.
Issued: 1990
Price: $248 £155 (R.R.P.)

MY FIRST FIGURINE HN3424
Designer: Nada Pedley
Height: 4¼in., 11cm.
Issued: 1993
Price: $80 £50 (R.R.P.)

MY FIRST PET HN3122
Designer: Alan Maslankowski
Height: 4½in., 11.5cm.
Issued: 1991-97
Price: $96 £60

MRS HUGH BONFOY
HN3319

MRS FITZHERBERT HN2007

MY LOVE HN2339
Designer: P. Davies
Height: 6¼in., 15.9cm.
Issued: 1969-1996
Price: $240 £150

MY PET HN2238
Designer: P. Davies
Height: 2¾in., 7cm.
Issued: 1962-1975
Price: $264 £165

MY PRETTY MAID HN2064
Designer: L. Harradine
Height: 5½in., 14cm.
Issued: 1950-1954
Price: $632 £395

MY TEDDY HN2177
Designer: P. Davies
Height: 3¼in., 8cm.
Issued: 1962-1967
Price: $560 £350

MYFANWY JONES HN39
Designer: E. W. Light
Height: 12in., 30.5cm.
Issued: 1914-1938
Price: $3600 £2250
See Welsh Girl

MYFANWY JONES HN92
Designer: E. W. Light
Height: 12in., 30.5cm.
Issued: 1918-1938
             Colour variation
Price: $4000 £2500
See Welsh Girl

MYFANWY JONES HN456
Designer: E. W. Light
Height: 12in., 30.5cm.
Issued: 1921-1938
             Colour variation
Price: $3600 £2250
See Welsh Girl

MYFANWY JONES HN514
Designer: E. W. Light
Height: 12in., 30.5cm.
Issued: 1921-1938
             Colour variation
Price: $4400 £2750
See Welsh Girl

MYFANWY JONES HN516
Designer: E. W. Light
Height: 12in., 30.5cm.
Issued: 1921-1938
             Colour variation
Price: $4400 £2750
See Welsh Girl

MYFANWY JONES HN519
Designer: E. W. Light
Height: 12in., 30.5cm.
Issued: 1921-1938
             Colour variation
Price: $4400 £2750
See Welsh Girl

ROYAL DOULTON FIGURES

MYFANWY JONES HN520
Designer: E. W. Light
Height: 12in., 30.5cm.
Issued: 1921-1938
           Colour variation
Price: $4400 £2750
See Welsh Girl

MYFANWY JONES HN660
Designer: E. W. Light
Height: 12in., 30.5cm.
Issued: 1924-1938
           Colour variation
Price: $3200 £2000
See Welsh Girl

MYFANWY JONES HN668
Designer: E. W. Light
Height: 12in., 30.5cm.
Issued: 1924-1938
           Colour variation
Price: £3200 £2000
See Welsh Girl

MYFANWY JONES HN669
Designer: E. W. Light
Height: 12in., 30.5cm.
Issued: 1924-1938
           Colour variation
Price: $2960 £1850
See Welsh Girl

MYFANWY JONES HN701
Designer: E. W. Light
Height: 12in., 30.5cm.
Issued: 1925-1938
           Colour variation
Price: $3200 £2000
See Welsh Girl

MYFANWY JONES HN792
Designer: E. W. Light:
Height: 12in., 30.5cm.
Issued: 1926-1938
           Colour variation
Price: $3200 £2000
See Welsh Girl

N

NADINE HN1885
Designer: L. Harradine
Height: 7¾in., 19.7cm.
Issued: 1938-1949
Price: $1200 £750

NADINE HN1886
Designer: L. Harradine
Height: 7¾in., 19.7cm.
Issued: 1938-1949
           Colour variation
Price: $1200 £750

NANA HN1766
Designer: L. Harradine
Height: 4¾in., 12cm.
Issued: 1936-1949
Price: $440 £275

MY FIRST FIGURINE HN3424

MUSICALE HN2756

MY FIRST PET HN3122

MY BEST FRIEND HN3011

MYFANWY JONES HN792

MY LOVE HN2339

255

ROYAL DOULTON FIGURES

NANA HN1767
Designer: L. Harradine
Height: 4¾in., 12cm.
Issued: 1936-1949
           Colour variation
Price: $440 £275

NANCY HN2955
Designer: P. Parsons
Height: 7½in., 19cm.
Issued: 1982-1994
Price: $152 £95

NANNY HN2221
Designer: P. Davies
Height: 6in., 15.2cm.
Issued: 1958-1991
Price: $280 £175

NAPOLEON AT WATERLOO HN3429
Designer: Alan Maslankowski
Height: 11½in., 29cm.
Issued: 1992 in a limited
           edition of 1500-1995
Price: $1360 £850

NATALIE HN3173
Designer: P. Davies
Height: 8in., 20cm.
Issued: 1988-1996
Price: $152 £95

NATALIE HN3498
Designer: P. Davies
Height: 8in., 20.3cm.
Issued: 1993
           Colour variation
           U.S.A. only
Price: $200 £125 (R.R.P.)

NEGLIGEE HN1219
Designer: L. Harradine
Height: 5in., 12.7cm.
Issued: 1927-1938
Price: $1360 £850

NEGLIGEE HN1228
Designer: L. Harradine
Height: 5in., 12.7cm.
Issued: 1927-1938
           Colour variation
Price: $1360 £850

NEGLIGEE HN1272
Designer: L. Harradine
Height: 5in., 12.7cm.
Issued: 1928-1938
           Colour variation
Price: $1360 £850

NEGLIGEE HN1273
Designer: L. Harradine
Height: 5in., 12.7cm.
Issued: 1928-1938
           Colour variation
Price: $1360 £850

NANCY HN2955

NANNY HN2221

NATALIE HN3498

NATALIE HN3173

NAPOLEON AT WATERLOO
HN3429

256

ROYAL DOULTON FIGURES

NEGLIGEE HN1454
Designer: L. Harradine
Height: 5in., 12.7cm.
Issued: 1931-1938
  Colour variation
Price: $1360 £850

NELL HN3014
Designer: P. Parsons
Height: 4in., 10cm.
Issued: 1983-1989
Price: $280 £175

NELL GWYNN HN1882
Designer: L. Harradine
Height: 6¾in., 17.2cm.
Issued: 1938-1949
  Colour variation
Price: $1360 £850

NELL GWYNN HN1887
Designer: L. Harradine
Height: 6¾in., 17.2cm.
Issued: 1938-1949
  Colour variation
Price: $1360 £850

NELSON HN2928 (Ship's figurehead)
Designer: S. Keenan
Height: 8¾in., 22.2cm.
Issued: 1981 in a limited
  edition of 950
Price: $720 £450

NESTLING DOWN HN3531
Designer: A. Hughes
Height: 13in., 33cm.
Issued: 1986-1994
Price: $440 £275

NEW ARRIVAL HN3551
Designer: Alan Maslankowski
Height: 3¼in., 8cm.
Issued: 1994
Price: $56 £35 (R.R.P.)

NEW BABY (Pink) HN3712
Designer: Valerie Annand
Height: 2in., 5cm.
Issued: 1997
Price: $80 £50 (R.R.P.)

NEW BABY (Blue) HN3713
Designer: Valerie Annand
Height: 2in., 5cm.
Issued: 1997
Price: $80 £50 (R.R.P.)

NEW BONNET HN1728
Designer: L. Harradine
Height: 7in., 17.8cm.
Issued: 1935-1949
Price: $960 £600

NEW BONNET HN1957
Designer: L. Harradine
Height: 7in., 17.8cm.
Issued: 1940-1949
  Colour variation
Price: $960 £600

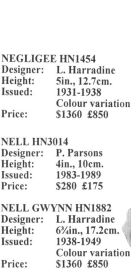

NEW BABY (Blue) HN3713

NEW BABY (Pink) HN3712

NELSON HN2928

NEGLIGEE HN1454

NEGLIGEE HN1219

NEW BONNET HN1728

NEGLIGEE HN1228

ROYAL DOULTON FIGURES

NEW COMPANIONS HN2770
Designer: W. K. Harper
Height: 7¾in., 19.5cm.
Issued: 1982-1986
Price: $264 £165

NEWHAVEN FISHWIFE HN1480
Designer: H. Fenton
Height: 7¾in., 19.7cm.
Issued: 1931-1938
Price: $4000 £2500

NEWS VENDOR HN2891
Designer: W. Harper
Height: 7in., 17.8cm.
Issued: 1986 in a limited edition of 2500
Price: $264 £165

NEWSBOY HN2244
Designer: P. Davies
Height: 8½in., 21.6cm.
Issued: 1959-1965
Price: $480 £300

NICOLA HN2839
Designer: P. Davies
Height: 7in., 17.8cm.
Issued: 1978-1995
Price: $280 £175

NICOLA HN2804
Michael Doulton Events
Designer: P. Davies
Height: 7½in., 19.1cm.
Issued: 1987 only
Price: $264 £165

NICOLE HN3421
Designer: Nada Pedley
Height: 7½in., 19.1cm.
Issued: 1993-1997
Price: $176 £110

NINA HN2347
Designer: P. Davies
Height: 7½in., 19.1cm.
Issued: 1969-1976
Price: $232 £145

NINETTE HN2379
Designer: P. Davies
Height: 7½in., 19.1cm.
Issued: 1971-1997
Price: $232 £145

NINETTE HN3215
Designer: P. Davies
Height: 3½in., 9cm.
Issued: 1988-1997
Price: $120 £75

NINETTE HN3417
Roadshow Events Figure
Designer: P. Davies
Height: 7½in., 19.1cm.
Issued: 1992 only
Price: $312 £195

NICOLE HN3421

NEWSBOY HN2244

NICOLA HN2839

NEW COMPANIONS HN2770

NINA HN2347

NEWS VENDOR HN2891

258

ROYAL DOULTON FIGURES

NOELLE HN2179
Designer: P. Davies
Height: 6¾in., 17.2cm.,
Issued: 1957-1967
Price: $472 £295

NORMA M36
Designer: Unknown
Height: 4½in., 11.4cm.
Issued: 1933-1945
Price: $720 £450

NORMA M37
Designer: Unknown
Height: 4½in., 11.4cm.
Issued: 1933-1945
 Colour variation
Price: $720 £450

NORTH AMERICAN INDIAN DANCER HN2809
Designer: P. Davies
Height: 8½in., 21.5cm.
Issued: 1982 in a limited
 edition of 750
Price: $680 £425

NOVEMBER HN2695
Designer: P. Davies
Height: 7¾in., 19.5cm.
Issued: 1987 only
Price: $200 £125

NOVEMBER HN3328
Designer: P. Davies
Height: 5¼in., 13.3cm.
Issued: 1991 only
 U.S.A.
Price: $152 £95

NUDE ON ROCK HN593
Designer: Unknown
Height: Unknown
Issued: 1924-1938
Price: $2000 £1250

O

OCTOBER HN2693
Designer: P. Davies
Height: 7¾in., 19.5cm.
Issued: 1987 only
Price: $200 £125

OCTOBER HN3327
Designer: P. Davies
Height: 5¼in., 13.3cm.
Issued: 1991 only
 U.S.A. only
Price: $152 £95

OCTOBER HN3410
Designer: P. Davies
Height: 7½in., 19.1cm.
Issued: 1991 only
 Canada only
Price: $200 £125

ODDS AND ENDS HN1844
Designer: L. Harradine
Height: 7¾in., 19.6cm.
Issued: 1938-1949
Price: $2000 £1250

NINETTE HN3215

NINETTE HN3417

NINETTE HN2379

NOELLE HN2179

NOVEMBER HN2695

NOVEMBER HN3328

NORTH AMERICAN INDIAN DANCER HN2809

259

ROYAL DOULTON FIGURES

OFF TO SCHOOL HN3768
Designer: Nada Pedley
Height: 5¼in., 14cm.
Issued: 1996
Price: $112 £70 (R.R.P.)

OFFICER OF THE LINE HN2733
Designer: W. K. Harper
Height: 9in., 23cm.
Issued: 1983-1986
Price: $360 £225

OLD BALLOON SELLER HN1315
Designer: L. Harradine
Height: 7½in., 19.1cm.
Issued: 1929-
Price: $232 £145 (R.R.P.)

OLD BALLOON SELLER HN2129
Designer: L. Harradine
Height: 3½in., 9cm.
Issued: 1989-1991
Price: $264 $165

OLD BALLOON SELLER AND BULLDOG HN1791
Designer: L. Harradine
Height: 7in., 17.8cm.
Issued: 1932-1938
Price: $880 £550

OLD BALLOON SELLER AND BULLDOG HN1912
Designer: L. Harradine
Height: 7in., 17.8cm.
Issued: 1939-1949
Price: $880 £550

OLD BEN HN3190
Designer: E. Griffiths
Height: 6½in., 16.5cm.
Issued: 1991 in a limited
edition if 1500
Price: $200 £125

OLD COUNTRY ROSES HN3483
Designer: P. Davies
Height: 6in., 15.2cm.
Issued: 1993-1995
Price: $192 £120

OLD COUNTRY ROSES HN3692
Designer: Nada Pedley
Height: 8in., 20cm.
Issued: 1995
Price: $248 £155 (R.R.P.)

OLD FATHER THAMES HN2993
Designer: Robert Tabbenor
Height: 6in., 15cm.
Issued: 1988 Commissioned
by Thames
Water
Price: $200 £125

OLD COUNTRY ROSES HN3483

OFF TO SCHOOL HN3768

OLD BEN HN3190

OLD COUNTRY ROSES HN3692

OFFICER OF THE LINE HN2733

OLD BALLOON SELLER HN1315

ROYAL DOULTON FIGURES

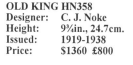

OLD KING HN358
Designer: C. J. Noke
Height: 9¾in., 24.7cm.
Issued: 1919-1938
Price: $1360 £800

OLD KING HN623
Designer: C. J. Noke
Height: 9¾in., 24.7cm.
Issued: 1924-1938
           Colour variation
Price: $1360 £800

OLD KING HN1801
Designer: C. J. Noke
Height: 9¾in., 24.7cm.
Issued: 1937-1954
Price: $1600 £1000

OLD KING HN2134
Designer: C. J. Noke
Height: 10¾in., 27.3cm.
Issued: 1954-1992
           Colour variation
Price: $560 £350

OLD KING COLE HN2217
Designer: P. Davies
Height: 6½in., 16.5cm.
Issued: 1963-1967
Price: $632 £395

**OLD LAVENDER SELLER
HN1492**
Designer: L. Harradine
Height: 6in., 15.2cm.
Issued: 1932-1949
Price: $840 £525

**OLD LAVENDER SELLER
HN1571**
Designer: L. Harradine
Height: 6½in., 16.5cm.
Issued: 1933-1949
Price: $840 £525

OLD MAN HN451
Designer: Unknown
Height: Unknown
Issued: 1921-1938
Price: $2400 £1500

OLD MEG HN2494
Designer: M. Nicoll
Height: 8¼in., 21cm.
Issued: 1974-1976
Price: $296 £185

**OLD MOTHER HUBBARD
HN2314**
Designer: M. Nicoll
Height: 8in., 20.3cm.
Issued: 1964-1975
Price: $392 £245

OLGA HN2463
Designer: J. Bromley
Height: 8¼in., 21cm.
Issued: 1972-1975
Price: $264 £165

OLD MEG HN2494

**OLD MOTHER HUBBARD
HN2314**

**OLD LAVENDER
SELLER HN1492**

OLD KING HN2134

OLGA HN2463

OLIVER HARDY HN2775
Designer: W. K. Harper
Height: 10in., 25cm.
Issued: 1992
Price: $312 £195

OLIVER TWIST M89
Designer: L. Harradine
Height: 4¼in., 10.8cm.
Issued: 1949-1982
Price: $80 £50

OLIVER HARDY HN2775

**OLIVER TWIST & THE ART-
FUL DODGER HN3786 (Resin)**
Designer: Arthur Dobson
Height: 8in., 20cm.
Issued: 1996 only.
Price: $120 £75

OLIVIA HN1995
Designer: L. Harradine
Height: 7½in., 19.1cm.
Issued: 1947-1951
Price: $720 £450

OLIVIA HN3339
G.U.S. Stores
Issued: 1992
Price: $280 £175

OLIVIA HN3717
Designer: Valerie Annand
Height: 8¾in., 22cm.
Issued: 1997
Price: $128 $80 (R.R.P.)

OLIVIA HN3339

**OMAR KHAYYAM (Style one)
HN408**
Designer: C. J. Noke
Height: 6in., 15.2cm.
Issued: 1920-1938
Price: $3200 £2000

**OMAR KHAYYAM (Style one)
HN409**
Designer: C. J. Noke
Height: 6in., 15.2cm.
Issued: 1920-1938
             Colour variation
Price: $4000 £2500

**OMAR KHAYYAM (Style two)
HN2247**
Designer: M. Nicoll
Height: 6¼in., 15.9cm.
Issued   1965-1983
Price: $296 £185

**OMAR KHAYYAM AND THE
BELOVED HN407**
Designer: C. J. Noke
Height: 10in., 25.4cm.
Issued: 1920-1938
Price: $3600 £2250

**OMAR KHAYYAM AND THE
BELOVED HN419**
Designer: C. J. Noke
Height: 6in., 15.2cm.
Issued: 1920-1938
Price: $3600 £2250

**OLIVER TWIST & THE ART-
FUL DODGER HN3786 (Resin)**

**OMAR KHAYYAM AND THE
BELOVED HN459**
Designer: C. J. Noke
Height: 10in., 25.4cm.
Issued: 1921-1938
Price: $3600 £2250

**OMAR KHAYYAM AND THE
BELOVED HN598**
Designer: C. J. Noke
Height: 10in., 25.4cm.
Issued: 1924-1938
Price: $4000 £2500

ON THE BEACH HN3877
Designer: Nada Pedley
Height: 3½in., 9cm.
Issued: 1997
Price: $96 £60 (R.R.P.)

ONCE UPON A TIME HN2047
Designer: L. Harradine
Height: 4¼in., 10.8cm.
Issued: 1949-1955
Price: $632 £395

**ONE OF THE FORTY
(Style one) HN417**
Designer: H. Tittensor
Height: 8¼in., 21cm.
Issued: 1920-1938
Price: $1600 £1000

**ONE OF THE FORTY
(Style one) HN490**
Designer: H. Tittensor
Height: 8¼in., 21cm.
Issued: 1921-1938
             Colour variation
Price: $1600 £1000

**ONE OF THE FORTY
(Style one) HN495**
Designer: H. Tittensor
Height: 8¼in., 21cm.
Issued: 1921-1938
             Colour variation
Price: $1600 £1000

**ONE OF THE FORTY
(Style one) HN501**
Designer: H. Tittensor
Height: 8¼in., 21cm.
Issued: 1921-1938
             Colour variation
Price: $1600 $1000

**ONE OF THE FORTY
(Style one) HN648**
Designer: H. Tittensor
Height: 8¼in., 21cm.
Issued: 1924-1938
             Colour variation
Price: $1600 £1000

**ONE OF THE FORTY
(Style one) HN528**
Designer: H. Tittensor
Height: 8¼in., 21cm.
Issued: 1921-1938
             Colour variation
Price: $1600 £1000

ONE OF THE FORTY
(Style one) HN1351
Designer: H. Tittensor
Height: 8¼in., 21cm.
Issued: 1929-1949
Colour variation
Price: $1600 £1000

ONE OF THE FORTY
(Style one) HN677
Designer: H. Tittensor
Height: 8¼in., 21cm.
Issued: 1924-1938
Colour variation
Price: $768 £480

ONE OF THE FORTY
(Style one) HN1352
Designer: H. Tittensor
Height: 8¼in., 21cm.
Issued: 1929-1949
Colour variation
Price: $1600 £1000

ONE OF THE FORTY
(Style two) HN494
Designer: H. Tittensor
Height: 7¼in., 18.4cm.
Issued: 1921-1938
Colour variation
Price: $1600 £1000

ONE OF THE FORTY
(Style two) HN418
Designer: H. Tittensor
Height: 7¼in., 18.4cm.
Issued: 1920-1938
Price: $1600 £1000

ONE OF THE FORTY
(Style two) HN498
Designer: H. Tittensor
Height: 7¼in., 18.4cm.
Issued: 1921-1938
Colour variation
Price: $1600 £1000

ONE OF THE FORTY
(Style two) HN647
Designer: H. Tittensor
Height: 7¼in., 18.4cm.
Issued: 1924-1938
Colour variation
Price: $1600 £1000

ONE OF THE FORTY
(Style two) HN666
Designer: H. Tittensor
Height: 7¼in., 18.4cm.
Issued: 1924-1938
Colour variation
Price: $1600 £1000

ONE OF THE FORTY
(Style two) HN704
Designer: H. Tittensor
Height: 7¼in., 18.4cm.
Issued: 1925-1938
Colour variation
Price: $1600 £1000

ONE OF THE FORTY
(Style three) HN423

ON THE BEACH HN3877

OMAR KHAYYAM (Style two)
HN2247

ONCE UPON A TIME HN2047

ONE OF THE FORTY
(Style ten) HN480

ONE OF THE FORTY
(Style two) HN1353
Designer: H. Tittensor
Height: 7¼in., 18.4cm.
Issued: 1929-1949
Colour variation
Price: $1600 £1000

ONE OF THE FORTY
(Style three) HN423
Designer: H. Tittensor
Height: 3in., 7.6cm.
Issued: 1921-1936
Price: $760 £475

ONE OF THE FORTY
(Style four) HN423A
Designer: H. Tittensor
Height: 3in., 7.6cm.
Issued: 1921-1938
Price: $760 £475

ONE OF THE FORTY
(Style five) HN423B
Designer: H. Tittensor
Height: 2¾in., 6.9cm.
Issued: 1921-1938
Price: $720 £450

ONE OF THE FORTY
(Style six) HN423C
Designer: H. Tittensor
Height: 2¾in., 6.9cm.
Issued: 1921-1938
Price: $760 £475

ONE OF THE FORTY
(Style seven) HN423D
Designer: H. Tittensor
Height: 2¾in., 6.9cm.
Issued: 1921-1938
Price: $720 £450

ONE OF THE FORTY
(Style eight) HN423E
Designer: H. Tittensor
Height: 3in., 7.6cm.
Issued: 1921-1938
Price: $1200 £750

ONE OF THE FORTY
(Style nine) HN427
Designer: H. Tittensor
Height: Unknown
Issued: 1921-1938
Price: $1600 £1000

ONE OF THE FORTY
(Style ten) HN480
Designer: H. Tittensor
Height: 7in., 17.8cm.
Issued: 1921-1938
Price: $1600 £1000

ONE OF THE FORTY
(Style ten) HN493
Designer: H. Tittensor
Height: 6¾in., 17.1cm.
Issued: 1921-1938
Price: $1600 £1000

ONE OF THE FORTY
(Style ten) HN499
Designer: H. Tittensor
Height: 6¾in., 17.1cm.
Issued: 1921-1938
Colour variation
Price: $1600 £1000

ONE OF THE FORTY
(Style ten) HN664
Designer: H. Tittensor
Height: 7¾in., 19.7cm.
Issued: 1924-1938
Colour variation
Price: $1600 £1000

ONE OF THE FORTY
(Style ten) HN714
Designer: H. Tittensor
Height: 6¾in., 17.1cm.
Issued: 1925-1938
Colour variation
Price: $1600 £1000

ONE OF THE FORTY
(Style ten) HN497
Designer: H. Tittensor
Height: 6¾in., 17.1cm.
Issued: 1921-1938
Colour variation
Price: $1600 £1000

ONE OF THE FORTY
(Style eleven) HN481
Designer: H. Tittensor
Height: Unknown
Issued: 1921-1938
Price: $1600 £1000

ONE OF THE FORTY
(Style eleven) HN491
Designer: H. Tittensor
Height: Unknown
Issued: 1921-1938
Colour variation
Price: $1600 £1000

ONE OF THE FORTY
(Style eleven) HN646
Designer: H. Tittensor
Height: Unknown
Issued: 1924-1938
Colour variation
Price: $1600 £1000

ONE OF THE FORTY
(Style eleven) HN483
Designer: H. Tittensor
Height: Unknown
Issued: 1921-1938
Colour variation
Price: $1600 £1000

ONE OF THE FORTY
(Style eleven) HN667
Designer: H. Tittensor
Height: Unknown
Issued: 1924-1938
Colour variation
Price: $1600 £1000

ONE OF THE FORTY
HN423

ONE OF THE FORTY
(Style eleven) HN483

ONE OF THE FORTY
(Style eleven) HN712
Designer: H. Tittensor
Height: Unknown
Issued: 1925-1938
Colour variation
Price: $1600 £1000

ONE OF THE FORTY
(Style eleven) HN1336
Designer: H. Tittensor
Height: Unknown
Issued: 1929-1938
Colour variation
Price: $1600 £1000

ONE OF THE FORTY
(Style eleven) HN1350
Designer: H. Tittensor
Height: Unknown
Issued: 1929-1949
Colour variation
Price: $1600 £1000

ONE OF THE FORTY
(Style twelve) HN482
Designer: H. Tittensor
Height: 6in., 15.2cm.
Issued: 1921-1938
Price: $1600 £1000

ONE OF THE FORTY
(Style twelve) HN484
Designer: H. Tittensor
Height: 6in., 15.2cm.
Issued: 1921-1938
Colour variation
Price: $1600 £1000

ONE OF THE FORTY
(Style twelve) HN492
Designer: H. Tittensor
Height: 6in., 15.2cm.
Issued: 1921-1938
Colour variation
Price: $1600 £1000

ONE OF THE FORTY
(Style twelve) HN645
Designer: H. Tittensor
Height: 6in., 15.2cm.
Issued: 1924-1938
Colour variation
Price: $1600 £1000

ONE OF THE FORTY
(Style twelve) HN663
Designer: H. Tittensor
Height: 6in., 15.2cm.
Issued: 1924-1938
Colour variation
Price: $1600 £1000

ONE OF THE FORTY
(Style twelve) HN713
Designer: H. Tittensor
Height: 6in., 15.2cm.
Issued: 1925-1938
Colour variation
Price: $1600 £1000

ONE OF THE FORTY
(Style thirteen) HN665
Designer: H. Tittensor
Height: 7¾in., 19.7cm.
Issued: 1924-1938
            Colour variation
Price: $1600 £1000

ONE OF THE FORTY
(Style thirteen) HN496
Designer: H. Tittensor
Height: 7¾in., 19.7cm.
Issued: 1921-1938
Price: $1600 £1000

ONE OF THE FORTY
(Style thirteen) HN500
Designer: H. Tittensor
Height: 7¾in., 19.7cm.
Issued: 1921-1938
            Colour variation
Price: $1600 £1000

ONE OF THE FORTY
(Style thirteen) HN649
Designer: H. Tittensor
Height: 7¾in., 19.7cm.
Issued: 1924-1938
            Colour variation
Price: $1600 £1000

ONE OF THE FORTY
(Style thirteen) HN1354
Designer: H. Tittensor
Height: 7¾in., 19.7cm.
Issued: 1929-1949
            Colour variation
Price: $1600 £1000

ONE THAT GOT AWAY
HN2153
Designer: P. Davies
Height: 6¼in., 15.9cm.
Issued: 1955-1959
Price: $472 £295

OPHELIA HN3674
In a limited edition of 5000
Designer: Pauline Parsons
Height: 7in., 18cm.
Issued: 1995
Price: $360 £225

ORANGE LADY HN1759
Designer: L. Harradine
Height: 8¾in., 22.2cm.
Issued: 1936-1975
Price: $280 £175

ORANGE LADY HN1953
Designer: L. Harradine
Height: 8½in., 21.6cm.
Issued: 1940-1975
            Colour variation
Price: $280 £175

ORANGE SELLER HN1325
Designer: L. Harradine
Height: 7in., 17.8cm.
Issued: 1929-1949
Price: $1040 £650

ONE THAT GOT AWAY
HN2153

ORANGE SELLER
HN1325

ORANGE LADY HN1953

ORANGE LADY HN1759

ONE OF THE FORTY
(Style thirteen) HN665

ORANGE VENDOR HN1966

ORANGE VENDOR HN72
Designer: C. J. Noke
Height: 6¼in., 15.8cm.
Issued: 1917-1938
Price: $1040 £650

ORANGE VENDOR HN508
Designer: C. J. Noke
Height: 6¼in., 15.8cm.
Issued: 1921-1938
Price: $1360 £850

ORANGE VENDOR HN521
Designer: C. J. Noke
Height: 6¼in., 15.8cm.
Issued: 1921-1938
             Colour variation
Price: $1600 £1000

ORANGE VENDOR HN1966
Designer: C. J. Noke
Height: 6¼in., 15.8cm
Issued: 1941-1949
             Colour variation
Price: $720 £450

ORGAN GRINDER HN2173
Designer: M. Nicoll
Height: 8¾in., 22.2cm.
Issued: 1956-1965
Price: $800 £500

OUR FIRST CHRISTMAS HN3452
Designer: Pauline Parsons
Height: 11½in., 29cm.
Issued: 1993
Price: $168 £105 (R.R.P.)

OUT FOR A WALK HN86
Designer: H. Tittensor
Height: Unknown
Issued: 1918-1936
Price: $2800 £1750

OUT FOR A WALK HN443
Designer: H. Tittensor
Height: Unknown
Issued: 1921-1936
Price: $3200 £2000

OUT FOR A WALK HN748
Designer: H. Tittensor
Height: 10in., 25.4cm.
Issued: 1925-1936
Price: $2800 £1750

OVER THE THRESHOLD HN3274
Designer: R. Tabbenor
Height: 12in., 30.5cm.
Issued: 1989
Price: $254 £159 (R.R.P.)

OWD WILLUM HN2042
Designer: H. Tittensor
Height: 6¾in., 17.2cm.
Issued: 1949-1973
Price: $360 £225

ORANGE
VENDOR HN72

OUR FIRST CHRISTMAS
HN3452

ORGAN GRINDER
HN2173

OWD WILLUM HN2042

P

PAINTING HN3012
Designer: P. Parsons
Height: 6in., 15cm.
Issued: 1988 in a limited
             edition of 750
Price: $1200 £750

PAISLEY SHAWL (Style one) HN1392
Designer: L. Harradine
Height: 8¼in., 21cm.
Issued: 1930-1949
Price: $440 £275

PAISLEY SHAWL (Style one) HN1460
Designer: L. Harradine
Height: 8¼in., 21cm.
Issued: 1931-1949
             Colour variation
Price: $560 £350

PAISLEY SHAWL (Style one) HN1707
Designer: L. Harradine
Height: 8¼in., 21cm.
Issued: 1935-1949
             Colour variation
Price: $600 £375

PAISLEY SHAWL (Style one) HN1739
Designer: L. Harradine
Height: 8¼in., 21cm.
Issued: 1935-1949
             Colour variation
Price: $600 £375

PAISLEY SHAWL (Style one) HN1987
Designer: L. Harradine
Height: 8¼in., 21cm.
Issued: 1946-1959
             Colour variation
Price: $440 £275

PAISLEY SHAWL (Style two) HN1914
Designer: L. Harradine
Height: 6½in., 16.5cm.
Issued: 1939-1949
Price: $360 £225

PAISLEY SHAWL (Style two) HN1988
Designer: L. Harradine
Height: 6¼in., 15.9cm.
Issued: 1946-1975
             Colour variation
Price: $360 £225

PAISLEY SHAWL M3
Designer: L. Harradine
Height: 4in., 10.1cm.
Issued: 1932-1938
Price: $472 £295

PAISLEY SHAWL M4
Designer: L. Harradine
Height: 4in., 10.1cm.
Issued: 1932-1945
           Colour variation
Price: $472 £295

PAISLEY SHAWL M26
Designer: L. Harradine
Height: 3¾in., 9.5cm.
Issued: 1932-1945
           Colour variation
Price: $472 £295

PALIO HN2428
Designer: P. Davies
Height: 17½in., 44.5cm.
Issued: 1971 in a limited
           edition of 500
Price: $6400 £4000

PAMELA HN1468
Designer: L. Harradine
Height: 7½in., 19.1cm.
Issued: 1931-1938
Price: $1200 £750

PAMELA HN1469
Designer: L. Harradine
Height: 7½in., 19.1cm.
Issued: 1931-1938
           Colour variation
Price: $1040 £650

PAMELA HN1564
Designer: L. Harradine
Height: 8in., 20.3cm.
Issued: 1933-1938
           Colour variation
Price: $1040 £650

PAMELA HN3223
Michael Doulton Events Figure
Designer: P. Davies
Height: 7in., 18cm.
Issued: 1989 only
Price: $280 £175

PAMELA HN2479
Designer: P. Davies
Height: 7in., 17.5cm.
Issued: 1986-1994
Price: $176 £110

PAMELA HN3756
(R.D.I.C.C. Figure 1996)
Designer: Tim Potts
Height: 8in., 20cm.
Issued: 1996 only
Price: $232 £145

PAN ON ROCK HN621
Designer: Unknown
Height: 5¼in., 13.3cm.
Issued: 1924-1938
Price: $2400 £1500

PAN ON ROCK HN622
Designer: Unknown
Height: 5¼in., 13.3cm.
Issued: 1924-1938
Price: $2400 £1500

PAISLEY SHAWL HN1988

PAMELA HN2479

PAMELA HN3756

PAMELA HN1469

PAINTING HN3012

ROYAL DOULTON FIGURES

PANORAMA HN3028
Designer: R. Jefferson
Height: 12¼in., 31cm.
Issued: 1987-1989
Price: $232 £145

PANTALETTES HN1362
Designer: L. Harradine
Height: 7¾in., 19.7cm.
Issued: 1929-1938
Price: $600 £375

PANTALETTES HN1412
Designer: L. Harradine
Height: 7¾in., 19.7cm.
Issued: 1930-1949
Colour variation
Price: $632 £395

PANTALETTES HN1507
Designer: L. Harradine
Height: 7¾in., 19.7cm.
Issued: 1932-1949
Colour variation
Price: $720 £450

PANTALETTES HN1709
Designer: L. Harradine
Height: 8in., 20.3cm.
Issued: 1935-1938
Colour variation
Price: $1040 £650

PANTALETTES M15
Designer: L. Harradine
Height: 3¾in., 9.5cm.
Issued: 1932-1945
Price: $552 £345

PANTALETTES M16
Designer: L. Harradine
Height: 3¾in., 9.5cm.
Issued: 1932-1945
Colour variation
Price: $480 £300

PANTALETTES M31
Designer: L. Harradine
Height: 4in., 10.1cm.
Issued: 1932-1945
Colour variation
Price: $520 £325

PARADISE HN3074
Designer: A. Hughes
Height: 13½in., 34.5cm.
Issued: 1985-1992
Price: $232 £145

PARISIAN HN2445
Designer: M. Nicoll
Height: 8in., 20.3cm.
Issued: 1972-1975
Price: $264 £165

PARK PARADE HN3116
Designer: A. Maslankowski
Height: 11¾in., 30cm.
Issued: 1987-1994
Price: $280 £175

PANTALETTES HN1412

PARADISE HN3074

PANTALETTES HN1709

PANORAMA HN3028

PARISIAN HN2445

PANTALETTES
HN1362

PARSON'S DAUGHTER HN337
Designer: H. Tittensor
Height: 10in., 25.4cm.
Issued: 1919-1938
Price: $1040 £650

**PARSON'S DAUGHTER
HN338**
Designer: H. Tittensor
Height: 10in., 25.4cm.
Issued: 1919-1938
  Colour variation
Price: $1040 £650

**PARSON'S DAUGHTER
HN441**
Designer: H. Tittensor
Height: 10in., 25.4cm.
Issued: 1921-1938
  Colour variation
Price: $1040 £650

**PARSON'S DAUGHTER
HN564**
Designer: H. Tittensor
Height: 9½in., 24.1cm.
Issued: 1923-1949
  Colour variation
Price: $440 £275

**PARSON'S DAUGHTER
HN790**
Designer: H. Tittensor
Height: 10in., 25.4cm.
Issued: 1926-1938
  Colour variation
Price: $1040 £650

**PARSON'S DAUGHTER
HN1242**
Designer: H. Tittensor
Height: 10in., 25.4cm.
Issued: 1927-1938
  Colour variation
Price: $1040 £650

**PARSON'S DAUGHTER
HN1356**
Designer: H. Tittensor
Height: 9¼in., 23.5cm.
Issued: 1929-1938
  Colour variation
Price: $960 £600

**PARSON'S DAUGHTER
HN2018**
Designer: H. Tittensor
Height: 9¾in., 24.7cm.
Issued: 1949-1953
  Colour variation
Price: $632 £395

PARTNERS HN3119
Designer: A. Maslankowski
Height: 6¾in., 17.2cm.
Issued: 1990-1992
Price: $264 £165

PARK PARADE HN3116

PARTNERS HN3119

**PARSON'S DAUGHTER
HN1356**

**PARSON'S DAUGHTER
HN564**

PAST GLORY HN2484
Designer: M. Nicoll
Height: 7½in., 19.1cm.
Issued: 1973-1978
Price: $520 £325

PATCHWORK QUILT HN1984
Designer: L. Harradine
Height: 6in., 15.2cm.
Issued: 1945-1959
Price: $520 £325

PATIENCE HN3533
Designer: Peter Gee
Height: 12¼in., 31cm.
Issued: 1987-1995
Price: $120 £75

PATRICIA HN1414
Designer: L. Harradine
Height: 8½in., 21.6cm.
Issued: 1930-1949
Price: $680 £425

PATRICIA HN1431
Designer: L. Harradine
Height: 8½in., 21.6cm.
Issued: 1930-1949
          Colour variation
Price: $680 £425

PATRICIA HN1462
Designer: L. Harradine
Height: 8in., 20.3cm.
Issued: 1931-1938
          Colour variation
Price: $840 £525

PATRICIA HN1567
Designer: L. Harradine
Height: 8½in., 21.6cm.
Issued: 1933-1949
          Colour variation
Price: $760 £475

PATRICIA M7
Designer: L. Harradine
Height: 4in., 10.1cm.
Issued: 1932-1945
Price: $560 £350

PATRICIA M8
Designer: L. Harradine
Height: 4in., 10.1cm.
Issued: 1932-1938
          Colour variation
Price: $560 £350

PATRICIA M28
Designer: L. Harradine
Height: 4in., 10.1cm.
Issued: 1932-1945
          Colour variation
Price: $560 £350

PATRICIA HN2715
Designer: E. Griffiths
Height: 7½in., 19cm.
Issued: 1982-1985
Price: $264 £165

PATRICIA HN3365
Figure of the year
Designer: Valerie Annand
Height: 8½in., 21.5cm.
Issued: 1993 only
Price: $400 £250

PATRICIA HN3365

PATRICIA HN1414

PAST GLORY HN2484

PATRICIA HN3907
Designer: Peggy Davies
Height: 7¾in., 19.5cm.
Issued: 1998
Price: $206 £129 (R.R.P.)

PAULA HN2906
Designer: P. Parsons
Height: 7in., 17.8cm.
Issued: 1980-1986
Price: $264 £165

PAULA HN3234
Designer: Pauline Parsons
Height: 7½in., 19cm.
Issued: 1990-1996
Price: $176 £110

PAULINE HN1444
Designer: L. Harradine
Height: 6in., 15.2cm.
Issued: 1931-1938
Price: $560 £350

PAULINE HN2441
Designer: P. Davies
Height: 5in., 12.5cm.
Issued: 1984-1989
Price: $360 £225

PAULINE HN3643
Roadshow Events Figure 1994
Designer: Nada Pedley
Height: 7¼in., 18.4cm.
Issued: 1994 (only) special
          commission
Price: $264 £165

PAVLOVA HN487
Designer: C. J. Noke
Height: 4¼in., 10.8cm.
Issued: 1921-1938
Price: $4800 £3000

PAVLOVA HN676
Designer: C.J. Noke
Height: 4¼in., 10.8cm.
Issued: 1924-1938
          Colour variation
Price: $4800 £3000

PEACE HN2443 (Black)
Designer: P. Davies
Height: 8in., 20.3cm.
Issued: 1981-1997
Price: $104 £65

PEACE HN2470 (White)
Designer: P. Davies
Height: 8in., 20.3cm.
Issued: 1981
Price: $80 £50 (R.R.P.)

PEARLY BOY (Style one)
HN1482
Designer: W. K. Harper
Height: 5½in., 14cm.
Issued: 1931-1949
Price: $360 £225

ROYAL DOULTON FIGURES

PEARLY BOY (Style one)
HN1547
Designer: W. K. Harper
Height: 5½in., 14cm.
Issued: 1933-1949
Colour variation
Price: $472 £295

PEARLY BOY (Style two)
HN2035
Designer: W. K. Harper
Height: 5½in., 14cm.
Issued: 1949-1959
Price: $280 £175

PEARLY BOY HN2767
Designer: W. K. Harper
Height: 8in., 20.3cm.
Issued: 1989-1992
Price: $280 £175

PEARLY GIRL (Style one)
HN1483
Designer: W. K. Harper
Height: 5½in., 14cm.
Issued: 1931-1949
Price: $360 £225

PEARLY GIRL (Style one)
HN1548
Designer: W. K. Harper
Height: 5½in., 14cm.
Issued: 1933-1949
Colour variation
Price: $472 £295

PEARLY GIRL (Style two)
HN2036
Designer: W. K. Harper
Height: 5½in., 14cm.
Issued: 1949-1959
Price: $260 £175

PEARLY GIRL HN2769
Designer: W. K. Harper
Height: 8in., 20.3cm.
Issued: 1989-1992
Price: $280 £175

PECKSNIFF (Style one) HN535
Designer: L. Harradine
Height: 3¾in., 9.5cm.
Issued: 1922-1932
Price: $80 £50

PECKSNIFF (Style two) HN553
Designer: L. Harradine
Height: 7in., 17.8cm.
Issued: 1923-1939
Price: $520 £325

PECKSNIFF (Style two)
HN1891
Designer: L. Harradine
Height: 7in., 17.8cm.
Issued: 1938-1952
Price: $440 £275

PAULA HN3234

PAULINE HN2441

PAULA HN2906

PEACE HN2470

PEACE HN2443

PATRICIA HN1567

PEARLY BOY (Style two)
HN2035

PEARLY GIRL (Style two)
HN2036

ROYAL DOULTON FIGURES

PECKSNIFF (Style three) HN2098
Designer: L. Harradine
Height: 7¼in., 18.4cm.
Issued: 1952-1967
Price: $392 £245

PECKSNIFF, MR M43
Designer: L. Harradine
Height: 4¼in., 10.8cm.
Issued: 1932-1982
Price: $80 £50

PEDLAR WOLF HN7
Designer: C. J. Noke
Height: 5½in., 14cm.
Issued: 1913-1938
Price: $2800 £1750

PEEK-A-BOO HN3363
Designer: Valerie Annand
Height: 2½in., 6.4cm.
Issued: 1992-1994
Price: $176 £110

PEGGY HN1941
Designer: L. Harradine
Height: 5in., 12.7cm.
Issued: 1940-1949
Price: $312 £195

PEGGY HN2038
Designer: L. Harradine
Height: 5in., 12.7cm.
Issued: 1949-1978
Price: $165 £110

PENELOPE HN1901
Designer: L. Harradine
Height: 7in., 17.8cm.
Issued: 1939-1975
Price: $440 £275

PENELOPE HN1902
Designer: L. Harradine
Height: 7in., 17.8cm.
Issued: 1939-1949
    Colour variation
Price: $960 £600

PENNY HN2338
Designer: P. Davies
Height: 4¾in., 12cm.
Issued: 1968-1995
Price: $104 £65

PENNY HN2424
Designer: P. Davies
Height: 4¾in., 12cm.
Issued: 1983-1992
Price: $120 £75

PENSIVE HN3109
Designer: R. Jefferson
Height: 13in., 33cm.
Issued: 1987-1989
Price: $232 £145

PENSIVE MOMENTS HN2704
Designer: P. Davies
Height: 5in., 12.7cm.
Issued: 1975-1982
Price: $280 £175

PENNY HN2424

PENSIVE HN3109

PERFECT PAIR HN581

PENSIVE MOMENTS HN2704

PEEK-A-BOO HN3363

PERFECT PAIR HN581
Designer: L. Harradine
Height: 6¾in., 17.2cm.
Issued: 1923-1938
Price: $880 £550

PERFORMANCE, THE HN3827
Designer: D.V.Tootle
Height: 10¼in., 26cm.
Issued: 1997
Price: $222 £139 (R.R.P.)

PHILIPPA OF HAINAULT HN2008
Designer: P. Davies
Height: 9¾in., 24.7cm.
Issued: 1948-1953
Price: $630 £395

PHILIPPINE DANCER HN2439
Designer: P. Davies
Height: 9½in., 24.1cm.
Issued: 1978 in a limited
    edition of 750
Price: $680 £425

PHYLLIS HN1420
Designer: L. Harradine
Height: 9in., 22.9cm.
Issued: 1930-1949
Price: $630 £395

PHYLLIS HN1430
Designer: L. Harradine
Height: 9in., 22.9cm.
Issued: 1930-1938
    Colour variation
Price: $880 £550

PHYLLIS HN1486
Designer: L. Harradine
Height: 9in., 22.9cm.
Issued: 1931-1949
    Colour variation
Price: $630 £395

PHYLLIS HN1698
Designer: L. Harradine
Height: 9in., 22.9cm.
Issued: 1935-1949
    Colour variation
Price: $760 £475

PHYLLIS HN3180
Designer: D. Tootle
Height: 7¼in., 18.5cm.
Issued: 1988-1991
Price: $264 £165

PICARDY PEASANT (Man) HN13
Designer: P. Stabler
Height: 9in., 22.9cm.
Issued: 1913-1938
Price: $2400 £1500

272

PICARDY PEASANT (Man)
HN17
Designer: P. Stabler
Height: 9½in., 24cm.
Issued: 1913-1938
Colour variation
Price: $2400 £1500

PICARDY PEASANT (Man)
HN19
Designer: P. Stabler
Height: 9½in., 24cm.
Issued: 1913-1938
Colour variation
Price: $2400 £1500

PICARDY PEASANT (Woman)
HN4
Designer: P. Stabler
Height: 9¼in., 23.5cm.
Issued: 1913-1938
Price: $2000 £1250

PICARDY PEASANT (Woman)
HN5
Designer: P. Stabler
Height: 9¼in., 23.5cm.
Issued: 1913-1938
Colour variation
Price: $2400 £1500

PICARDY PEASANT (Woman)
HN17A
Designer: P. Stabler
Height: 9½in., 24cm.
Issued: 1913-1938
Colour variation
Price: $2400 £1500

PICARDY PEASANT (Woman)
HN351
Designer: P. Stabler
Height: 9½in., 24cm.
Issued: 1919-1938
Colour variation
Price: $1600 £1000

PICARDY PEASANT (Woman)
HN513
Designer: P. Stabler
Height: 9½in., 24cm.
Issued: 1921-1938
Colour variation
Price: $2400 £1500

PICNIC HN2308
Designer: P. Davies
Height: 3¾in., 9.5cm.
Issued: 1965-1988
Price: $200 £125

PIED PIPER HN1215
Designer: L. Harradine
Height: 8¼in., 21cm.
Issued: 1926-1938
Price: $1200 £750

PIED PIPER HN2102
Designer: L. Harradine
Height: 8½in., 21.6cm.
Issued: 1953-1976
Colour variation
Price: $352 £220

PICNIC HN2308

PHYLLIS HN1420

PHILIPPA OF
HAINAULT   HN2008

PHILIPPINE DANCER HN2439

PICARDY PEASANT (Woman)
HN351

PIED PIPER HN3721 (Resin)
Designer: Alan Maslankowski
Height: 8¾in., 22cm.
Issued: 1993-1996
Price: $120 £75

PIERRETTE (Style one) HN642
Designer: L. Harradine
Height: 7¼in., 18.4cm.
Issued: 1924-1938
Price: $2400 £1500

PIERRETTE (Style one) HN643
Designer: L. Harradine
Height: 7¼in., 18.4cm.
Issued: 1924-1938
           Colour variation
Price: $1760 £1100

PIERRETTE (Style one) HN644
Designer: L. Harradine
Height: 7¼in., 18.4cm.
Issued: 1924-1938
           Colour variation
Price: $1520 £950

PIERRETTE (Style one) HN691
Designer: L. Harradine
Height: 7¼in., 18.4cm.
Issued: 1925-1938
           Colour variation
Price: $2000 £1250

PIERRETTE (Style one) HN721
Designer: L. Harradine
Height: 7¼in., 18.4cm.
Issued: 1925-1938
           Colour variation
Price: $2240 £1400

PIERRETTE (Style one) HN731
Designer: L. Harradine
Height: 7¼in., 18.4cm.
Issued: 1925-1938
           Colour variation
Price: $2320 £1450

PIERRETTE (Style one) HN732
Designer: L. Harradine
Height: 7¼in., 18.4cm.
Issued: 1925-1938
           Colour variation
Price: $2400 £1500

PIERRETTE (Style one) HN784
Designer: L. Harradine
Height: 7¼in., 18.4cm.
Issued: 1926-1938
           Colour variation
Price: $2000 £1250

PIERRETTE (Style two) HN795
Designer: L. Harradine
Height: 3½in., 8.9cm.
Issued: 1926-1938
Price: $1600 £1000

PIED PIPER HN3721

PIED PIPER HN1215

PIERRETTE
HN731

PIERRETTE
HN644

PIERRETTE HN643

PIERRETTE HN1749

ROYAL DOULTON FIGURES

PIERRETTE (Style two)
HN796
Designer: L. Harradine
Height: 3½in., 8.9cm.
Issued: 1926-1938
Price: $1600 £1000

PIERRETTE (Style three)
HN1391
Designer: L. Harradine
Height: 8½in., 21.6cm.
Issued: 1930-1938
Price: $2800 £1750

PIERRETTE (Style three)
HN1749
Designer: L. Harradine
Height: 8½in., 21.6cm.
Issued: 1936-1949
           Colour variation
Price: $2160 £1350

PILLOW FIGHT HN2270
Designer: P. Davies
Height: 5in., 12.7cm.
Issued: 1965-1969
Price: $312 £195

PINKIE HN1552
Designer: L. Harradine
Height: 5in., 12.7cm.
Issued: 1933-1938
Price: $880 £550

PINKIE HN1553
Designer: L. Harradine
Height: 5in., 12.7cm.
Issued: 1933-1938
           Colour variation
Price: $960 £600

PIPER HN2907
Designer: M. Abberley
Height: 8in., 20.3cm.
Issued: 1980-1992
Price: $296 £185

PIPER HN3444
Designer: Peter Gee
Height: 10in., 25.5cm.
Issued: 1993-1995
Price: $264 £165

PIRATE KING HN2901
Designer: W. K Harper
Height: 10in., 25.4cm.
Issued: 1981-1986
Price: $680 £425

PIROUETTE HN2216
Designer: P. Davies
Height: 5¾in., 14.6cm.
Issued: 1959-1967
Price: $264 £165

PLAYFUL HN3534
Designer: Adrian Hughes
Height: 7½in., 19.5cm.
Issued: 1987-1993
Price: $152 £95

PIPER HN3444   PIPER HN2907

PIERRETTE
HN1391

PIRATE KING HN2901   PIROUETTE HN2216

ROYAL DOULTON FIGURES

PLAYMATES HN3127
Designer: P. Parsons
Height: 8½in., 22cm.
Issued: 1988-1992
Price: $232 £145

PLAYTIME HN3544
(Cat & Kittens)
Designer: John Ablitt
Height: 8in., 20.3cm.
Issued: 1990-1992
Price: $176 £110

PLEASE KEEP STILL HN2967
Designer: P. Parsons
Height: 4½in., 11.5cm.
Issued: 1982-1985
Price: $264 £165

PLEASE SIR IIN3302
In a limited edition of 7500
Designer: Adrian Hughes
Height: 8in., 20.5cm.
Issued: 1992-1996
Price: $360 £225

POACHER HN2043
Designer: L. Harradine
Height: 6in., 15.2cm.
Issued: 1949-1959
Price: $360 £225

POCAHONTAS HN2930
(Ship's figurehead)
Designer: S. Keenan
Height: 8in., 20.3cm.
Issued: 1982 in a limited
edition of 950
Price: $632 £395

POKE BONNET HN362
Designer: C. J. Noke
Height: 8¾in., 22.2cm.
Issued: 1919-1938
Price: $1760 £1100

POKE BONNET HN612
Designer: C. J. Noke
Height: 9½in., 24.1cm.
Issued: 1924-1938
Colour variation
Price: $1760 £1100

POKE BONNET HN765
Designer: C. J. Noke
Height: 8¾in., 22.2cm.
Issued: 1925-1938
Colour variation
Price: $1920 £1200
Also called In Grandma's Days
and Lilac Shawl

POLISH DANCER HN2836
Designer: P. Davies
Height: 9½in., 24.1cm.
Issued: 1980 in a limited
edition of 750
Price: $880 £550

POACHER HN2043

POCAHONTAS
HN2930

POKE BONNET
HN612

POLISH DANCER HN2836

POLKA HN2156
Designer: P. Davies
Height: 7½in., 19.1cm.
Issued: 1955-1969
Price: $360 £225

POLLY HN3178
Designer: D. Tootle
Height: 8¼in., 21cm.
Issued: 1988
Price: $280 £175

POLLY PEACHUM M23
Designer: L. Harradine
Height: 2¼in., 5.7cm.
Issued: 1932-1938
Colour variation
Price: $720 £450

POLLY PEACIIUM (Style one) HN463
Designer: L. Harradine
Height: 6¼in., 15.9cm.
Issued: 1921-1949
Price: $720 £450

POLLY PEACHUM (Style one) HN465
Designer: L. Harradine
Height: 6½in., 16.5cm.
Issued: 1921-1949
Colour variation
Price: $720 £450

POLLY PEACHUM (Style one) HN550
Designer: L. Harradine
Height: 6½in., 16.5cm.
Issued: 1922-1949
Colour variation
Price: $560 £350

POLLY PEACHUM (Style one) HN589
Designer: L. Harradine
Height: 6½in., 16.5cm.
Issued: 1924-1949
Colour variation
Price: $600 £375

POLLY PEACHUM (Style one) HN614
Designer: L. Harradine
Height: 6½in., 16.5cm.
Issued: 1924-1949
Colour variation
Price: $680 £425

POLLY PEACHUM (Style one) HN680
Designer: L. Harradine
Height: 6½in., 16.5cm.
Issued: 1924-1949
Colour variation
Price: $800 £500

ROYAL DOULTON FIGURES

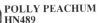

POLLY PEACHUM (Style one)
HN693
Designer:	L. Harradine
Height:	6½in,. 16.5cm.
Issued:	1925-1949
	Colour variation
Price:	$600 £375

POLLY PEACHUM (Style two)
HN489
Designer:	L. Harradine
Height:	4¼in., 10.8cm.
Issued:	1921-1938
Price:	$600 £375

POLLY PEACHUM (Style two)
HN549
Designer:	L. Harradine
Height:	4¼in., 10.8cm.
Issued:	1922-1949
	Colour variation
Price:	$472 £295

POLLY PEACHUM (Style two)
HN620
Designer:	L. Harradine
Height:	4¼in., 10.8cm.
Issued:	1924-1938
	Colour variation
Price:	$520 £325

POLLY PEACHUM (Style two)
HN694
Designer:	L. Harradine
Height:	4¼in., 10.8cm.
Issued:	1925-1949
	Colour variation
Price:	$560 £350

POLLY PEACHUM (Style two)
HN734
Designer:	L. Harradine
Height:	4¼in., 10.8cm.
Issued:	1925-1949
	Colour variation
Price:	$840 £525

POLLY PEACHUM (Style three) HN698
Designer:	L. Harradine
Height:	2¼in., 5.7cm.
Issued:	1925-1949
Price:	$560 £350

POLLY PEACHUM (Style three) HN699
Designer:	L. Harradine
Height:	2¼in., 5.7cm.
Issued:	1925-1949
	Colour variation
Price:	$760 £475

POLLY PEACHUM (Style three) HN757
Designer:	L. Harradine
Height:	2¼in., 5.7cm.
Issued:	1925-1949
	Colour variation
Price:	$720 £450

POLLY PEACHUM
HN489

POLLY PEACHUM
HN463

POLLY PEACHUM (Style one)
HN550

POLLYANNA HN2965

POLLY PUT THE KETTLE ON HN3021

POLLY PEACHUM (Style three) HN758
Designer:	L. Harradine
Height:	2¼in., 5.7cm.
Issued:	1925-1949
	Colour variation
Price:	$720 £450

POLLY PEACHUM (Style three) HN759
Designer:	L. Harradine
Height:	2¼in., 5.7cm.
Issued:	1925-1949
	Colour variation
Price:	$720 £450

POLLY PEACHUM (Style three) HN760
Designer:	L. Harradine
Height:	2¼in., 5.7cm.
Issued:	1925-1949
	Colour variation
Price:	$720 £450

POLLY PEACHUM (Style three) HN761
Designer:	L. Harradine
Height:	2¼in., 5.7cm.
Issued:	1925-1949
	Colour variation
Price:	$720 £450

POLLY PEACHUM (Style three) HN762
Designer:	L. Harradine
Height:	2¼in., 5.7cm.
Issued:	1925-1949
	Colour variation
Price:	$720 £450

POLLY PEACHUM M21
Designer:	L. Harradine
Height:	2¼in., 5.7cm.
Issued:	1932-1945
Price:	$440 £275

POLLY PEACHUM M22
Designer:	L. Harradine
Height:	2¼in., 5.7cm.
Issued:	1932-1938
	Colour variation
Price:	$440 £275

POLLY PUT THE KETTLE ON HN3021
Designer:	P. Parsons
Height:	8in., 20cm.
Issued:	1984-1987
Price:	$232 £145

POLLYANNA HN2965
Designer:	P. Parsons
Height:	6¾in., 17cm.
Issued:	1982-1985
Price:	$232 £145

POLLYANNA HN2965

POPE JOHN PAUL II
HN2888
Designer: E. Griffiths
Height: 10in., 25.4cm.
Issued: 1982-1992
Price: $264 £165

POSY FOR YOU, A, HN3606
Designer: Nada Pedley
Height: 4¾in., 12cm.
Issued: 1994-1997
Price: $96 £60

POTTER HN1493
Designer: C. J. Noke
Height: 7in., 17.8cm.
Issued: 1932-1992
Price: $400 £250

POTTER HN1518
Designer: C. J. Noke
Height: 6¾in., 17.2cm.
Issued: 1932-1949
               Colour variation
Price: $640 £400

POTTER HN1522
Designer: C. J. Noke
Height: 6¾in., 17.2cm.
Issued: 1932-1949
               Colour variation
Price: $800 £500

PREMIERE HN2343
Designer: P. Davies
Height: 7½in., 19.1cm.
Issued: 1969-1978
Price: $280 £175

PRETTY LADY HN69
Designer: H. Tittensor
Height: 9½in., 24.1cm.
Issued: 1916-1938
Price: $960 £600

PRETTY LADY HN70
Designer: H. Tittensor
Height: 9¾in., 24.1cm.
Issued: 1916-1938
               Colour variation
Price: $1600 £1000

PRETTY LADY HN302
Designer: H. Tittensor
Height: 9½in., 24.1cm.
Issued: 1918-1938
               Colour variation
Price: $1600 £1000

PRETTY LADY HN330
Designer: H. Tittensor
Height: 9½in., 24.1cm.
Issued: 1918-1938
               Colour variation
Price: $1920 £1200

PRETTY LADY HN361
Designer: H. Tittensor
Height: 9½in., 24.1cm.
Issued: 1919-1938
               Colour variation
Price: $1600 £1000

PREMIERE HN2343

POPE JOHN PAUL II
HN2888

POSY FOR YOU, A, HN3606

OTTER HN1493

ROYAL DOULTON FIGURES

PRETTY LADY HN384
Designer: H. Tittensor
Height: 9½in., 24.1cm.
Issued: 1920-1938
  Colour variation
Price: $1600 £1000

PRETTY LADY HN565
Designer: H. Tittensor
Height: 10in., 25.4cm.
Issued: 1923-1938
  Colour variation
Price: $1520 £950

PRETTY LADY HN700
Designer: H. Tittensor
Height: 9½in., 24.1cm.
Issued: 1925-1938
  Colour variation
Price: $1520 £950

PRETTY LADY HN763
Designer: H. Tittensor
Height: 9½in., 24.1cm.
Issued: 1925-1938
  Colour variation
Price: $1920 £1200

PRETTY LADY HN783
Designer: H. Tittensor
Height: 9½in., 24.1cm.
Issued: 1926-1938
  Colour variation
Price: $1760 £1100

PRETTY POLLY HN2768
Designer: W. K. Harper
Height: 6in., 15cm.
Issued: 1984-1988
Price: $264 £165

PRIDE AND JOY HN2945
Designer: R. Tabbenor
Height: 7in., 17.8cm.
Issued: 1984
Price: $480 £300

PRIMA BALLERINA HN4024
Designer: D.V. Tootle
Height: 5½in., 14cm.
Issued: 1997
Price: $112 £70 (R.R.P.)

PRIMROSE HN3710
Designer: V. Annand
Height: 9in., 23cm.
Issued: 1996
Price: $224 £140 (R.R.P.)

PRIMROSES HN1617
Designer: L. Harradine
Height: 6½in., 16.5cm.
Issued: 1934-1949
Price: $920 £575

PRINCE OF WALES HN1217
Designer: L. Harradine
Height: 7½in., 19.1cm.
Issued: 1926-1938
Price: $1120 £700

PRETTY POLLY HN2768

PRIMROSE HN3710

PRIDE AND JOY HN2945

PRETTY LADY HN763

279

PRINCE OF WALES HN2883
Designer: E. Griffiths
Height: 8in., 20.3cm.
Issued: 1981 in a limited
              edition of 1500
Price: $2000 £1250

PRINCE OF WALES HN2884
Designer: E. Griffiths
Height: 8in., 20.3cm.
Issued: 1981 in a limited
              edition of 1500
Price: $720 £450

PRINCESS HN391
Designer: Unknown
Height: 9¼in., 23.5cm.
Issued: 1920-1938
Price: $3200 £2000

PRINCESS HN392
Designer: Unknown
Height: 9¼in., 23.5cm.
Issued: 1920-1938
              Colour variation
Price: $3200 £2000

PRINCESS HN420
Designer: Unknown
Height: 9¼in., 23.5cm.
Issued: 1920-1938
              Colour variation
Price: $3200 £2000

PRINCESS HN430
Designer: Unknown
Height: 9¼in., 23.5cm.
Issued: 1921-1938
              Colour variation
Price: $3200 £2000

PRINCESS HN431
Designer: Unknown
Height: 9¼in., 23.5cm.
Issued: 1921-1938
              Colour variation
Price: $3200 £2000

PRINCESS HN633
Designer: Unknown
Height: 9¼in., 23.5cm.
Issued: 1924-1938
              Colour variation
Price: $3200 £2000

PRINCESS BADOURA HN2081
Designer: H. Tittensor, H.E.
              Stanton and F. Van
              Allen Phillips
Height: 20in., 50.8cm.
Issued: 1952-
Price: $21200 £13250
              (R.R.P.)

PRINCESS BADOURA HN2081

PRINCE OF WALES HN2884

PRINCE OF WALES HN2883

ROYAL DOULTON FIGURES

PRINCESS BADOURA HN3921
Designer: H. Tittensor, H.
               Stanton, F. Van
               Allen Phillips
Height: 20in., 50cm.
Issued: 1996
               Colour variation
Price: $21200 £13250
               (R.R.P.)

**PRINCESS ELIZABETH
HN3682**
In limited edition of 5000
Designer: Pauline Parsons
Height: 8½in., 21.6cm.
Issued: 1996
Price: $400 £225

PRINCESS OF WALES HN2887
Designer: E. Griffiths
Height: 7¾in., 19.6cm.
Issued: 1982 in a limited
               edition of 1500
Price: $1600 £1000

PRINTEMPS HN3066
Designer: R. Jefferson
Height: 11½in., 29cm.
Issued: 1987 in a limited
               edition of 300
Price: $1040 £650

PRISCILLA HN1337
Designer: L. Harradine
Height: 8in., 20.3cm.
Issued: 1929-1938
Price: $680 £425

PRISCILLA HN1340
Designer: L. Harradine
Height: 8in., 20.3cm.
Issued: 1929-1949
               Colour variation
Price: $440 £275

PRISCILLA HN1495
Designer: L. Harradine
Height: 8in., 20.3cm.
Issued: 1932-1949
               Colour variation
Price: $600 £375

PRISCILLA HN1501
Designer: L. Harradine
Height: 8in., 20.3cm.
Issued: 1932-1938
               Colour variation
Price: $760 £475

PRISCILLA HN1559
Designer: L. Harradine
Height: 8in., 20.3cm.
Issued: 1933-1949
               Colour variation
Price: $480 £300

PRISCILLA M13
Designer: L. Harradine
Height: 4in., 10.1cm.
Issued: 1932-1938
Price: $560 £350

PRINTEMPS HN3066

PRINCESS BADOURA HN3921

PRISCILLA HN1340

PRINCESS OF WALES HN2887

PRISCILLA M14
Designer: L. Harradine
Height: 3¾in., 9.5cm.
Issued: 1932-1945
Colour variation
Price: $480 £300

PRISCILLA M24
Designer: L. Harradine
Height: 3¾in., 9.5cm.
Issued: 1932-1945
Colour variation
Price: $480 £300

PRIVATE, CONNECTICUT REGIMENT 1777 HN2845
Designer: E. J. Griffiths
Height: 11¼in., 28.5cm.
Issued: 1978 in a limited edition of 350
Price: $880 £550

PRIVATE, DELAWARE REGIMENT 1776 HN2761
Designer: E. J. Griffiths
Height: 12in., 30.5cm.
Issued: 1977 in a limited edition of 350
Price: $880 £550

PRIVATE, 1ST GEORGIA REGIMENT 1777 HN2779
Designer: E. J. Griffiths
Height: 11in., 27.9cm.
Issued: 1975 in a limited edition of 350
Price: $880 £550

PRIVATE, MASSACHUSETTS REGIMENT 1778 HN2760
Designer: E. J. Griffiths
Height: 12½in., 31.7cm.
Issued: 1977 in a limited edition of 350
Price: $880 £550

PRIVATE, PENNSYLVANIA RIFLE BATTALION 1776 HN2846
Designer: E. J. Griffiths
Height: 11¼in., 28.5cm.
Issued: 1978 in a limited edition of 350
Price: $880 £550

PRIVATE, RHODE ISLAND REGIMENT 1781 HN2759
Designer: E. J. Griffiths
Height: 11¾in., 29.8cm.
Issued: 1977 in a limited edition of 350
Price: $880 £550

PRIVATE, 2ND SOUTH-CAROLINA REGIMENT 1781 HN2717
Designer: E. J. Griffiths
Height: 11½in., 29.2cm.
Issued: 1975 in a limited edition of 350
Price: $880 £550

PRIZED POSSESSIONS
HN2942

PROFESSOR HN2281

PRIVATE, 3RD NORTH CAROLINA REGIMENT 1778 HN2754
Designer: E. J. Griffiths
Height: 11in., 27.9cm.
Issued: 1976 in a limited edition of 350
Price: $880 £550

PRIZED POSSESSIONS HN2942
Designer: R. Tabbenor
Height: 7in., 17.8cm.
Issued: 1982
Price: $680 £425

PROFESSOR HN2281
Designer: M. Nicoll
Height: 7¼in., 18.4cm.
Issued: 1965-1980
Price: $264 £165

PROMENADE HN2076
Designer: P. Davies
Height: 8in., 20.3cm.
Issued: 1951-1953
Price: $2400 £1500

PROMENADE HN3072
Designer: A. Hughes
Height: 13in., 33cm.
Issued: 1987-1995
Price: $232 £145

PROPOSAL (Man) HN725
Designer: Unknown
Height: 5½in., 14cm.
Issued: 1925-1938
Price: $1520 £950

PROPOSAL (Man) HN1209
Designer: Unknown
Height: 5½in., 14cm.
Issued: 1926-1938
Colour variation
Price: $1520 £950

PROPOSAL (Woman) HN715
Designer: Unknown
Height: 5¾in., 14.6cm.
Issued: 1925-1938
Price: $1520 £950

PROPOSAL (Woman) HN716
Designer: Unknown
Height: 5¾in., 14.6cm.
Issued: 1925-1938
Colour variation
Price: $1520 £950

PROPOSAL (Woman) HN788
Designer: Unknown
Height: 5¾in., 14.6cm.
Issued: 1926-1938
Colour variation
Price: $1520 £950

PRUDENCE HN1883
Designer: L. Harradine
Height: 6¾in., 17.2cm.
Issued: 1938-1949
Price: $760 £475

PROPOSAL (Woman) HN715

PROPOSAL (Man) HN725

PRUDENCE HN1883

PROPOSAL (Woman) HN716

PROMENADE HN3072

PROMENADE HN2076

PRUDENCE HN1884
Designer: L. Harradine
Height: 6¾in., 17.2cm.
Issued: 1938-1949
            Colour variation
Price: $760 £475

PRUE HN1996
Designer: L. Harradine
Height: 6¾in., 17.2cm.
Issued: 1947-1955
Price: $560 £350

PUFF AND POWDER HN397
Designer: L. Harradine
Height: 6½in., 16.4cm.
Issued: 1920-1938
Price: $2640 £1650

PUFF AND POWDER IIN398
Designer: L. Harradine
Height: 6½in., 16.4cm.
Issued: 1920-1938
            Colour variation
Price: $2880 £1800

PUFF AND POWDER HN400
Designer: L. Harradine
Height: 6½in., 16.4cm.
Issued: 1920-1938
            Colour variation
Price: $2880 £1800

PUFF AND POWDER HN432
Designer: L. Harradine
Height: 6½in., 16.4cm.
Issued: 1921-1938
            Colour variation
Price: $2880 £1800

PUFF AND POWDER HN433
Designer: L. Harradine
Height: 6½in., 16.4cm.
Issued: 1921-1938
            Colour variation
Price: $2400 £1500

PUNCH AND JUDY MAN HN2765
Designer: W. K. Harper
Height: 9in., 22.9cm.
Issued: 1981-
Price: $280 £175

PUPPETMAKER HN2253
Designer: M. Nicoll
Height: 8in., 20.3cm.
Issued: 1962-1973
Price: $560 £350

PUPPY LOVE HN3371
Designer: Nada Pedley
Height: 7¼in., 18.5cm.
Issued: 1991-1994 in a
            limited edition of
            9500
Price: $264 £165

PUPPY LOVE HN3371

**PUNCH AND JUDY MAN
HN2765**

PUSSY HN18
Designer: F. C. Stone
Height: 7¾in., 19.7cm.
Issued: 1913-1238
Price: $4000 £2500

PUSSY HN325
Designer: F. C. Stone
Height: 7½in., 19.1cm.
Issued: 1918-1938
            Colour variation
Price: $2560 £1600

PUSSY HN507
Designer: F. C. Stone
Height: 7½in., 19.1cm.
Issued: 1921-1938
            Colour variation
Price: $2880 £1800

PYJAMAS HN1942
Designer: L. Harradine
Height: 5¼in., 13.3cm.
Issued: 1940-1949
Price: $560 £350

Q

QUALITY STREET HN1211
Designer: Unknown
Height: 7¼in., 18.4cm.
Issued: 1926-1936
Price: $1200 £750

QUALITY STREET HN1211A
Designer: Unknown
Height: 7¼in., 18.4cm.
Issued: 1926-1936
            Colour variation
Price: $1200 £750

QUEEN ANNE HN3141
Designer: P. Parsons
Height: 9½in., 24cm.
Issued: 1989 in a limited
            edition of 5000
Price: $360 £225

QUEEN ELIZABETH I HN3099
Designer: P. Parsons
Height: 9in., 22.5cm.
Issued: 1987 in a limited
            edition of 5000
Price: $472 £295

QUEEN ELIZABETH II HN2502
Designer: P. Davies
Height: 7¾in., 19.7cm.
Issued: 1973 in a limited
            edition of 750
Price: $1200 £750

QUEEN ELIZABETH II HN2878
Designer: E. Griffiths
Height: 10¼in., 26.5cm.
Issued: 1983
Price: $520 £325

QUEEN ELIZABETH II
HN3436
Designer: Alan Maslankowski
Height: 8¼in., 21cm.
Issued: 1992 in a limited
             edition of 5000
Price: $880 £550

QUEEN ELIZABETH II
HN3440
Designer: P. Gee
Height: 4½in., 19cm.
Issued: 1992 in a limited
             edition of 3500
Price: $472 £295

QUEEN MOTHER HN2882
Designer: E. Griffiths
Height: 8in., 20.3cm.
Issued: 1980 in a limited
             edition of 1500
Price: $1040 £650

QUEEN MOTHER (90TH Birth-
day) HN3189
Designer: E. Griffiths
Height: 8¼in., 21cm.
Issued: 1990
Price: $520 £325

QUEEN MOTHER AS THE
DUCHESS OF YORK HN3230
Designer: P. Parsons
Height: 9in., 22.5cm.
Issued: 1989 in a limited
             edition of 9500
Price: $560 £375

QUEEN OF SHEBA HN2328
Designer: P. Davies
Height: 9in., 22.8cm.
Issued: 1982 in a limited
             edition of 750
Price: $1040 £650

QUEEN OF THE DAWN
HN2437
Designer: P. Davies
Height: 8½in., 21.5cm.
Issued: 1983-1986
Price: $296 £185

QUEEN OF THE ICE HN2435
Designer: P. Davies
Height: 8in., 20cm.
Issued: 1983-1986
Price: $264 £165

QUEEN VICTORIA HN3125
Designer: P. Parsons
Height: 8in., 20cm.
Issued: 1988 in a limited
             edition of 5000
Price: $1040 £650

QUIET, THEY'RE SLEEPING
HN3657
Designer: Nada Pedley
Height: 5½in., 14cm.
Issued: 1994-1997
Price: $152 £95

QUEEN OF THE ICE HN2435

QUEEN ANNE HN3141

QUEEN ELIZABETH II
HN2502

QUEEN ELIZABETH I HN3099

ROYAL DOULTON FIGURES

QUEEN ELIZABETH II
HN3436

QUEEN ELIZABETH II
HN3440

QUEEN MOTHER HN2882

QUEEN VICTORIA
HN3125

QUEEN OF SHEBA HN2328

QUEEN OF THE DAWN
HN2437

QUEEN MOTHER AS THE
DUCHESS OF YORK HN3230

R

RACHEL HN2919
Designer: P. Gee
Height: 7½in., 19.1cm.
Issued: 1980-1984
Price: $312 £195

RACHEL HN2936
Designer: P. Gee
Height: 7¾in., 19.5cm.
Issued: 1985-1997
Colour variation
Price: $264 £165

RAG DOLL HN2142
Designer: P. Davies
Height: 4¾in., 12cm.
Issued: 1954-1986
Price: $176 £110

RAG DOLL SELLER HN2944
Designer: R. Tabbenor
Height: 7in., 17.5cm.
Issued: 1984-1995
Price: $232 £145

REBECCA HN2815
Designer: P. Davies
Height: 7¼in., 18.4cm.
Issued: 1980-1996
Price: $318 £199

REBECCA HN3414
Designer: Peggy Davies
Height: 3½in., 9cm.
Issued: 1992-1997
Price: $104 £65

REBECCA HN4041
1998 Figure of the year.
Designer: Valerie Annand
Height: 8¾in., 22.5cm.
Issued: 1998
Price: $160 £100 (R.R.P.)

REFLECTION HN3039
Designer: A. Hughes
Height: 8in., 22cm.
Issued: 1988-1989
Price: $232 £145

REFLECTIONS HN1820
Designer: L. Harradine
Height: 5in., 12.7cm.
Issued: 1937-1938
Price: $2640 £1650

REFLECTIONS HN1821
Designer: L. Harradine
Height: 5in., 12.7cm.
Issued: 1937-1938
Colour variation
Price: $2640 £1650

REFLECTIONS HN1847
Designer: L. Harradine
Height: 4½in., 11.4cm.
Issued: 1938-1949
Colour variation
Price: $1760 £1100

RACHEL HN2936

RACHEL HN2919

REFLECTIONS HN1847

REBECCA HN2805

RAG DOLL SELLER HN2944

REBECCA HN3414

REFLECTIONS HN1848
Designer: L. Harradine
Height: 5in., 12.7cm.
Issued: 1938-1949
Colour variation
Price: $1760 £1100

REGAL LADY HN2709
Designer: P. Davies
Height: 7½in., 19.1cm.
Issued: 1975-1984
Price: $232 £145

REGENCY HN1752
Designer: L. Harradine
Height: 8in., 20.3cm.
Issued: 1936-1949
Price: $1112 £695

REGENCY BEAU HN1972
Designer: H. Fenton
Height: 8in., 20.3cm.
Issued: 1941-1949
Price: $1272 £795

RENDEZVOUS HN2212
Designer: P. Davies
Height: 7¼in., 18.4cm.
Issued: 1962-1971
Price: $472 £295

REPOSE HN2272
Designer: P. Davies
Height: 5¼in., 13.3cm.
Issued: 1972-1978
Price: $360 £225

REST A WHILE HN2728
Designer: W. K. Harper
Height: 8in., 20.3cm.
Issued: 1981-1984
Price: $264 £165

RETURN OF PERSE-PHONE HN31
Designer: C. Vyse
Height: 16in., 40.6cm.
Issued: 1913-1938
Price: $4000 £2500

REVERIE HN2306
Designer: P. Davies
Height: 6½in., 16.5cm.
Issued: 1964-1982
Price: $360 £225

REWARD HN3391
Designer: Alan Maslankowski
Height: 4½in., 11.5cm.
Issued: 1992-1996
Price: $104 £65

RHAPSODY HN2267
Designer: P. Davies
Height: 6¾in., 17.2cm.
Issued: 1961-1973
Price: $280 £175

RHODA HN1573
Designer: L. Harradine
Height; 10¼in., 26.7cm.
Issued: 1933-1949
Price: $880 £550

REPOSE HN2272

REGENCY HN1752

REST A WHILE HN2728

REWARD HN3391

REVERIE HN2306

RHODA HN1574
Designer: L. Harradine
Height: 10¼in., 26.7cm.
Issued: 1933-1938
            Colour variation
Price: $880 £550

RHODA HN1688
Designer: L. Harradine
Height: 10¼in., 26.7cm.
Issued: 1935-1949
            Colour variation
Price: $880 £550

RHYTHM HN1903
Designer: L. Harradine
Height: 6¾in., 17.2cm.
Issued: 1939-1949
Price: $2000 £1250

RHYTHM HN1904
Designer: L. Harradine
Height: 6¾in., 17.2cm.
Issued: 1939-1949
            Colour variation
Price: $2560 £1600

RICHARD THE LIONHEART HN3675
Designer: Pauline Parsons
Height: 10in., 25.5cm.
Issued: 1995
Price: $400 £250

RITA HN1448
Designer: L. Harradine
Height: 7in., 17.8cm.
Issued: 1931-1938
Price: $800 £500

RITA HN1450
Designer: L. Harradine
Height: 7in., 17.8cm.
Issued: 1931-1938
            Colour variation
Price: $920 £575

RITZ BELL BOY HN2772
Designer: W. Harper
Height: 8in., 20cm.
Issued: 1989-1993
Price: $232 £145

RIVER BOY HN2128
Designer: P. Davies
Height: 4in., 10.1cm.
Issued: 1962-1975
Price: $280 £175

ROBERT BURNS HN42
Designer: E. W. Light
Height: 18in., 45.7cm.
Issued: 1914-1938
Price: $2800 £1750

ROBERT BURNS HN3641
Designer: Robert Tabbenor
Height: 7½in., 19cm.
Issued: 1996-1997
Price: $232 £145

RHYTHM HN1903

RHODA HN1573

RHYTHM HN1904

RICHARD THE LIONHEART HN3675

ROBERT BURNS HN3641

RITZ BELL BOY HN2772

ROYAL DOULTON FIGURES

ROBERT E. LEE, GEN. HN3404
Designer: Robert Tabbenor
Height: 11½in., 29cm.
Issued: 1993 in a limited edition of 5000
Price: $792 £495

ROBIN M38
Designer: Unknown
Height: 2½in., 6.4cm.
Issued: 1933-1945
Price: $600 £375

ROBIN M39
Designer: L. Harradine
Height: 2½in., 6.4cm.
Issued: 1933-1945 Colour variation
Price: $680 £425

ROBIN HOOD HN2773
Designer: W. K. Harper
Height: 8in., 20cm.
Issued: 1985-1990
Price: $264 £165

ROBIN HOOD HN3720
Designer: Alan Maslankowski
Height: 10½in., 27cm.
Issued: 1993-1996
Price: $120 £75

ROBIN HOOD AND MAID MARIAN HN3111
Designer: Robert Jefferson
Height: 12in., 30.5cm.
Issued: 1994 in a limited edition of 150
Price: $3192 £1995 (R.R.P.)

ROCKING HORSE HN2072
Designer: L. Harradine
Height: 7in., 17.8cm.
Issued: 1951-1953
Price: $2240 £1400

ROMANCE HN2430
Designer: P. Davies
Height: 5¼in., 13.3cm.
Issued: 1972-1980
Price: $260 £175

ROMANY SUE HN1757
Designer: L. Harradine
Height: 9¼in., 23.5cm.
Issued: 1936-1949
Price: $1200 £750

ROMANY SUE HN1758
Designer: L. Harradine
Height: 9½in., 24.1cm.
Issued: 1936-1949 Colour variation
Price: $1200 £750

ROBIN HOOD HN2773

ROBERT E. LEE, GEN. HN3404

ROBIN HOOD HN3720

ROBIN HOOD AND MAID MARIAN HN3111

ROMEO AND JULIET HN3113
Designer: Robert Jefferson
Height: 12in., 30.5cm.
Issued: 1993 in a limited
                edition of 150
Price: $3192 £1995
                (R.R.P.)

ROSABELL HN1620
Designer: L. Harradine
Height: 6¾in., 17.1cm.
Issued: 1934-1938
Price: $1000 £625

ROSALIND HN2393
Designer: P. Davies
Height: 5½in., 14cm.
Issued: 1970-1975
Price: $280 £175

**ROSAMUND (Style one)
HN1320**
Designer: L. Harradine
Height: 7¼in., 18.4cm.
Issued: 1929-1938
Price: $1600 £1000

**ROSAMUND (Style two)
HN1497**
Designer: L. Harradine
Height: 8½in., 21.6cm.
Issued: 1932-1938
Price: $1440 £900

**ROSAMUND (Style two)
HN1551**
Designer: L. Harradine
Height: 8½in., 21.6cm.
Issued: 1933-1938
                Colour variation
Price: $2320 £1450

ROSAMUND M32
Designer: L. Harradine
Height: 4¼in., 10.8cm.
Issued: 1932-1945
Price: $640 £400

ROSAMUND M33
Designer: L. Harradine
Height: 4in., 10.1cm.
Issued: 1932-1945
                Colour variation
Price: $680 £425

ROSE HN1387
Designer: L. Harradine
Height: 4½in., 11.4cm.
Issued: 1930-1938
                Colour variation
Price: $360 £225

ROSE HN1368
Designer: L. Harradine
Height: 4½in., 11.4cm.
Issued: 1930-1995
Price: $96 £60

ROMANY SUE HN1757

ROSE HN1368

ROMANCE HN2430

ROSAMUND (Style one)
HN1320

ROMEO AND JULIET HN3113

ROYAL DOULTON FIGURES

ROSE HN1416
Designer: L. Harradine
Height: 4½in., 11.4cm.
Issued: 1930-1949
            Colour variation
Price: $280 £175

ROSE HN1506
Designer: L. Harradine
Height: 4½in., 11.4cm.
Issued: 1932-1938
            Colour variation
Price: $400 £250

ROSE HN1654
Designer: L. Harradine
Height: 4½in., 11.4cm.
Issued: 1934-1938
Price: $440 £275

ROSE HN2123
Designer: L. Harradine
Height: 4½in., 11.4cm.
Issued: 1983-1995
Price: $96 £60

ROSE HN3709
Designer: V. Annand
Height: 8½in., 21.5cm.
Issued: 1996
Price: $224 £140 (R.R.P.)

ROSE ARBOUR HN3145
Designer: D. Brindley
Height: 12in., 30.5cm.
Issued: 1987-1990
Price: $232 £145

ROSEANNA HN1921
Designer: L. Harradine
Height: 8in., 20.3cm.
Issued: 1940-1949
Price: $880 £550

ROSEANNA HN1926
Designer: L. Harradine
Height: 8in., 20.3cm.
Issued: 1940-1959
            Colour variation
Price: $472 £295

ROSEBUD (Style one) HN1580
Designer: L. Harradine
Height: 3in., 7.6cm.
Issued: 1933-1938
Price: $680 £425

ROSEBUD (Style one) HN1581
Designer: L. Harradine
Height: 3in., 7.6cm.
Issued: 1933-1938
            Colour variation
Price: $680 £425

ROSEBUD (Style two) HN1983
Designer: L. Harradine
Height: 7½in., 19.1cm.
Issued: 1945-1952
Price: $560 £350

ROSE HN3709

ROSEANNA HN1926

ROSE ARBOUR HN3145

ROSEMARY HN2091
Designer: L. Harradine
Height: 7in., 17.8cm.
Issued: 1952-1959
Price: $680 £425

ROSEMARY HN3143
Designer: P. Parsons
Height: 7½in., 19cm.
Issued: 1988-1991
Price: $232 £145

ROSEMARY HN3691
Designer: Nada Pedley
Height: 8in., 20.3cm.
Issued: 1995
Price: $240 £150

ROSIE HN4093
Designer: Nada Pedley
Height: 8in., 20.5cm.
Issued: 1998
Price: $160 £100 (R.R.P.)

ROSINA HN1358
Designer: L. Harradine
Height: 5¾in., 14.6cm.
Issued: 1929-1938
Price: $1040 £650

ROSINA HN1364
Designer: L. Harradine
Height: 5¼in., 13.3cm.
Issued: 1929-1938
            Colour variation
Price: $1040 £650

ROSINA HN1556
Designer: L. Harradine
Height: 5¾in., 14.6cm.
Issued: 1933-1938
            Colour variation
Price: $1040 £650

ROWENA HN2077
Designer: L. Harradine
Height: 7¼in., 18.4cm.
Issued: 1951-1955
Price: $720 £450

**ROYAL CANADIAN
MOUNTED POLICE 1873
(BUST.) HN2555**
Designer: D. Tootle
Height: 8¼in., 21cm.
Issued: 1973 in a limited
            edition of 1500
Price: $560 £350

**ROYAL CANADIAN
MOUNTED POLICE 1973
HN2547**
Designer: D. Tootle
Height: 8in., 20.3cm.
Issued: 1973 in a limited
            edition of 1500
Price: $720 £450

ROYAL GOVERNOR'S COOK
HN2233
Designer: P. Davies
Height: 6in., 15.2cm.
Issued: 1960-1984
Price: $440 £275

RUBY HN1724
Designer: L. Harradine
Height: 5¼in., 13.3cm.
Issued: 1935-1949
Price: $520 £325

RUBY HN1725
Designer: L. Harradine
Height: 5¼in., 13.3cm.
Issued: 1935-1949
Colour variation
Price: $520 £325

RUMPELSTILTSKIN HN3025
Designer: R. Jefferson
Height: 8in., 20cm.
Issued: 1983-1986
Price: $320 £200

RUSTIC SWAIN HN1745
Designer: L. Harradine
Height: 5¼in., 13.3cm.
Issued: 1935-1949
Price: $1920 £1200

RUSTIC SWAIN HN1746
Designer: L. Harradine
Height: 5¼in., 13.3cm.
Issued: 1935-1949
Colour variation
Price: $1920 £1200

RUTH HN2799
Designer: P. Davies
Height: 6in., 15.2cm.
Issued: 1976-1982
Price: $280 £175

RUTH THE PIRATE MAID
HN2900
Designer: W. K. Harper
Height: 11¾in., 29.8cm.
Issued: 1981-1986
Price: $680 £425

S

SABBATH MORN HN1982
Designer: L. Harradine
Height: 7¼in., 18.4cm.
Issued: 1945-1959
Price: $360 £225

SAILOR'S HOLIDAY HN2442
Designer: M. Nicoll
Height: 6¼in., 15.9cm.
Issued: 1972-1978
Price: $360 £225

SAIREY GAMP M46
Designer: L. Harradine
Height: 4in., 10.1cm.
Issued: 1932-1982
Price: $80 £50

ROSEBUD (Style one) HN1580

ROYAL GOVERNOR'S COOK HN2233

ROSEMARY HN3143

SAIREY GAMP HN558

RUMPELSTILTSKIN HN3025

RUTH THE PIRATE MAID HN2900

RUSTIC SWAIN HN1746

RUSTIC SWAIN
HN1745

SABBATH MORN HN1982

SAILOR'S HOLIDAY HN2442

SAIREY GAMP (Style one)
HN533
Designer: L. Harradine
Height: 4in., 10.1cm.
Issued: 1922-1932
Price: $88 £55

SAIREY GAMP (Style two)
HN558
Designer: L. Harradine
Height: 7in., 17.8cm.
Issued: 1923-1939
Price: $632 £395

SAIREY GAMP (Style two)
HN1896
Designer: L. Harradine
Height: 7in., 17.8cm.
Issued: 1938-1952
             Colour variation
Price: $520 £325

SAIREY GAMP (Style three)
HN2100
Designer: L. Harradine
Height: 7¼in., 18.4cm.
Issued: 1952-1967
Price: $472 £295

SALLY HN2741
Designer: D. Tootle
Height: 5½in., 13.5cm.
Issued: 1988-1991
Price: $200 £125

SALLY HN3851
Designer: Tim Potts
Height: 8¼in., 21cm.
Issued: 1996
Price: $168 £105 (R.R.P.)

SALOME HN1775
Designer: R. Garbe
Height: 8in., 24.4cm.
Issued: 1933 in a limited
             edition of 100
Price: $4000 £2500

SALOME HN1828
Designer: R. Garbe
Height: 8in., 24.4cm.
Issued: 1937-1949
             Colour variation
Price: $3200 £2000

SALOME HN3267
Designer: P. Davies
Height: 9½in., 24.1cm.
Issued: 1990 in a limited
             edition of 1000
Price: $880 £550

SAM WELLER HN531
Designer: L. Harradine
Height: 4in., 10.1cm.
Issued: 1922-1932
Price: $80 £50

SAM WELLER M48
Designer: L. Harradine
Height: 4in., 10.1cm.
Issued: 1932-1982
Price: $72 £45

SAMANTHA HN2954
Designer: P. Parsons
Height: 7in., 17.5cm.
Issued: 1982-1984
Price: $264 £165

SAMANTHA HN3304
Designer: Peggy Davies
Height: 7½in., 18.5cm.
Issued: 1990-1995
Price: $192 £120

SAMANTHA HN4043
Designer: Valerie Annand
Height: 8¼in., 20.9cm.
Issued: 1998
Price: $160 £100

SAMURAI WARRIOR HN3402
(Flambé)
Designer: R. Tabbenor
Height: 9in., 22.7cm.
Issued: 1992 in a limited
             edition of 950
Price: $480 £300

SAMWISE HN2925
Designer: D. Lyttleton
Height: 4½in., 11.5cm.
Issued: 1982-1984
Price: $440 £275

SANDRA HN2275
Designer: P. Davies
Height: 7¾in., 19.7cm.
Issued: 1969-1997
Price: $200 £125

SANDRA HN2401
Designer: P. Davies
Height: 8in., 20cm.
Issued: 1983
Price: $232 £145

SANTA CLAUS HN2725
Designer: W. K. Harper
Height: 9½in., 24cm.
Issued: 1982-1992
Price: $312 £195

SANTA'S HELPER HN3301
Designer: A. Hughes
Height: 6½in., 16.5cm.
Issued: 1991-1994
Price: $280 £175

SARA HN2265
Designer: P. Davies
Height: 7½in., 19.1cm.
Issued: 1981-
Price: $280 £175 (R.R.P.)

SARA HN3219
Designer: P. Davies
Height: 3¾in., 9.5cm.
Issued: 1988
Price: $104 £65 (R.R.P.)

SALLY HN3851

SALOME HN3267

SAMANTHA
HN3304

SAMANTHA HN2954

SANTA'S HELPER HN3301

SAMWISE HN2925

SAMURAI WARRIOR
HN3402

SANDRA HN2275

SANTA CLAUS HN2725

SARA HN3219

SARA HN2265

SARA (Blue/crimson) HN3308

SARA (Blue/crimson) HN3308
Designer: Peggy Davies
Height: 7¾in., 19.5cm.
Issued: 1981-1996
Price: $280 £175

SARAH HN3384
Designer: Tim Potts
Height: 8in., 20cm.
Issued: 1995
Price: $160 £100 (R.R.P.)

SARAH HN3852 (Green)
Designer: Tim Potts
Height: 8in., 20cm.
Issued: 1997
Price: $216 £135 (R.R.P.)

SARAH IN WINTER IIN3005
Designer: Peter Gee
Height: 8in., 20.5cm.
Issued: 1986 Danbury Mint
             commission
Price: $360 £225

SAUCY NYMPH HN1539
Designer: Unknown
Height: 4½in., 11.4cm.
Issued: 1933-1949
Price: $320 £200

SAVE SOME FOR ME HN2959
Designer: P. Parsons
Height: 7¼in., 18cm.
Issued: 1982-1985
Price: $264 £165

SCHEHERAZADE HN3835
Designer: Pauline Parsons
Height: 10½in., 26.7cm.
Issued: 1996 in a limited
             edition of 1500
Price: $632 £395

SCHOOLMARM HN2223
Designer: P. Davies
Height: 6¾in., 17.2cm.
Issued: 1958-1980
Price: $360 £225

SCOTCH GIRL HN1269
Designer: L. Harradine
Height: 7½in., 19.1cm.
Issued: 1928-1938
Price: $1520 £950

SCOTLAND HN3629
Designer: Valerie Annand
Height: 7¾in., 19.5cm.
Issued: 1995
Price: $288 £180 (R.R.P.)

SCOTTIES HN1281
Designer: L. Harradine
Height: 5½in., 14cm.
Issued: 1928-1938
Price: $2160 £1350

SCOTTIES HN1349
Designer: L. Harradine
Height: 5¼in., 13.3cm.
Issued: 1929-1949
             Colour variation
Price: $2000 £1250

SARAH HN3852 (Green)

SAUCY NYMPH HN1539

SAVE SOME FOR ME HN2959

SARAH HN3384

SCHOOLMARM HN2223

SCOTTIES HN1349

SCOTLAND HN3629

SCOTTIES HN1281

**SCOTTISH HIGHLAND
DANCER HN2436**
Designer: P. Davies
Height: 9½in., 24.1cm.
Issued: 1978 in a limited
            edition of 750
Price: $880 £550

SCRIBE HN305
Designer: C. J. Noke
Height: 6in., 15.2cm.
Issued: 1918-1936
Price: $1200 £750

SCRIBE HN324
Designer: C. J. Noke
Height: 6in., 15.2cm.
Issued: 1918-1938
            Colour variation
Price: $1200 £750

SCRIBE HN1235
Designer: C. J. Noke
Height: 6in., 15.2cm.
Issued: 1927-1938
            Colour variation
Price: $1360 £850

SCROOGE M87
Designer: L. Harradine
Height: 4in., 10.1cm.
Issued: 1949-1982
Price: $80 £50

SEA HARVEST HN2257
Designer: M. Nicoll
Height: 7½in., 19.1cm.
Issued: 1969-1976
Price: $360 £225

SEA SHORE HN2263
Designer: P. Davies
Height: 3½in., 8.9cm.
Issued: 1961-1965
Price: $360 £225

**SEA SPRITE (Style one)
HN1261**
Designer: L. Harradine
Height: 5in., 12.7cm.
Issued: 1927-1938
Price: $800 £500

**SEA SPRITE (Style two)
HN2191**
Designer: P. Davies
Height: 7in., 17.8cm.
Issued: 1958-1962
Price: $440 £275

SEAFARER HN2455
Designer: M. Nicoll
Height: 8½in., 21.6cm.
Issued: 1972-1976
Price: $312 £195

SECOND VIOLIN HN3705
In a limited edition of 1500
Designer: Valerie Annand
Height: 9in., 23cm.
Issued: 1996
Price: $472 £295

SCRIBE HN305

SCOTTISH HIGHLAND
DANCER HN2436

SEA HARVEST HN2257

SEAFARER HN2455

ROYAL DOULTON FIGURES

SECRET MOMENT HN3106
Designer: R. Jefferson
Height: 12¼in., 31cm.
Issued: 1987-1989
Price: $264 £165

SECRET THOUGHTS HN2382
Designer: P. Davies
Height: 6¼in., 15.9cm.
Issued: 1971-1988
Price: $312 £195

SENTIMENTAL PIERROT HN36
Designer: C. J. Noke
Height: 5½in., 14cm.
Issued: 1914-1938
Price: $3200 £2000

SENTIMENTAL PIERROT HN307
Designer: C. J. Noke
Height: 5½in., 14cm.
Issued: 1918-1938
Price: $3200 £2000

SENTINEL HN523
Designer: Unknown
Height: 17½in., 44.4cm.
Issued: 1921-1938
Price: $3200 £2000

SEPTEMBER HN3166
Designer: P. Davies
Height: 7¾in., 19.7cm.
Issued: 1987
Price: $200 £125

SEPTEMBER HN3326
Designer: P. Davies
Height: 7½in., 19.1cm.
Issued: 1991 only
U.S.A. only
Price: $165 £110

SEPTEMBER HN3409
Designer: P. Davies
Height: 7½in., 19.1cm.
Issued: 1991 only
Canada only
Price: $200 £125

SERENA HN1868
Designer: L. Harradine
Height: 11in., 27.9cm.
Issued: 1938-1949
Price: $1040 £650

SERENADE HN2753
Designer: E. Griffiths
Height: 9in., 23cm.
Issued: 1983-1986
Price: $232 £145

SERENITY HN3542
Designer: John Ablitt
Height: 11in., 28cm.
Issued: 1990-1995
Price: $65 £39

SEPTEMBER HN3326

SECRET MOMENT HN3106

SEPTEMBER HN3166

SEPTEMBER HN3409

SERENADE HN2753

SECRET THOUGHTS HN2382

299

SERGEANT, 6th MARYLAND REGIMENT 1777 HN2815
Designer: E. J. Griffiths
Height: 13¾in., 34.9cm.
Issued: 1976 in a limited edition of 350
Price: $880 £550

SERGEANT, VIRGINIA 1st REGIMENT CONTINENTAL LIGHT DRAGOONS, 1777 HN2844
Designer: E. J. Griffiths
Height: 14¼in., 36.1cm.
Issued: 1978 in a limited edition of 350
Price: $2000 £1250

SHADOW PLAY HN3526
Designer: Russell Willis
Height: 10in., 25.5cm.
Issued: 1982
Price: $136 £80 (R.R.P.)

SHARON HN3047
Designer: P. Parsons
Height: 5½in., 14cm.
Issued: 1984-1993
Price: $176 £110

SHARON HN3455
Designer: P. Parsons
Height: 5½in., 14cm.
Issued: 1994 Colour variation
Price: $104 £65 (R.R.P.)

SHARON HN3603
Designer: Nada Pedley
Height: 8in., 20.5cm.
Issued: 1994 only. (Michael Doulton events)
Price: $232 £145

SHE LOVES ME NOT HN2045
Designer: L. Harradine
Height: 5½in., 14cm.
Issued: 1949-1962
Price: $264 £165

SHEIKH HN3083
Designer: E. J. Griffiths
Height: 9¾in., 25cm.
Issued: 1988-1989
Price: $264 £165

SHEILA HN2742
Designer: D. Tootle
Height: 8¼in., 21cm.
Issued: 1984-1991
Price: $232 £145

SHEPHERD (Style one) HN81
Designer: C. J. Noke
Height: 13¼in., 33.6cm.
Issued: 1918-1938
Price: $3200 £2000

SHARON HN3047

SHEPHERD HN751

SHEPHERD (Style four) HN1975

SHEPHERD (Style one) HN617
Designer: C. J. Noke
Height: 13¼in., 33.6cm.
Issued: 1924-1938 Colour variation
Price: $3680 £2300

SHEPHERD (Style one) HN632
Designer: C. J. Noke
Height: 13¼in., 33.6cm.
Issued: 1924-1938 Colour variation
Price: $3680 £2300

SHEPHERD (Style two) HN709
Designer: Unknown
Height: 3½in., 8.8cm.
Issued: 1925-1938
Price: $1600 £1000

SHEPHERD (Style three) HN751
Designer: Unknown
Height: 7½in., 19.1cm.
Issued: 1925-1938
Price: $1600 £1000

SHEPHERD (Style four) HN1975
Designer: H. Fenton
Height: 8½in., 21.6cm.
Issued: 1945-1975
Price: $280 £175

SHEPHERD HN3160
Designer: A. Hughes
Height: 8½in., 22cm.
Issued: 1988-1989
Price: $296 £185

SHEPHERD M17
Designer: Unknown
Height: 3¾in., 9.5cm.
Issued: 1932-1938
Price: $2000 £1250

SHEPHERD M19
Designer: Unknown
Height: 3¾in., 9.5cm.
Issued: 1932-1938 Colour variation
Price: $2000 £1250

SHEPHERDESS (Style one) HN708
Designer: Unknown
Height: 3½in., 8.8cm.
Issued: 1925-1948
Price: $1200 £750

SHEPHERDESS (Style two) HN735
Designer: Unknown
Height: 7in., 17.8cm.
Issued: 1925-1938
Price: $1520 £950

SHEPHERDESS (Style two) HN750
Designer: Unknown
Height: 7in., 17.8cm.
Issued: 1925-1938 Colour variation
Price: $1520 £950

ROYAL DOULTON FIGURES

SHEPHERDESS HN2990
Designer: R. Tabbenor
Height: 8in., 20.3cm.
Issued: 1988-1989
Price: $256 £160

SHEPHERDESS M18
Designer: Unknown
Height: 3½in., 8.9cm.
Issued: 1932-1938
Price: $2000 £1250

SHEPHERDESS M20
Designer: Unknown
Height: 3¾in., 9.5cm.
Issued: 1932-1938
Colour variation
Price: $1920 £1200

SHEPHERDESS HN2420
Designer: J. Bromley
Height: 9in., 22.9cm.
Issued: 1991 in a limited
edition of 12500
Price: $312 £195

SHERLOCK HOLMES HN3639
Designer: Robert Tabbenor
Height: 8½in., 21.5cm.
Issued: 1995-1996
Price: $160 £100

SHIRLEY HN2702
Designer: P. Davies
Height: 7¼in., 18cm.
Issued: 1985-1997
Price: $192 £120

SHORE LEAVE HN2254
Designer: M. Nicoll
Height: 7½in., 19.1cm.
Issued: 1965-1978
Price: $312 £195

SHY ANNE HN60
Designer: L. Perugini
Height: 7¾in., 19.7cm.
Issued: 1916-1938
Price: $4000 £2500

SHY ANNE HN64
Designer: L. Perugini
Height: 7¾in., 19.7cm.
Issued: 1916-1936
Colour variation
Price: $3200 £2000

SHY ANNE HN65
Designer: L. Perugini
Height: 7¾in., 19.7cm.
Issued: 1916-1936
Colour variation
Price: $3200 £2000

SHY ANNE HN568
Designer: L. Perugini
Height: 7½in., 19.1cm.
Issued: 1923-1936
Colour variation
Price: $2800 £1750

SHEPHERDESS (Style two) HN735

SHEPHERDESS HN2420

SHIRLEY HN2702

SHY ANNE HN64

SHORE LEAVE HN2254

SHERLOCK HOLMES HN3639

SHYLOCK HN79
Designer: C. J. Noke
Height: Unknown
Issued: 1917-1938
Price: $2880 £1800

SHYLOCK HN317
Designer: C. J. Noke
Height: Unknown
Issued: 1918-1938
Colour variation
Price: $2400 £1500

SIBELL HN1668
Designer: L. Harradine
Height: 6½in., 16.5cm.
Issued: 1934-1949
Price: $760 £475

SIBELL HN1695
Designer: L. Harradine
Height: 6½in., 16.5cm.
Issued: 1935-1949
Colour variation
Price: $760 £475

SIBELL HN1735
Designer: L. Harradine
Height: 6½in., 16.5cm.
Issued: 1935-1949
Colour variation
Price: $880 £550

SIESTA HN1305
Designer: L. Harradine
Height: 4¾in., 12cm.
Issued: 1928-1938
Price: $2800 £1750

SILKS AND RIBBONS HN2017
Designer: L. Harradine
Height: 6in., 15.2cm.
Issue: 1949-
Price: $192 £120 (R.R.P.)

SILVERSMITH OF WILLIAMSBURG HN2208
Designer: P. Davies
Height: 6¼in., 15.9cm.
Issued: 1960-1983
Price: $264 £165

SIMONE HN2378
Designer: P. Davies
Height: 7¼in., 18.4cm.
Issued: 1971-1982
Price: $264 £165

SINGLE RED ROSE HN3376
Designer: Nada Pedley
Height: 8in., 20cm.
Issued: 1992-1995
Price: $240 £150

SIR EDWARD HN2370
Designer: J. Bromley
Height: 11in., 27.9cm.
Issued: 1979 in a limited edition of 500
Price: $440 £275

SIBELL HN1668

SHYLOCK HN317

SIBELL HN1695

SILKS AND RIBBONS HN2017

SIR EDWARD HN2370

SIESTA HN1305

SIR FRANCIS DRAKE HN3770
Designer: David Biggs
Height: 8½in., 21.5cm.
Issued: 1996 only.
Price: $120 £75

**SIR HENRY DOULTON
HN3891**
In a limited edition of 1997
Designer: R. Tabbenor
Height: 8¾in., 27cm.
Issued: 1997 only
Price: $360 £225

**SIR JOHN A. McDONALD
HN2860**
Designer: William K. Harper
Height: 9¼in., 23.5cm.
Issued: 1987 to
commemorate the
centenary of the
Dominion of
Canada General
Insurance Co.
Price: $265 £165

SIR RALPH HN2371
Designer: J. Bromley
Height: 7½in., 19.1cm.
Issued: 1979 in a limited
edition of 500
Price: $440 £275

SIR THOMAS HN2372
Designer: J. Bromley
Height: 11in., 27.9cm.
Issued: 1979 in a limited
edition of 500
Price: $440 £275

SIR THOMAS LOVELL HN356
Designer: C. J. Noke
Height: 7¾in., 19.7cm.
Issued: 1919-1938
Price: $3200 £2000

**SIR WALTER RALEIGH
HN1742**
Designer: L. Harradine
Height: 10½in., 26.7cm.
Issued: 1935-1949
Price: $2000 £1250

**SIR WALTER RALEIGH
HN1751**
Designer: L. Harradine
Height: 11½in.,, 29.2cm.
Issued: 1936-1949
Colour variation
Price: $1200 £750

**SIR WALTER RALEIGH
HN2015**
Designer: L. Harradine
Height: 11½in., 29.2cm.
Issued: 1948-1955
Colour variation
Price: $720 £450

SILVERSMITH OF
WILLIAMSBURG HN2208

SIMONE HN2378

SIR FRANCIS DRAKE HN3770

SIR HENRY DOULTON
HN3891

SINGLE RED ROSE HN3376

SIR WINSTON CHURCHILL
HN3057

SIR RALPH HN2371

SIR THOMAS HN2372

SIR WALTER RALEIGH
HN2015

SIR WINSTON CHURCHILL
HN3057
Designer: A. Hughes
Height: 10½in., 26.5cm.
Issued: 1985-
Price: $160 £100 (R.R.P.)

SISTERLY LOVE HN3130
Designer: P. Parsons
Height: 8½in., 21.5cm.
Issued: 1987-1995
Price: $200 £125

SISTERS HN3018
Designer: P. Parsons
Height: 8½in., 21.5cm.
Issued: 1983-
Price: $80 £50 (R.R.P.)

SISTERS HN3019
Designer: P. Parsons
Height: 8½in., 21.5cm.
Issued: 1983-1997
              Colour variation
Price: $96 £60

SIT HN3123
Designer: Alan Maslankowski
Height: 4½in., 11.5cm.
Issued: 1991
Price: $80 £50 (R.R.P.)

SKATER HN2117
Designer: P. Davies
Height: 7¼in., 18.4cm.
Issued: 1953-1971
Price: $440 £275

SKATER, THE HN3439
Designer: Peter Gee
Height: 8in., 20cm.
Issued: 1992-1997
Price: $256 £160 (R.R.P.)

SKETCH GIRL Model 444
Designer: L. Harradine
Height: 7in., 17.7cm.
Issued: 1924-1938
Price: $2000 £1250

SLAPDASH HN2277
Designer: Mary Nicoll
Height: 10in., 25.5cm.
Issued: 1990-1994
Price: $264 £165

SLEEP HN24
Designer: P. Stabler
Height: 8¼in., 21cm.
Issued: 1913-1936
Price: $1360 £850

SLEEP HN24A
Designer: P. Stabler
Height: 8¼in., 21cm.
Issued: 1913-1936
              Colour variation
Price: $1360 £850

ROYAL DOULTON FIGURES

SISTERS HN3018

SISTERS HN3019

SKATER HN2117

SISTERLY LOVE HN3130

SIT HN3123

SLAPDASH HN2277

SKATER, THE HN3439

SLEEP HN25
Designer: P. Stabler
Height: 8¼in., 21cm.
Issued: 1913-1936
Colour variation
Price: $1360 £850

SLEEP HN25A
Designer: P. Stabler
Height: 8¼in., 21cm.
Issued: 1913-1936
Colour variation
Price: $1360 £850

SLEEP HN424
Designer: P. Stabler
Height: 6in., 15.2cm.
Issued: 1921-1936
Colour variation
Price: $1360 £850

SLEEP HN692
Designer: P. Stabler
Height: 8¼in., 21cm.
Issued: 1925-1936
Colour variation
Price: $1520 £950

SLEEP HN710
Designer: P. Stabler
Height: 8¼in., 21cm.
Issued: 1925-1936
Colour variation
Price: $1360 £850

SLEEPING BEAUTY HN3079
Designer: A. Hughes
Height: 4½in., x 8in.,
11cm. x 22cm.
Issued: 1987-1989
Price: $312 £195

SLEEPY DARLING HN2953
(R.D.I.C.C.)
Designer: P. Parsons
Height: 7¼in., 18.4cm.
Issued: Only available in
1981
Price: $312 £195
(Collectors Club Issue)

SLEEPY HEADS (Cats) HN3761
Designer: Robert Tabbenor
Height: 3¼in., 8.5cm.
Issued: 1998
Price: $65 £40 (R.R.P.)

SLEEPY SCHOLAR HN15
Designer: W. White
Height: 6¾in., 17.2cm.
Issued: 1913-1938
Price: $3200 £2000

SLEEPY SCHOLAR HN16
Designer: W. White
Height: 6¾in., 17.2cm.
Issued: 1913-1938
Colour variation
Price: $3200 £2000

SLEEPY DARLING HN2953

SLEEPY SCHOLAR HN16

SLEEPYHEAD HN3761

SONG OF THE SEA HN2729

SLEEPY SCHOLAR HN29
Designer: W. White
Height: 6¾in., 17.2cm.
Issued: 1913-1938
Colour variation
Price: $3200 £2000

SLEEPYHEAD HN2114
Designer: P. Davies
Height: 5in., 12.7cm.
Issued: 1953-1955
Price: $2000 £1250

SLEEPYHEAD HN3761
Designer: Nada Pedley
Height: 4in., 10cm.
Issued: 1996
Price: $64 £40 (R.R.P.)

SMILING BUDDHA HN454
Designer: C. J. Noke
Height: 6¼in., 15.9cm.
Issued: 1921-1936
Price: $2720 £1700

SNAKE CHARMER HN1317
Designer: Unknown
Height: 4in., 10.1cm.
Issued: 1929-1938
Price: $1600 £1000

SNOW WHITE HN3678
In a limited edition of 2500
Designer: Pauline Parsons
Height: 8in., 20.3cm.
Issued: 1995
Price: $360 £225

SOIRÉE HN2312
Designer: P. Davies
Height: 7½in., 19.1cm.
Issued: 1967-1984
Price $232 £145

SOLITUDE HN2810
Designer: P. Davies
Height: 5½in., 14cm.
Issued: 1977-1983
Price: $360 £225

SONATA HN2438
Designer: P. Davies
Height: 6½in., 16.5cm.
Issued: 1983-1986
Price: $264 £165

SONG OF THE SEA HN2729
Designer: W. K. Harper
Height: 7¼in., 18cm.
Issued: 1983-1991
Price: $295 £185

SONIA HN1692
Designer: L. Harradine
Height: 6¼in., 15.9cm.
Issued: 1935-1949
Price: $1120 £700

ROYAL DOULTON FIGURES

SONIA HN1738
Designer: L. Harradine
Height: 6½in., 16.5cm.
            Colour variation
Issued: 1935-1949
Price: $1120 £700

SONNY HN1313
Designer: L. Harradine
Height: 3½in., 8.9cm.
Issued: 1929-1938
Price: $1040 £650

SONNY HN1314
Designer: L. Harradine
Height: 3½in., 8.9cm.
Issued: 1929-1938
            Colour variation
Price: $1040 £650

SOPHIA CHARLOTTE, LADY SHEFFIELD HN3008
Designer: Peter Gee
Height: 10in., 24.5cm.
Issued: 1991 in a limited
            edition of 5000-1994
Price: $472 £295

SOPHIE HN2833
Designer: P. Davies
Height: 6in., 15.2cm.
Issued: 1977-1987
Price: $232 £145

SOPHIE HN3257
Designer: Douglas Tootle
Height: 8in., 20cm.
Issued: 1990-1992
Price: $280 £175

SOPHIE HN3715
Designer: Valerie Annand
Height: 8¾in., 22cm.
Issued: 1997
Price: $160 £100 (R.R.P.)

SOPHIE (Ivory/Gold) HN3791
Designer: Alan Maslankowski
Height: 9in., 23cm.
Issued: 1996-1997
Price: $160 £100

SOPHIE (Blue) HN3793
Designer: Alan Maslankowski
Height: 9in., 23cm.
Issued: 1996-1997
Price: $160 £100

SOPHIE HN3994
(Compton & Woodhouse)
Designer: John Bromley
Height: 8½in., 21.5cm
Issued: 1998
Price: $224 £140 (R.R.P.)

SOPHISTICATION HN3059
Designer: A. Hughes
Height: 11½in., 29cm.
Issued: 1988-1990
Price: $264 £165

SOUTHERN BELLE HN2229
Designer: P. Davies
Height: 7½in., 19.1cm.
Issued: 1958-1997
Price: $240 £150

SONIA HN1692

SOPHIA CHARLOTTE, LADY SHEFFIELD HN3008

SONNY HN1314

SOLITUDE HN2810

SONATA HN2438

SOPHIE HN3793   SOPHIE HN3791

ROYAL DOULTON FIGURES

SOUTHERN BELLE HN2425
Designer: P. Davies
Height: 7½in., 19.1cm.
Issued: 1983-1994
Colour variation
Price: $264 £165

SOUTHERN BELLE HN3174
Designer: P. Davies
Height: 4in., 10cm.
Issued: 1988-1997
Price: $104 £65

SPANISH FLAMENCO DANCER HN2831
Designer: P. Davies
Height: 7¼in., 18.4cm.
Issued: 1977 in a limited edition of 750
Price: $790 £495

SPANISH LADY HN1262
Designer: L. Harradine
Height: 8½in., 21.6cm.
Issued: 1927-1938
Price: $1200 £750

SPANISH LADY HN1290
Designer: L. Harradine
Height: 8¼in., 21cm.
Issued: 1928-1938
Colour variation
Price: $1360 £850

SPANISH LADY HN1293
Designer: L. Harradine
Height: 8¼in., 21cm.
Issued: 1928-1938
Colour variation
Price: $1160 £725

SPANISH LADY HN1294
Designer: L. Harradine
Height: 8¼in., 21cm.
Issued: 1928-1938
Colour variation
Price: $1280 £800

SPANISH LADY HN1309
Designer: L. Harradine
Height: 8¼in., 21cm.
Issued: 1929-1938
Colour variation
Price: $1200 £750

SPECIAL FRIEND HN3607
Designer: Nada Pedley
Height: 4¼in., 11cm.
Issued: 1994
Price: $80 £50 (R.R.P.)

SPECIAL TREAT HN3663
Designer: Nada Pedley
Height: 6in., 15cm.
Issued: 1995-1997
Price: $120 £75

SOUTHERN BELLE
HN3174

SOUTHERN BELLE
HN2229

SPANISH FLAMENCO
DANCER HN2831

SPINNING HN2390
Designer: P. Davies
Height: 7½in., 19cm.
Issued: 1984 in a limited edition of 750
Price: £1360 £850

SPIRIT OF THE WIND HN1777
Designer: R. Garbe
Height: Unknown
Issued: 1933 in a limited edition of 50
Price: $4400 £2750

SPIRIT OF THE WIND HN1825
Designer: R. Garbe
Height: Unknown
Issued: 1937-1949
Colour variation
Price: $3200 £2000

SPOOK HN50
Designer: H. Tittensor
Height: 7in., 17.8cm.
Issued: 1916-1936
Price: $2000 £1250

SPOOK HN51
Designer: H. Tittensor
Height: 7in., 17.8cm.
Issued: 1916-1936
Colour variation
Price: $2000 £1250

SPOOK HN51A
Designer: H. Tittensor
Height: 7in., 17.8cm.
Issued: 1916-1936
Colour variation
Price: $2000 £1250

SPOOK HN51B
Designer: H. Tittensor
Height: 7in., 17.8cm.
Issued: 1916-1936
Colour variation
Price: $2000 £1250

SPOOK HN58
Designer: H. Tittensor
Height: 7in., 17.8cm.
Issued: 1916-1936
Colour variation
Price: $2000 £1250

SPOOK HN512
Designer: H. Tittensor
Height: 7in., 17.8cm.
Issued: 1921-1936
Colour variation
Price: $3200 £2000

SPOOK HN625
Designer: H. Tittensor
Height: 7in., 17.8cm.
Issued: 1924-1936
Colour variation
Price: $2000 £1250

ROYAL DOULTON FIGURES

SPOOK HN1218
Designer: H. Tittensor
Height: 7in., 17.8cm.
Issued: 1926-1936
             Colour variation
Price: $1760 £1100

SPOOKS HN88
Designer: C. J. Noke
Height: 7¼in., 18.4cm.
Issued: 1918-1936
Price: $3200 £2000

SPOOK HN89
Designer: C. J. Noke
Height: 7¼in., 18.4cm.
Issued: 1918-1936
             Colour variation
Price: $3200 £2000

SPOOKS HN372
Designer: C. J. Noke
Height: 7¼in., 18.4cm.
Issued: 1920-1936
             Colour variation
Price: $3200 £2000

SPRING (Style one) HN312
Designer: Unknown
Height: 7½in., 19.1cm.
Issued: 1918-1938
Price: $1360 £850

SPRING (Style one) HN472
Designer: Unknown
Height: 7½in., 19.1cm.
Issued: 1921-1938
             Colour variation
Price: $1440 £900

SPRING (Style two) HN1774
Designer: R. Garbe
Height: 21in., 53.3cm.
Issued: 1933 in a limited
             edition of 100
Price: $1600 £1000

SPRING (Style two) HN1827
Designer: R. Garbe
Height: 21in., 53.3cm.
Issued: 1937-1949
             Colour variation
Price: $2000 £1250

SPRING(Style three) HN2085
Designer: P. Davies
Height: 7¾in., 19.6cm.
Issued: 1952-1959
Price: $560 £350

SPRING FLOWERS HN1807
Designer: L. Harradine
Height: 7¼in., 18.4cm.
Issued: 1937-1959
Price: $632 £395

SPRING FLOWERS HN1945
Designer: L. Harradine
Height: 7¼in., 18.4cm.
Issued: 1940-1949
Price: $960 £600

SPECIAL FRIEND
HN3607

SPECIAL TREAT
HN3663

SPOOK HN50

SPINNING
HN2390

SPRING(Style three) HN2085

SPRING FLOWERS
HN1945

SPRING FLOWERS HN1807

SPRING MORNING HN1922
Designer: L. Harradine
Height: 7½in., 19.1cm.
Issued: 1940-1973
Price: $360 £225

SPRING MORNING HN1923
Designer: L. Harradine
Height: 7½in., 19.1cm.
Issued: 1940-1949
Colour variation
Price: $560 £350

SPRING MORNING HN3725
Designer: A. Maslankowski
Height: 7¾in., 19.5cm.
Issued: 1995
Price: $128 £80 (R.R.P.)

SPRING SERENADE HN3956
Designer: Alan Maslankowski
Height: 7¾in., 19.5cm.
Issued: 1997
Price: $216 £135 (R.R.P.)

SPRING SONG HN3446
Designer: P. Gee
Height: 7in., 17.8cm.
Issued: 1993 Special
colourway yellow
Price: $170 £110

SPRING WALK HN3120
Designer: A. Maslankowski
Height: 13in., 32.9cm.
Issued: 1990-1992
Price: $312 £195

SPRINGTIME HN1971
Designer: L. Harradine
Height: 6in., 15.2cm.
Issued: 1941-1949
Price: $1040 £650

SPRINGTIME HN3033
Designer: A. Hughes
Height: 8in., 20cm.
Issued: 1983
Price: $440 £275

SPRINGTIME HN3477
Designer: V. Annand
Height: Unknown
Issued: 1993-1996
Price: $312 £195

SQUIRE HN1814
Designer: Unknown
Height: 9¾in., 24.7cm.
Issued: 1937-1949
Price: $3200 £2000
Also called "Hunting Squire"

ST.GEORGE (Style one) HN385
Designer: S. Thorogood
Height: 16in., 40.6cm.
Issued: 1920-1938
Price: $3200 £2000

SPRING SONG HN3446

SPRINGTIME HN1971

SPRING MORNING HN3725

SPRING WALK HN3120

SPRINGTIME HN3477

SPRINGTIME HN3033

ST. GEORGE (Style one) HN386
Designer: S. Thorogood
Height: 16in., 40.6cm.
Issued: 1920-1938
Colour variation
Price: $3200 £2000

ST. GEORGE (Style one) HN1800
Designer: S. Thorogood
Height: 16in., 40.6cm.
Issued: 1934-1950
Colour variation
Price: $3200 £2000

ST. GEORGE (Style one) HN2067
Designer: S. Thorogood
Height: 15¾in., 40cm.
Issued: 1950-1976
Colour variation-
Price: $2400 £1500

ST. GEORGE (Style two) HN2051
Designer: P. Davies
Height: 7½in., 19.1cm.
Issued: 1950-1986
Price: $600 £375

ST. GEORGE AND THE DRAGON (Style three) HN2856
Designer: W. K. Harper
Height: 16in., 40.6cm
Issued: 1978-1994
Price: $8000 £5000

STAGE STRUCK HN3951
Designer: Alan Maslankowski
Height: 3¾in., 9.5cm.
Issued: 1997
Price: $64 £40 (R.R.P.)

STAN LAUREL HN2774
Designer: W. K. Harper
Height: 10in., 25.5cm.
Issued: 1992-1994
Price: $360 £225

STAR GAZER HN3182
Designer: D. V. Tootle
Height: 10½in., 26.5cm.
Issued: 1988-1990
Price: $280 £175

STAR PERFORMER HN3950
Designer: Alan Maslankowski
Height: 4in., 10cm.
Issued: 1997
Price: $64 £40 (R.R.P.)

STATESMAN HN2859
Designer: W. Harper
Height: 9¼in., 23.5cm.
Issued: 1988-1990
Price: $264 £165

STAN LAUREL HN2774

ST. GEORGE (Style one) HN2067

ST. GEORGE AND THE DRAGON (Style three) HN2856

STEPHANIE HN2807

ST. GEORGE (Style two) HN2051

STAYED AT HOME HN2207
Designer: P. Davies
Height: 5in., 12.7cm.
Issued: 1958-1969
Price: $264 £165

STEPHANIE HN2807
Designer: P. Davies
Height: 7¼in., 18.4cm.
Issued: 1977-1982
Price: $264 £165

STEPHANIE HN2811
Designer: P. Davies
Height: 7½in., 19cm.
Issued: 1983-1994
Price: $216 £135

STICK 'EM UP HN2981
Designer: A. Hughes
Height: 7in., 17.5cm.
Issued: 1984-1985
Price: $264 £165

STIGGINS HN536
Designer: L. Harradine
Height: 3¾in., 9.5cm.
Issued: 1922-1932
Price: $80 £50

STIGGINS M50
Designer: L. Harradine
Height: 4in., 10.1cm.
Issued: 1932-1982
Price: $72 £45

STITCH IN TIME HN2352
Designer: M. Nicoll
Height: 6¼in., 15.9cm.
Issued: 1966-1980
Price: $312 £195

STOP PRESS HN2683
Designer: M. Nicoll
Height: 7½in., 19.1cm.
Issued: 1977-1980
Price: $312 £195

STORYTIME HN3126
Designer: P. Parsons
Height: 6in., 15.2cm.
Issued: 1987-1992
Price: $200 £125

STORYTIME HN3695
Designer: Nada Pedley
Height: 4in., 10cm.
Issued: 1995
Price: $112 £70 (R.R.P.)

STROLLING HN3073
Designer: A. Hughes
Height: 13½in., 34.5cm.
Issued: 1985-1995
Price: $264 £165

STROLLING HN3755
Designer: Tim Potts
Height: 8in., 20cm.
Issued: 1996
Price: $152 £95 (R.R.P.)

STITCH IN TIME HN2352

STROLLING HN3755

STROLLING HN3073

STOP PRESS HN2683

SUMMER BREEZE HN3724

STORYTIME HN3695

ROYAL DOULTON FIGURES

SUITOR HN2132
Designer: P. Davies
Height: 7¼in., 18.4cm.
Issued: 1962-1971
Price: $560 £350

SUMMER (Style one) HN313
Designer: Unknown
Height: 7½in., 19.1cm.
Issued: 1918-1938
Price: $1360 £850

SUMMER (Style one) HN473
Designer: Unknown
Height: 7½in., 19.1cm.
Issued: 1921-1938
Price: $1600 £1000

SUMMER (Style two) HN2086
Designer: P. Davies
Height: 7¼in., 18.4cm.
Issued: 1952-1959
Price: $520 £325

SUMMER BREEZE HN3724
Designer: A. Maslankowski
Height: 7¾in., 19.5cm.
Issued: 1995
Price: $128 £80 (R.R.P.)

SUMMER ROSE HN3085
Designer: E. Griffiths
Height: 8½in., 21.5cm.
Issued: 1987-1992
Price: $232 £145

SUMMER ROSE HN3309
Designer: Peggy Davies
Height: 7¾in., 19.5cm.
Issued: 1991-1997
Price: $192 £120

SUMMER SCENT HN3955
Designer: Alan Maslankowski
Height: 7¾in., 19.5cm.
Issued: 1997
Price: $216 £135 (R.R.P.)

SUMMER SERENADE HN3610
Designer: P. Davies
Height: 7in., 17.8cm.
Issued: 1993 Special
colourway blue
Price: $200 £125

SUMMER'S DARLING HN3091
Designer: P. Parsons
Height: 11¼in., 28cm.
Issued: 1986-1995
Price: $232 £145

SUMMER'S DAY HN2181
Designer: P. Davies
Height: 5¾in., 14.6cm.
Issued: 1957-1962
Price: $360 £225

SUMMER'S DAY HN3378
Designer: Tim Potts
Height: 8½in., 22cm.
Issued: 1991-1996
Price: $224 £140

SUMMER'S DARLING HN3091

SUMMER SERENADE HN3610

SUMMER (Style two) HN2086

SUMMER ROSE HN3085

SUMMER ROSE HN3309

SUMMER'S DAY HN3378

SUMMERTIME HN3137
Designer: P. Parsons
Height: 8in., 20cm.
Issued: 1987
Price: $264 £165

SUMMERTIME HN3478
Designer: V. Annand
Height: 8½in., 21.5cm.
Issued: 1994-1996
Price: $280 £175

SUNDAY BEST HN3218
Designer: P. Davies
Height: 3¾in., 9.5cm.
Issued: 1988-1993
Price: $120 £75

SUNDAY BEST HN2206
Designer: P. Davies
Height: 7½in., 19.1cm.
Issued: 1979-1984
Price: $232 £145

SUNDAY BEST HN2698
Designer: P. Davies
Height: 7½in., 19.1cm.
Issued: 1985-1995
Price: $200 £125

SUNDAY MORNING HN2184
Designer: P. Davies
Height: 7½in., 19.1cm.
Issued: 1963-1969
Price: $360 £225

SUNSHINE GIRL HN1344
Designer: L. Harradine
Height: 5in., 12.7cm.
Issued: 1929-1938
Price: $4000 £2500

SUNSHINE GIRL HN1348
Designer: L. Harradine
Height: 5in., 12.7cm.
Issued: 1929-1938
            Colour variation
Price: $4400 £2750

SUSAN HN2056
Designer: L. Harradine
Height: 7in., 17.8cm.
Issued: 1950-1959
Price: $472 £295

SUSAN HN2952
Designer: P. Parsons
Height: 8½in., 21.5cm.
Issued: 1982-
Price: $264 £165

SUSAN (Red) HN3050
Designer: P. Parsons
Height: 8½in., 21.5cm.
Issued: 1986-1994
Price: $264 £165

SUSAN HN3871
Designer: Nada Pedley
Height: 8in., 20cm.
Issued: 1997 only.
Price: $256 £160

SUMMERTIME HN3478

SUMMERTIME HN3137

SUNDAY BEST HN2206

SUSAN HN3871

SUNSHINE GIRL HN1344

ROYAL DOULTON FIGURES

SUSANNA HN1233
Designer: L. Harradine
Height: 6in., 15.2cm.
Issued: 1927-1936
Price: $1600 £1000

SUSANNA HN1288
Designer: L. Harradine
Height: 6in., 15.2cm.
Issued: 1928-1936
Price: $1920 £1200

SUSANNA HN1299
Designer: L. Harradine
Height: 6in., 15.2cm.
Issued: 1928-1936
        Colour variation
Price: $1760 £1100

SUZETTE HN1487
Designer: L. Harradine
Height: 7½in., 19.1cm.
Issued: 1931-1950
Price: $520 £325

SUZETTE HN1577
Designer: L. Harradine
Height: 7½in., 19.1cm.
Issued: 1933-1949
        Colour variation
Price: $520 £325

SUZETTE HN1585
Designer: L. Harradine
Height: 7½in., 19.1cm.
Issued: 1933-1938
        Colour variation
Price: $720 £450

SUZETTE HN1696
Designer: L. Harradine
Height: 7½in., 19.1cm.
Issued: 1935-1949
        Colour variation
Price: $520 £325

SUZETTE HN2026
Designer: L. Harradine
Height: 7¼in., 18.4cm.
Issued: 1949-1959
Price: $475 £295

SWEET AND FAIR HN1864
Designer: L. Harradine
Height: 7½in., 19.1cm.
Issued: 1938-1949
Price: $1760 £1100

SWEET AND FAIR HN1865
Designer: L. Harradine
Height: 7¼in., 18.4cm.
Issued: 1938-1949
        Colour variation
Price: $1760 £1100

SWEET AND TWENTY(Style one) HN1298
Designer: L. Harradine
Height: 5¾in., 14.6cm.
Issued: 1928-1969
Price: $520 £325

SUSAN HN2952

SUZETTE HN1487

SUZETTE HN2026

SUZETTE HN1696

SWEET AND TWENTY(Style one) HN1298

SWEET AND TWENTY(Style one) HN1360
Designer: L. Harradine
Height: 6in., 15.2cm.
Issued: 1929-1938
             Colour variation
Price: $720 £450

SWEET AND TWENTY(Style one) HN1437
Designer: L. Harradine
Height: 6in., 15.2cm.
Issued: 1930-1938
             Colour variation
Price: $760 £475

SWEET AND TWENTY (Style one) HN1438
Designer: L. Harradine
Height: 6in., 15.2cm.
Issued: 1930-1938
             Colour variation
Price: $760 £475

SWEET AND TWENTY(Style one) HN1549
Designer: L. Harradine
Height: 6in., 15.2cm.
Issued: 1933-1949
             Colour variation
Price: $520 £325

SWEET AND TWENTY(Style one) HN1563
Designer: L. Harradine
Height: 6in., 15.2cm.
Issued: 1933-1938
Price: $720 £450

SWEET AND TWENTY(Style one) HN1649
Designer: L. Harradine
Height: 6in., 15.2cm.
Issued: 1934-1936
             Colour variation
Price: $880 £550

SWEET AND TWENTY(Style two) HN1589
Designer: L. Harradine
Height: 3½in., 8.9cm.
Issued: 1933-1949
Price: $520 £325

SWEET AND TWENTY(Style two) HN1610
Designer: L. Harradine
Height: 3½in., 8.9cm.
Issued: 1933-1938
             Colour variation
Price: $680 £425

SWEET ANNE HN1318
Designer: L. Harradine
Height: 7½in., 19.1cm.
Issued: 1929-1949
Price: $310 £195

SWEET ANNE HN1330
Designer: L. Harradine
Height: 7¼in., 18.4cm.
Issued: 1929-1949
             Colour variation
Price: $310 £195

SWEET ANNE HN1453

SWEET ANNE HN1318

SWEET ANNE HN1496

SWEET DREAMS HN2380

SWEET ANNE HN1331
Designer: L. Harradine
Height: 7¼in., 18.4cm.
Issued: 1929-1949
             Colour variation
Price: $310 £195

SWEET ANNE HN1453
Designer: L. Harradine
Height: 7in., 17.8cm.
Issued: 1931-1949
             Colour variation
Price: $392 £245

SWEET ANNE HN1496
Designer: L. Harradine
Height: 7in., 17.8cm.
Issued: 1932-1967
             Colour variation
Price: $360 £225

SWEET ANNE IIN1631
Designer: L. Harradine
Height: 7in., 17.8cm.
Issued: 1934-1938
             Colour variation
Price: $720 £450

SWEET ANNE HN1701
Designer: L. Harradine
Height: 7in., 17.8cm.
Issued: 1935-1938
Price: $880 £550

SWEET ANNE M5
Designer: L. Harradine
Height: 4in., 10.1cm.
Issued: 1932-1945
Price: $400 £250

SWEET ANNE M6
Designer: L. Harradine
Height: 4in., 10.1cm.
Issued: 1932-1945
             Colour variation
Price: $400 £250

SWEET ANNE M27
Designer: L. Harradine
Height: 4in., 10.1cm.
Issued: 1932-1945
             Colour variation
Price: $400 £250

SWEET APRIL HN2215
Designer: P. Davies
Height: 7¼in., 18.4cm.
Issued: 1965-1967
Price: $425 £265

SWEET DREAMS HN2380
Designer: P. Davies
Height: 5in., 12.7cm.
Issued: 1971-1990
Price: $264 £165

SWEET DREAMS HN3394
Designer: Alan Maslankowski
Height: 6in., 15cm.
Issued: 1992
Price: $65 £40 (R.R.P.)

ROYAL DOULTON FIGURES

SWEET LAVENDER HN1373
Designer: L. Harradine
Height: 9in., 22.8cm.
Issued: 1930-1949
Price: $800 £500

SWEET MAID (Style one)
HN1504
Designer: L. Harradine
Height: 8in., 20.3cm.
Issued: 1932-1936
Price: $1040 £650

SWEET MAID (Style one)
HN1505
Designer: L. Harradine
Height: 8in., 20.3cm.
Issued: 1932-1936
Price: $1040 £650

SWEET MAID (Style two)
HN2092
Designer: L. Harradine
Height: 7in., 17.8cm.
Issued: 1952-1955
           Colour variation
Price: $680 £425

SWEET PERFUME HN3094
Designer: P. Parsons
Height: 13in., 33cm.
Issued: 1986-1995
Price: $232 £145

SWEET SEVENTEEN
HN273
Designer: D. V. Tootle
Height: 7½in., 19.1cm.
Issued: 1975-1993
Price: $232 £145

SWEET SIXTEEN HN2231
Designer: P. Davies
Height: 7¼in., 18.4cm.
Issued: 1958-1965
Price: $440 £275

SWEET SIXTEEN HN3648
Designer: Nada Pedley
Height: 8in., 20cm.
Issued: 1994
Price: $168 £105 (R.R.P.)

SWEET SUZY HN1918
Designer: L. Harradine
Height: 6½in., 16.5cm.
Issued: 1939-1949
Price: $800 £500

SWEET VIOLETS HN3175
Designer: D. Tootle
Height: 10¼in., 26cm.
Issued: 1988-1989
Price: $232 £145

SWEETING HN1935
Designer: L. Harradine
Height: 6in., 15.2cm.
Issued: 1940-1973
Price: $232 £145

SWEET PERFUME HN3094

SWEET AND TWENTY(Style one) HN1549

SWEET LAVENDER HN1373

SWEET SEVENTEEN HN2734

SWEET MAID HN1505

SWEET SIXTEEN HN3648

SWEET DREAMS HN3394

SWEETING HN1938
Designer: L. Harradine
Height: 6in., 15.2cm.
Issued: 1940-1949
Colour variation
Price: $280 £175

SWIMMER HN1270
Designer: L. Harradine
Height: 7¼in., 18.4cm.
Issued: 1928-1938
Price: $2240 £1400

SWIMMER HN1326
Designer: L. Harradine
Height: 7½in., 19.1cm.
Issued: 1929-1938
Colour variation
Price: $2400 £1500

SWIMMER HN1329
Designer: L. Harradine
Height: 7½in., 19.1cm.
Issued: 1929-1938
Colour variation
Price: $2320 £1450

SYLVIA HN1478
Designer: L. Harradine
Height: 10½in., 26.7cm.
Issued: 1931-1938
Price: $560 £350

SYMPATHY HN2838 (Black)
Designer: P. Davies
Height: 11¾in., 29.8cm.
Issued: 1981-1986
Price: $192 £120

SYMPATHY HN2876 (White)
Designer: P. Davies
Height: 11¾in., 29.8cm.
Issued: 1981-1986
Price: $192 £120

SYMPHONY HN2287
Designer: D. B. Lovegrove
Height: 5¼in., 13.3cm.
Issued: 1961-1965
Price: $352 £220

T

TAILOR HN2174
Designer: M. Nicoll
Height: 5in., 12.7cm.
Issued: 1956-1959
Price: $880 £550

TAKE ME HOME HN3662
Designer: Nada Pedley
Height: 8in., 20cm.
Issued: 1995
Price: $152 £95 (R.R.P.)

TAKING THINGS EASY HN2677
Designer: M. Nicoll
Height: 6¾in., 17.2cm.
Issued: 1975-1987
Price: $312 £195

SWIMMER HN1270

SYLVIA HN1478

TAKING THINGS EASY HN2680

TAKE ME HOME HN3662

TAKING THINGS EASY HN2677

ROYAL DOULTON FIGURES

TAKING THINGS EASY
HN2680
Designer: M. Nicoll
Height: 7½in., 19.5cm.
Issued: 1987-1996
Price: $240 £150

TALL STORY HN2248
Designer: M. Nicoll
Height: 6½in., 16.5cm.
Issued: 1986-1975
Price: $360 £225

TANGO HN3075
Designer: A. Hughes
Height: 13in., 33cm.
Issued: 1985-1992
Price: $264 £165

TAPESTRY WEAVING
HN3048
Designer: P. Parsons
Height: 7½in., 19cm.
Issued: 1985 in a limited
edition of 750
Price: $1040 £650

TEATIME HN2255
Designer: M. Nicoll
Height: 7¼in., 18.4cm.
Issued: 1972-1995
Price: $200 £125

TEEING OFF HN3276
Designer: Robert Tabbenor
Height: 8½in., 21.5cm.
Issued: 1990-1997
Price: $240 £150

TEENAGER HN2203
Designer: P. Davies
Height: 7¼in., 18.4cm.
Issued: 1957-1962
Price: $400 £250

TENDER MOMENT HN3303
Designer: Peggy Davies
Height: 7in., 17.5cm.
Issued: 1990-1997
Price: $176 £110

TENDERNESS HN2713
Designer: E. Griffiths
Height: 11¾in., 29.5cm.
Issued: 1982-1997
Colour variation
White
Price: $120 £75

TENDERNESS HN2714
Designer: E. Griffiths
Height: 11¾in., 29.5cm.
Issued: 1982-1992
Price: $176 £110

TERESA HN1682
Designer: L. Harradine
Height: 5¾in., 14.6cm.
Issued: 1935-1949
Price: $1600 £1000

TENDERNESS
HN2713

TANGO HN3075

TEEING OFF HN3276

TENDER MOMENT
HN3303

TEATIME HN2255

TAPESTRY WEAVING
HN3048

ROYAL DOULTON FIGURES

TERESA HN1683
Designer: L. Harradine
Height: 5¾in., 14.6cm.
Issued: 1935-1938
              Colour variation
Price: $2000 £1250

TERESA HN3206
Designer: A. Hughes
Height: 7¾in., 19.6cm.
Issued: 1989-1992
Price: $190 £120

TESS HN2865
Designer: P. Davies
Height: 5¾in., 14.6cm.
Issued: 1978-1983
Price: $310 £195

TÊTE-À-TÊTE (Style one) HN798
Designer: L. Harradine
Height: 5¾in., 14.6cm.
Issued: 1926-1938
Price: $2320 £1450

TÊTE-À-TÊTE (Style one) HN799
Designer: L. Harradine
Height: 5¾in., 14.6cm.
Issued: 1926-1940
              Colour variation
Price: $2080 £1300

TÊTE-À-TÊTE (Style two) HN1236
Designer: C. J. Noke
Height: 3in., 7.6cm.
Issued: 1927-1938
Price: $2320 £1450

TÊTE-À-TÊTE HN1237
Designer: C. J. Noke
Height: 3in., 7.6cm.
Issued: 1927-1938
              Colour variation
Price: $2320 £1450

THANK YOU HN2732
Designer: W. K. Harper
Height: 8¼in., 21cm.
Issued: 1982-1986
Price: $264 £165

THANK YOU HN3390
Designer: Alan Maslankowski
Height: 6¼in., 16cm.
Issued: 1991
Price: $64 £40 (R.R.P.)

THANKFUL (White) HN3129
Designer: P. Parsons
Height: 8½in., 21.5cm.
Issued: 1987
Price: $80 £50 (R.R.P.)

THANKFUL (Black) HN3135
Designer: P. Parsons
Height: 8½in., 21.5cm.
Issued: 1987
Price: $80 £50 (R.R.P.)

THANKFUL HN3129

TERESA HN1682

TERESA HN3206

THANK YOU HN2732

THANK YOU HN3390

TÊTE-À-TÊTE (Style one) HN799

THANKS DOC HN2731
Designer: W. K. Harper
Height: 8¾in., 22.2cm.
Issued: 1975-1990
Price: $264 £165

THANKSGIVING HN2446
Designer: M. Nicoll
Height: 8in., 20.3cm.
Issued: 1972-1976
Price: $256 £160

THINKING OF YOU HN3124
Designer: Alan Maslankowski
Height: 6¾in., 17cm.
Issued: 1991
Price: $64 £40 (R.R.P.)

THINKING OF YOU HN3490
Designer: Alan Maslankowski
Height: 6¾in., 17cm.
Issued: 1993 only
Colour variation
Price: $120 £75

THIS LITTLE PIG HN1793
Designer: L. Harradine
Height: 4in., 10.1cm.
Issued: 1936-1995
Price: $120 £75

THIS LITTLE PIG HN1794
Designer: L. Harradine
Height: 4in., 10.1cm.
Issued: 1936-1949
Colour variation
Price: $520 £325

THIS LITTLE PIG HN2125
Designer: L. Harradine
Height: 4in., 10.1cm.
Issued: 1984-1995
Colour variation
Price: $88 £55

TIGER HN2646
Designer: Charles Noke
Height: 5¾in., 14.6cm.
Issued: 1955-1992
Price: $1040 £650

TIGER ON THE ROCK HN2639
Designer: Charles Noke
Height: 12in., 30.5cm.
Issued: 1952-1992
Price: $1200 £750

TILDY HN1576
Designer: L. Harradine
Height: 5in., 12.7cm.
Issued: 1933-1939
Price: $1200 £750

TILDY HN1859
Designer: L. Harradine
Height: 5½in., 14cm.
Issued: 1934-1939
Colour variation
Price: $1360 £850

TILDY HN1859

THINKING OF YOU HN3124

THANKSGIVING HN2446

TILDY HN1576

THANKS DOC HN2731

THIS LITTLE PIG HN1793

321

ROYAL DOULTON FIGURES

TIME FOR BED HN3762
Designer: Nada Pedley
Height: 5¼in., 13cm.
Issued: 1996
Price: $112 £70 (R.R.P.)

TINA HN3494
Commissioned by G.U.S.
Designer: P. Davies
Height: 7½in., 19.1cm.
Issued: 1993
        Colour variation
        U.K. only
Price: $200 £125

TINKLE BELL HN1677
Designer: L. Harradine
Height: 4¾in., 12cm.
Issued: 1935-1988
Price: $136 £85

TINSMITH HN2146
Designer: M. Nicoll
Height: 6½in., 16.5cm.
Issued: 1962-1967
Price: $520 £325

TINY TIM HN539
Designer: L. Harradine
Height: 3½in., 8.9cm.
Issued: 1922-1932
Price: $70 £45

TINY TIM M56
Designer: L. Harradine
Height: 3¾in., 9.5cm.
Issued: 1932-1983
Price: $80 £50

TIPTOE HN3293
Designer: Adrian Hughes
Height: 9in., 23cm.
Issued: 1990-1994
Price: $240 £150

TITANIA HN3679
In a limited edition of 5000
Designer: Pauline Parsons
Height: 8¾in., 22cm.
Issued: 1995
Price: $360 £225

TO BED HN1805
Designer: L. Harradine
Height: 6in., 15.2cm.
Issued: 1937-1959
Price: $280 £175

TO BED HN1806
Designer: L. Harradine
Height: 6in., 15.2cm.
Issued: 1937-1949
        Colour variation
Price: $440 £275

TOINETTE HN1940
Designer: L. Harradine
Height: 6¾in., 17.1cm.
Issued: 1940-1949
Price: $1400 £875
Also called 'Meryll'

TINA HN3494

TIME FOR BED HN3762

TINKLE BELL HN1677

TOINETTE HN1940

TIPTOE HN3293

TINSMITH HN2146

322

ROYAL DOULTON FIGURES

TOM HN2864
Designer: P. Davies
Height: 5¾in., 14.6cm.
Issued: 1978-1981
Price: $440 £275

TOM BOMBADIL HN2924
Designer: D. Lyttleton
Height: 5¾in., 14.6cm.
Issued: 1982-1984
Price: $440 £275

TOM BROWN HN2941
Designer: R. Tabbenor
Height: 6¾in., 17cm.
Issued: 1983-1985
Price: $200 £125

TOM SAWYER HN2926
Designer: D. Lyttleton
Height: 5¼in., 13cm.
Issued: 1982-1985
Price: $200 £125

TOM, TOM THE PIPER'S SON HN3032
Designer: A. Hughes
Height: 7in., 17.5cm.
Issued: 1984-1987
Price: $200 £125

TOMORROW'S DREAMS HN3128
Designer: P. Parsons
Height: 6½in., 16.5cm.
Issued: 1987-1992
Price: $200 £125

TOMORROW'S DREAMS HN3665
Designer: Peter Gee
Height: 8½in., 21.5cm.
Issued: 1995
Price: $128 £80 (R.R.P.)

TONY WELLER (Style one) HN346
Designer: C. J. Noke
Height: 10½in., 26.7cm.
Issued: 1919-1938
Price: $2400 £1500

TONY WELLER (Style one) HN368
Designer: C. J. Noke
Height: 10½in., 26.7cm.
Issued: 1920-1938
Colour variation
Price: $1600 £1000

TONY WELLER (Style one) HN684
Designer: C. J. Noke
Height: 10¼in., 26cm.
Issued: 1924-1938
Colour variation
Price: $1520 £950

TOM, TOM THE PIPER'S SON HN3032

TOM BOMBADIL HN2924

TOMORROW'S DREAMS HN3665

TOM BROWN HN2941

TONY WELLER (Style one) HN684

TOM SAWYER HN2926

TONY WELLER (Style two) HN544
Designer: L. Harradine
Height: 3½in., 8.9cm.
Issued: 1922-1932
Price: $80 £50

TONY WELLER (Style two)M47
Designer: L. Harradine
Height: 4in., 10.1cm.
Issued: 1932-1982
Price: $72 £45

TOOTLES HN1680
Designer: L. Harradine
Height: 4¾in., 12cm.
Issued: 1935-1975
Price: $165 £110

TOP O' THE HILL HN1833
Designer: L. Harradine
Height: 7in., 17.8cm.
Issued: 1937-1971
Price: $264 £165

TOP O' THE HILL HN1834
Designer: L. Harradine
Height: 7in., 17.8cm.
Issued: 1937-
             Colour variation
Price: $232 £145 (R.R.P.)

TOP O' THE HILL HN1849
Designer: L. Harradine
Height: 7¼in., 18.4cm.
Issued: 1938-1975
             Colour variation
Price: $264 £165

TOP O' THE HILL HN2126 (R.D.I.C.C.)
Designer: P. Gee
Height: 4in., 10cm.
Issued: 1988 only
Price: $200 £125

TOP O'THE HILL HN2127
Designer: Leslie Harradine
Height: 7in., 18cm.
Issued: 1988 (Australian
             Bicentenary
             colourway)
Price: $360 £225

TOP O' THE HILL HN3499
Designer: Leslie Harradine
Height: 4in., 10cm.
Issued: 1993
Price: $104 £65 (R.R.P.)

TOP O'THE HILL HN3735
In a limited edition of 3500
Designer: Leslie Harradine
Height: 7in., 18cm.
Issued: 1997
             Colour variation
Price: $238 £149 (R.R.P.)

HN3499

HN1833

HN1849

HN3735

HN2126

HN1834

TOP O' THE HILL

ROYAL DOULTON FIGURES

TOWN CRIER HN3261
Designer: P. Davies
Height: 4½in., 11.5cm.
Issued: 1989-1992
Price: $152 £95

TOWN CRIER HN2119
Designer: P. Davies
Height: 8½in., 21.6cm.
Issued: 1953-1976
Price: $360 £225

TOYMAKER HN2250
Designer: M. Nicoll
Height: 6in., 15.2cm.
Issued: 1959-1973
Price: $472 £295

TOYS HN1316
Designer: L. Harradine
Height: Unknown
Issued: 1929-1938
Price: $3200 £2000

TRACY HN2736
Designer: D. Tootle
Height: 7½in., 19cm.
Issued: 1983-1994
Price: $176 £110

TRACY HN3291
Designer: D. V. Tootle
Height: 7½in., 19.1cm.
Issued: 1993
Colour variation
U.S.A. only
Price: $200 £125 (R.R.P.)

TRANQUILLITY HN2426
(Black)
Designer: P. Davies
Height: 12in., 30.5cm.
Issued: 1981-1986
Price: $192 £120

TRANQUILLITY HN2469
(White)
Designer: P. Davies
Height: 12in., 30.5cm.
Issued: 1981-1986
Price: $192 £120

TRAVELLERS' TALES
HN3185
Designer: E. J. Griffiths
Height: 9½in., 23.5cm.
Issued: 1988-1989
Price: $232 £145

TREASURE ISLAND HN2243
Designer: P. Davies
Height: 4¾in., 12cm.
Issued: 1962-1975
Price: $232 £145

TROTTY VECK M91
Designer: L. Harradine
Height: 4¼in., 10.8cm.
Issued: 1949-1982
Price: $80 £50

TOWN CRIER HN3261   TRACY HN3291

TUPPENCE A BAG HN2320

TWILIGHT HN2256   TUMBLING HN3283

TULIPS HN466
Designer: Unknown
Height: 9½in., 24.1cm.
Issued: 1921-1938
Price: $2800 £1750

TULIPS HN488
Designer: Unknown
Height: 9½in., 24.1cm.
Issued: 1921-1938
Price: $2800 £1750

TULIPS HN672
Designer: Unknown
Height: 9½in., 24.1cm.
Issued: 1924-1936
Colour variation
Price: $2320 £1450

TULIPS HN747
Designer: Unknown
Height: 9½in., 24.1cm.
Issued: 1925-1936
Colour variation
Price: $2000 £1250

TULIPS HN1334
Designer: Unknown
Height: 9½in., 24.1cm.
Issued: 1929-1936
Colour variation
Price: $1920 £1200

TUMBLER HN3181
Designer: D. Tootle
Height: 9in., 23cm.
Issued: 1989-1991
Price: $264 £165

TUMBLING HN3283
Designer: D. Tootle
Height: 9in., 23cm.
Issued: 1990-1994
Price: $240 £150

TUMBLING HN3289
For National Playing Fields
Association.
Designer: D. V. Tootle
Height: 9in., 23cm.
Issued: 1991 in a limited
edition of 2500
Price: $312 £195

TUPPENCE A BAG HN2320
Designer: M. Nicoll
Height: 5½in., 14cm.
Issued: 1968-1995
Price: $200 £125

TWILIGHT HN2256
Designer: M. Nicoll
Height: 5in., 12.7cm.
Issued: 1971-1976
Price: $312 £195

TWILIGHT HN3466
Designer: Adrian Hughes
Height: 5¾in., 14.5cm.
Issued: 1996
Price: $80 £50 (R.R.P.)

TWO-A-PENNY HN1359
Designer: L. Harradine
Height: 8¼in., 21cm.
Issued: 1929-1938
Price: $3200 £2000

TZ'U HSI, THE EMPRESS-DOWAGER HN2391
Designer: P. Davies
Height: 8in., 20cm.
Issued: 1983 in a limited
            edition of 750
Price: $1040 £650

U

ULYSSES S. GRANT HN3403
Designer: Robert Tabbenor
Height: 11¾in., 30cm.
Issued: 1993 in a limited
            edition of 5000
Price: $792 £495

UNCLE NED HN2094
Designer: H. Fenton
Height: 6¾in., 17.2cm.
Issued: 1952-1965
Price: $392 £245

UNDER THE GOOSEBERRY BUSH HN49
Designer: C. J. Noke
Height: 3½in., 8.9cm.
Issued: 1916-1938
Price: $2000 £1250

"UPON HER CHEEKS SHE WEPT" HN59
Designer: L. Perugini
Height: 9in., 22.8cm.
Issued: 1916-1938
Price: $2560 £1600

"UPON HER CHEEKS SHE WEPT" HN511
Designer: L. Perugini
Height: 9in., 22.8cm.
Issued: 1921-1938
            Colour variation
Price: $3200 £2000

"UPON HER CHEEKS SHE WEPT" HN522
Designer: L. Perugini
Height: 9in., 22.8cm.
Issued: 1921-1938
Price: $3200 £2000

URIAH HEEP (Style one) HN545
Designer: L. Harradine
Height: 4in., 10.1cm
Issued: 1922-1932
Price: $80 £50

URIAH HEEP (Style one) M45
Designer: L. Harradine
Height: 4in., 10.1cm.
Issued: 1932-1982
Price: $72 £45

TZ'U HSI, THE EMPRESS-DOWAGER HN2391

UNCLE NED HN2094

"UPON HER CHEEKS SHE WEPT" HN59

ULYSSES S. GRANT HN3403

URIAH HEEP (Style two)HN554
Designer: L. Harradine
Height: 7¼in., 18.4cm.
Issued: 1923-1939
Price: $440 £275

URIAH HEEP (Style two) HN1892
Designer: L. Harradine
Height: 7in., 17.8cm.
Issued: 1938-1952
Price: $400 £250

URIAH HEEP (Style three) HN2101
Designer: L. Harradine
Height: 7½in., 19.1cm.
Issued: 1952-1967
Price: $360 £225

V

VALERIE HN2107
Designer: P. Davies
Height: 4¾in., 12cm.
Issued: 1953-1995
Price: $136 £85

VALERIE HN3620
Designer: P. Davies
Height: 4¾in., 12cm.
Issued: 1994
Colour variation
Price: $116 £75 (R.R.P.)

VALERIE HN3904
Designer: Peggy Davies
Height: 7¾in., 19.5cm.
Issued: 1997
Price: $206 £129 (R.R.P.)

VANESSA HN1836
Designer: L. Harradine
Height: 7½in., 19.1cm.
Issued: 1938-1949
Price: $1200 £750

VANESSA HN1838
Designer: L. Harradine
Height: 7½in., 19.1cm.
Issued: 1938-1949
Colour variation
Price: $1200 £750

VANESSA HN3198
Designer: A. Hughes
Height: 8½in., 21.5cm.
Issued: 1989-1990
Price: $296 £185

VANITY HN2475
Designer: P. Davies
Height: 5¼in., 13.3cm.
Issued: 1973-1992
Price: $176 £110

VENETA HN2722
Designer: W. K. Harper
Height: 8in., 20.3cm.
Issued: 1974-1980
Price: $232 £145

VALERIE HN2107

VANITY HN2475

VENETA HN2722

VERENA HN1835

VERA HN1729
Designer: L. Harradine
Height: 4¼in., 10.8cm.
Issued: 1935-1938
Price: $960 £600

VERA HN1730
Designer: L. Harradine
Height: 4¼in., 10.8cm.
Issued: 1935-1938
Colour variation
Price: $960 £600

VERENA HN1835
Designer: L. Harradine
Height: 8¼in., 21cm.
Issued: 1938-1949
Price: $1000 £625

VERENA HN1854
Designer: L. Harradine
Height: 8¼in., 21cm.
Issued: 1938-1949
Colour variation
Price: $1200 £750

VERONICA (Style one) HN1517
Designer: L. Harradine
Height: 8in., 20.3cm.
Issued: 1932-1951
Price: $392 £245

VERONICA (Style one) HN1519
Designer: L. Harradine
Height: 8in., 20.3cm.
Issued: 1932-1938
Price: $472 £295

VERONICA (Style one) HN1650
Designer: L. Harradine
Height: 8in., 20.3cm.
Issued: 1934-1949
Colour variation
Price: $440 £275

VERONICA (Style one) HN1943
Designer: L. Harradine
Height: 8in., 20.3cm.
Issued: 1940-1949
Colour variation
Price: $600 £375

VERONICA (Style two) HN1915
Designer: L. Harradine
Height: 5¾in.. 14.6cm.
Issued: 1939-1949
Price: $440 £275

VERONICA HN3205
Designer: A. Hughes
Height: 8in., 20.3cm.
Issued: 1989-1992
Price: $232 £145

VERONICA M64
Designer: L. Harradine
Height: 4½in., 10.8cm.
Issued: 1934-1949
Price: $632 £395

VERONICA M70
Designer: L. Harradine
Height: 4¼in., 10.8cm.
Issued: 1936-1949
Price: $632 £395

VICTORIA HN2471
Designer: P. Davies
Height: 6½in., 16.5cm.
Issued: 1973-
Price: $232 £145 (R.R.P.)

VICTORIA HN3416
Roads Show Events Piece
Designer: P. Davies
Height: 6½in., 16.5cm.
Issued: 1972 only
Price: $280 £175

VICTORIA HN3744
Designer: Peggy Davies
Height: 3¼in., 8cm.
Issued: 1995
Price: $104 £65 (R.R.P.)

VICTORIA AND ALBERT
HN3256
Designer: D. V. Tootle
Height: 9¼in., 23.5cm.
Issued: 1990 in a limited
   edition of 2500
Price: $720 £450

VICTORIAN LADY HN726
Designer: L. Harradine
Height: 7½in., 19.1cm.
Issued: 1925-1938
Price: $520 £325

VICTORIAN LADY HN727
Designer: L. Harradine
Height: 7½in., 19.1cm.
Issued: 1925-1938
   Colour variation
Price: $520 £325

VICTORIAN LADY HN728
Designer: L. Harradine
Height: 7¾in., 19.7cm.
Issued: 1925-1952
   Colour variation
Price: $440 £275

VICTORIAN LADY HN736
Designer: L. Harradine
Height: 7¾in., 19.7cm.
Issued: 1925-1938
   Colour variation
Price: $520 £325

VICTORIAN LADY HN739
Designer: L. Harradine
Height: 7¾in., 19.7cm.
Issued: 1925-1938
   Colour variation
Price: $520 £325

VICTORIAN LADY HN740
Designer: L. Harradine
Height: 7¾in., 19.7cm.
Issued: 1925-1938
   Colour variation
Price: $472 £295

VICTORIA HN2471

VICTORIA HN3416

VICTORIA HN3744

VICTORIAN LADY HN726

VERONICA (Style one) HN1517

ROYAL DOULTON FIGURES

VICTORIAN LADY HN742
Designer: L. Harradine
Height: 7¾in., 19.7cm.
Issued: 1925-1938
Colour variation
Price: $560 £350

VICTORIAN LADY HN745
Designer: L. Harradine
Height: 7¾in., 19.7cm.
Issued: 1925-1938
Colour variation
Price: $600 £375

VICTORIAN LADY HN1208
Designer: L. Harradine
Height: 7¾in., 19.7cm.
Issued: 1926-1938
Colour variation
Price: $520 £325

VICTORIAN LADY HN1258
Designer: L. Harradine
Height: 7¾in., 19.7cm.
Issued: 1927-1938
Colour variation
Price: $520 £325

VICTORIAN LADY HN1276
Designer: L. Harradine
Height: 7½in., 19.1cm.
Issued: 1928-1938
Colour variation
Price: $560 £350

VICTORIAN LADY HN1277
Designer: L. Harradine
Height: 7¾in., 19.7cm.
Issued: 1928-1938
Colour variation
Price: $560 £350

VICTORIAN LADY HN1345
Designer: L. Harradine
Height: 7¾in., 19.7cm.
Issued: 1929-1949
Colour variation
Price: $472 £295

VICTORIAN LADY HN1452
Designer: L. Harradine
Height: 7¾in., 19.7cm.
Issued: 1931-1949
Colour variation
Price: $440 £275

VICTORIAN LADY HN1529
Designer: L. Harradine
Height: 7¾in., 19.7cm.
Issued: 1932-1938
Colour variation
Price: $600 £375

VICTORIAN LADY M1
Designer: L. Harradine
Height: 3¾in., 9.5cm.
Issued: 1932-1945
Price: $440 £275

VICTORIAN LADY HN1452

VICTORIAN LADY HN1277

VICTORIAN LADY HN728

VICTORIAN LADY HN740

VICTORIA AND ALBERT HN3256

VICTORIAN LADY M2
Designer: L. Harradine
Height: 3¾in., 9.5cm.
Issued: 1932-1945
            Colour variation
Price: $440 £275

VICTORIAN LADY M25
Designer: L. Harradine
Height: 3¾in., 9.5cm.
Issued: 1932-1945
            Colour variation
Price: $472 £295

VIKING HN2375
Designer: J. Bromley
Height: 8¾in., 22.2cm.
Issued: 1973-1976
Price: $392 £245

VIOLA HN3706
In a limited edition of 1500
Designer: Valerie Annand
Height: 8¾in., 22cm.
Issued: 1996
Price: $472 £295

VIOLA D'AMORE HN2797
Designer: P. Davies
Height: 6in., 15.2cm.
Issued: 1976 in a limited
            edition of 750
Price: $960 £600

VIOLIN HN2432
Designer: P. Davies
Height: 6¼in., 15.9cm.
Issued: 1972 in a limited
            edition of 750
Price: $960 £600

VIRGINALS HN2427
Designer: P. Davies
Height: 6¼in., 15.9cm.
Issued: 1971 in a limited
            edition of 750
Price: $1040 £650

VIRGINIA HN1693
Designer: L. Harradine
Height: 7½in., 19.1cm.
Issued: 1935-1949
Price: $960   £600

VIRGINIA HN1694
Designer: L. Harradine
Height: 7½in., 19.1cm.
Issued: 1935-1949
            Colour variation
Price: $960   £600

VIVIENNE HN2073
Designer: L. Harradine
Height: 7¾in., 19.7cm.
Issued: 1951-1967
Price: $360 £225

VOTES FOR WOMEN HN2816
Designer: W. K. Harper
Height: 9¾in., 24.7cm.
Issued: 1978-1981
Price: $312 £195

VIRGINIA HN1693

VIOLA D'AMORE
HN2797

VIRGINALS
HN2427

VIVIENNE
HN2073

VIOLIN HN2432

VIKING HN2375

W

W. SHAKESPEARE HN3633
Designer: Robert Tabbenor
Height: 11¾in., 30cm.
Issued: 1994
Price: $1200 £750

W. G. GRACE HN3640
In a limited edition of 9500
Designer: Robert Tabbenor
Height: 8in., 20.5cm.
Issued: 1996
Price: $200 £125

**WAITING FOR A TRAIN
HN3315**
Designer: P. Gee
Height: 8½in., 21.6cm.
Issued: 1991 in a limited
        edition of 500
Price: $440 £275

WALES HN3622
Designer: Valerie Annand
Height: 8½in., 19.5cm.
Issued: 1995
Price: $288 £180 (R.R.P.)

**WANDERING MINSTREL
HN1224**
Designer: L. Harradine
Height: 7in., 17.8cm.
Issued: 1927-1936
Price: $2640 £1650

**WARDROBE MISTRESS
HN2145**
Designer: P. Davies
Height: 5¾in., 14.6cm.
Issued: 1954-1967
Price: $600 £375

WATER MAIDEN HN3155
Designer: A. Hughes
Height: 12in., 30.5cm.
Issued: 1987-1991
Price: $232 £145

WAYFARER HN2362
Designer: M. Nicoll
Height: 5½in., 14cm.
Issued: 1970-1976
Price: $312 £195

WEDDING DAY HN2748
Designer: D. Tootle
Height: 12½in., 31.5cm.
Issued: 1987
Price: $254 £159 (R.R.P.)

WEDDING MORN HN1866
Designer: L. Harradine
Height: 10½in., 26.7cm.
Issued: 1938-1949
Price: $2160 £1350

WALES HN3622

VOTES FOR WOMEN
HN2816

WARDROBE MISTRESS
HN2145

WANDERING MINSTREL
HN1224

WAITING FOR A TRAIN
HN3315

WEDDING MORN HN1867
Designer: L. Harradine
Height: 10½in., 26.7cm.
Issued: 1938-1949
             Colour variation
Price: $2160 £1350

WEDDING MORN HN3853
Designer: Tim Potts
Height: 8in., 20cm.
Issued: 1996
Price: $248 £155 (R.R.P.)

WEDDING VOWS HN2750
Designer: D. Tootle
Height: 8in., 20cm.
Issued: 1988-1992
Price: $264 £165

WEE WILLIE WINKIE HN2050
Designer: P. Davies
Height: 5¼in., 13.3cm.
Issued: 1949-1953
Price: $440 £275

WEE WILLIE WINKIE HN3031
Designer: A. Hughes
Height: 7¾in., 19.5cm.
Issued: 1984-1987
Price: $296 £185

WELCOME HN3764 (R.D.I.C.C.)
Designer: Nada Pedley
Height: 5½in., 14cm.
Issued: 1996 only
Price: $104 £65

WELCOME HOME HN3299
Designer: A. Hughes
Height: 8½in., 21.6cm.
Issued: 1992 in a limited
             edition of 9500
Price: $440 £275

WELL DONE HN3362
Designer: V. Annand
Height: 4in., 10.1cm.
Issued: 1992-1994
Price: $176 £110

WELSH GIRL HN39
Designer: E. W. Light
Height: 12in., 30.5cm.
Issued: 1914-1936
Price: $3600 £2250

WELSH GIRL HN92
Designer: E. W. Light
Height: 12in., 30.5cm.
Issued: 1918-1936
             Colour variation
Price: $4400 £2750

WELSH GIRL HN456
Designer: E. W Light
Height: 12in., 30.5cm.
Issued: 1921-1936
             Colour variation
Price: $3600 £2250

WELSH GIRL HN514
Designer: E. W. Light
Height: 12in., 30.5cm.
Issued: 1921-1936
             Colour variation
Price: $4400 £2750

WELSH GIRL HN516
Designer: E. W. Light
Height: 12in., 30.5cm.
Issued: 1921-1936
Price: $4400 £2750

WELSH GIRL HN519
Designer: E. W. Light
Height: 12in., 30.5cm.
Issued: 1921-1936
             Colour variation
Price: $4400 £2750

WELSH GIRL HN520
Designer: E. W. Light
Height: 12in., 30.5cm.
Issued: 1921-1936
             Colour variation
Price: $4400 £2750

WELSH GIRL HN660
Designer: E. W. Light
Height: 12in., 30.5cm.
Issued: 1924-1936
             Colour variation
Price: $4000 £2500

WELSH GIRL HN668
Designer: E. W. Light
Height: 12in., 30.5cm.
Issued: 1924-1936
             Colour variation
Price: $3600 £2250

WELSH GIRL HN669
Designer: E. W. Light
Height: 12in., 30.5cm.
Issued: 1924-1936
             Colour variation
Price: $3360 £2100

WELSH GIRL HN701
Designer: E. W. Light
Height: 12in., 30.5cm.
Issued: 1925-1936
             Colour variation
Price: $4000 £2500

WELSH GIRL HN792
Designer: E. W. Light
Height: 12in., 30.5cm.
Issued: 1926-1938
             Colour variation
Price: $4000 £2500

WENDY HN2109
Designer: L. Harradine
Height: 5in., 12.7cm.
Issued: 1953-1995
Price: $104 £65

WEE WILLIE WINKIE HN2050

WEDDING MORN HN3853

WELSH GIRL HN39

WEE WILLIE WINKIE HN3031

WELL DONE HN3362

WELCOME HOME HN3299

ROYAL DOULTON FIGURES

WEST INDIAN DANCER
HN2384
Designer: P. Davies
Height: 8¾in., 22.2cm.
Issued: 1981 in a limited
edition of 750
Price: $600 £375

WEST WIND HN1776
Designer: R. Garbe
Height: 14½in., 36.8cm.
Issued: 1933 in a limited
edition of 25
Price: $4800 £3000

WEST WIND HN1826
Designer: R. Garbe
Height: 14½in., 36.8cm.
Issued: 1937-1949
Price: $4800 £3000

WHAT FUN HN3364
Designer: V. Annand
Height: 4in., 10.1cm.
Issued: 1992-1994
Price: $176 £110

WHAT'S THE MATTER?
HN3684
Designer: Nada Pedley
Height: 5½in., 14cm.
Issued: 1995
Price: $112 £70 (R.R.P.)

WHEN I WAS YOUNG HN3457
Designer: Pauline Parsons
Height: 5½in., 14cm.
Issued: 1994
Price: $240 £150 (R.R.P.)

WIGMAKER OF WILLIAMS-
BURG HN2239
Designer: P. Davies
Height: 7½in., 19.1cm.
Issued: 1960-1983
Price: $264 £165

WILL HE - WON'T HE ?
HN3275
Designer: Robert Tabbenor
Height: 9in., 23cm.
Issued: 1990-1994
Price: $232 £145

WILLIAM III HN4022
Designer: D. Tootle
Height: 10½in., 26.7cm.
Issued: 1997 in a limited
edition of 1500
Price: $792 £495

WILLY-WON'T-HE HN1561
Designer: L. Harradine
Height: 6in., 15.2cm.
Issued: 1933-1949
Price: $720 £450

WILLY-WON'T-HE HN1584
Designer: L. Harradine
Height: 6in., 15.2cm.
Issued: 1933-1949
Colour variation
Price: $600 £375

WENDY HN2109

WIGMAKER OF WILLIAMS-
BURG HN2239

WILL HE - WON'T HE ?
HN3275

WHAT FUN HN3364

WHAT'S THE MATTER?
HN3684

WEST INDIAN DANCER
HN2384

WHEN I WAS YOUNG HN3457

ROYAL DOULTON FIGURES

WILLY- WON'T-HE
HN2150
Designer: L. Harradine
Height: 5½in., 14cm.
Issued: 1955-1959
             Colour variation
Price: $400 £250

WIMBLEDON HN3366
Designer: Valerie Annand
Height: 8in., 20cm.
Issued: 1995-1997 in a
             limited edition of
             5000
Price: $392 £245 (R.R.P.)

WINDFLOWER (Style one)
HN1763
Designer: L. Harradine
Height: 7¼in., 18.4cm.
Issued: 1936-1949
Price: $632 £395

WINDFLOWER (Style one)
HN1764
Designer: L. Harradine
Height: 7¼in., 18.4cm.
Issued: 1936-1949
             Colour variation
Price: $880 £550

WINDFLOWER (Style one)
HN2029
Designer: L. Harradine
Height: 7¾in., 19.6cm.
Issued: 1949-1952
             Colour variation
Price: $960 £600

WINDFLOWER (Style two)
HN1920
Designer: L. Harradine
Height: 11in., 27.9cm.
Issued: 1939-1949
Price: $2000 £1250

WINDFLOWER (Style two)
HN1939
Designer: L. Harradine
Height: 11in., 27.9cm.
Issued: 1940-1949
             Colour variation
Price: $2000 £1250

WINDFLOWER M78
Designer: L. Harradine
Height: 4in., 10.1cm.
Issued: 1939-1949
Price: $880 £550

WINDFLOWER M79
Designer: L. Harradine
Height: 4in., 10.1cm.
Issued: 1939-1949
             Colour variation
Price: $880 £550

WINDFLOWER HN3077
Designer: A. Hughes
Height: 12¼in., 31cm.
Issued: 1987-1992
Price: $232 £145

WIMBLEDON HN3366

WINDFLOWER
HN2029

WINDFLOWER HN3077

WINDMILL LADY HN1400
Designer: L. Harradine
Height: 8½in., 21.6cm.
Issued: 1930-1938
Price: $2400 £1500

WINDSWEPT HN3027
Designer: R. Jefferson
Height: 12in., 30.5cm.
Issued: 1985-1994
Price: $200 £125

WINNER HN1407
Designer: Unknown
Height: 6¾in., 17.2cm.
Issued: 1930-1938
Price: $4000 £2500

WINNING PUTT HN3279
Designer: Robert Tabbenor
Height: 8in., 20cm.
Issued: 1991-1995
Price: $232 £145

WINSOME HN2220
Designer: P. Davies
Height: 8in., 20.3cm.
Issued: 1960-1985
Price: $232 £145

WINSTON S. CHURCHILL
HN3433
Designer: Alan Maslankowski
Height: 12in., 30.5cm.
Issued: 1993 in a limited
             edition of 5000
Price: $472 £295 (R.R.P.)

WINTER (Style one) HN315
Designer: Unknown
Height: 7½in., 19.1cm.
Issued: 1918-1938
Price: $1360 £850

WINTER (Style one) HN475
Designer: Unknown
Height: 7½in., 19.1cm.
Issued: 1921-1938
             Colour variation
Price: $1600 £1000

WINTER (Style two) HN2088
Designer: P. Davies
Height: 6¼in., 15.9cm.
Issued: 1952-1959
Price: $560 £350

WINTER WELCOME HN3611
Designer: P. Davies
Height: 7½in., 19.1cm.
Issued: 1993 Colourway
             red
Price: $175 £110 (R.R.P.)

WINTER'S DAY HN3769
Designer: Nada Pedley
Height: 7¾in., 19.5cm.
Issued: 1997 only.
Price: $232 £145

WINTER'S WALK HN3052
Designer: A. Hughes
Height: 12¼in., 31cm.
Issued: 1987-1995
Price: $280 £175

ROYAL DOULTON FIGURES

WINTER (Style two) HN2088

WINTER'S DAY HN3769

WINTER'S WALK HN3052

WINNING PUTT HN3279

WINSTON S. CHURCHILL
HN3433

WINTER WELCOME HN3611

WINDSWEPT HN3027

ROYAL DOULTON FIGURES

WINTERTIME HN3060
(R.D.I.C.C.)
Designer: A. Hughes
Height: 8¾in., 22.2cm.
Issued: 1985
Price: $290 £195

WINTERTIME HN3622
Designer: V. Annand
Height: 8½in., 21.5cm.
Issued: 1995-1996
Price: $312 £195

WISTFUL HN2396
Designer: P. Davies
Height: 6½in., 16.5cm.
Issued: 1979-1990
Price: $264 £165

WISTFUL HN2472
Designer: P. Davies
Height: 6½in., 16.5cm.
Issued: 1985 only
Price: $312 £195

WISTFUL HN3664
Designer: Peter Gee
Height: 12¼in., 31cm.
Issued: 1994
Price: $80 £50 (R.R.P.)

WITH LOVE HN3393
Designer: Alan Maslankowski
Height: 6in., 15cm.
Issued: 1992
Price: $64 £40 (R.R.P.)

WITH LOVE HN3492
Designer: A. Maslankowski
Height: 6in., 15cm.
Issued: 1994
            Colour variation
            Canada only
Price: $62 £39 (R.R.P.)

WIZARD HN2877
Designer: A. Maslankowski
Height: 9¾in., 24.8cm.
Issued: 1979
Price: $240 £150 (R.R.P.)

WIZARD HN3121 (Flambé)
Designer: A. Maslankowski
Height: 10in., 25.4cm.
Issued: 1990-1995
Price: $360 £225

WIZARD HN3722
Designer: Alan Maslankowski
Height: 10in., 25.5cm.
Issued: 1994-1996
Price: $160 £100

**WOMAN HOLDING CHILD
HN462**
Designer: Unknown
Height: 9¼in., 23.5cm.
Issued: 1921-1938
Price: $4000 £2500

**WOMAN HOLDING CHILD
HN570**
Designer: Unknown
Height: 9¼in., 23.5cm.
Issued: 1923-1938
            Colour variation
Price: $4000 £2500

WINTERTIME HN3622

WINTERTIME HN3060

WOOD NYMPH HN2192

WIZARD HN3722

WISTFUL HN2396

WITH LOVE HN3393

WIZARD HN2877

336

**WOMAN HOLDING CHILD
HN703**
Designer: Unknown
Height: 9¼in., 23.5cm.
Issued: 1925-1938
          Colour variation
Price: $4400 £2750

**WOMAN HOLDING CHILD
HN743**
Designer: Unknown
Height: 9¼in., 23.5cm.
Issued: 1925-1938
          Colour variation
Price: $4400 £2750

**WOMAN OF THE TIME OF
HENRY VI HN43**
Designer: E. W. Light
Height: 9¼in., 23.4cm.
Issued: 1914-1938
Price: $4400 £2500

WOOD NYMPH HN2192
Designer: P. Davies
Height: 7¼in., 18.4cm.
Issued: 1958-1962
Price: $360 £225

WRITING HN3049
Designer: P. Parsons
Height: 7¾in., 19.5cm.
Issued: 1986 in a limited
          edition of 750
Price: $1040 £650

Y

YEARNING HN2920 (White)
Designer: P. Gee
Height: 11¾in., 29.8cm.
Issued: 1982-1986
Price: $200 £125

YEARNING HN2921 (Black)
Designer: P. Gee
Height: 11¾in., 29.8cm.
Issued: 1982-1986
Price: £200 £125

**YEOMAN OF THE GUARD
HN688**
Designer: L. Harradine
Height: 5¾in., 14.6cm.
Issued: 1924-1938
Price: $1040 £650

**YEOMAN OF THE GUARD
HN2122**
Designer: L. Harradine
Height: 5¾in., 14.6cm.
Issued: 1954-1959
Price: $880 £550

YOUNG DREAMS HN3176
Designer: D. Tootle
Height: 6¼in., 16cm.
Issued: 1988-1992
Price: $264 £165

YOUNG MASTER HN2872

YOUNG LOVE HN2735

YOURS FOREVER HN3354

WRITING HN3049

ROYAL DOULTON FIGURES

YOUNG KNIGHT HN94
Designer: C. J. Noke
Height: 9½in., 24.1cm.
Issued: 1918-1936
Price: $4000 £2500

YOUNG LOVE HN2735
Designer: D. V. Tootle
Height: 10in., 25.4cm.
Issued: 1975-1990
Price: $600 £375

YOUNG MASTER HN2872
Designer: P. Davies
Height: 7in., 17.8cm.
Issued: 1980-1989
Price: $360 £225

YOUNG MELODY HN3654
Designer: Nada Pedley
Height: 4¼in., 11cm.
Issued: 1994-1996
Price: $88 £55

YOUNG MISS NIGHTINGALE HN2010
Designer: P. Davies
Height: 9¼in., 23.5cm.
Issued: 1948-1953
Price: $880 £550

YOUNG WIDOW HN1399
Designer: L. Harradine
Height: 8in., 20.3cm.
Issued: 1930-1938
Price: $2000 £1250
Also called 'Little Mother'(Style two)

YOURS FOREVER HN3354
Designer: Pauline Parsons
Height: 8in., 20cm.
Issued: 1992-1997
Price: $200 £125

YUM-YUM (Style one) HN1268
Designer: L. Harradine
Height: 5in., 12.7cm.
Issued: 1928-1938
Price: $880 £550

YUM-YUM (Style one) HN1287
Designer: L. Harradine
Height: 5in., 12.7cm.
Issued: 1928-1939
   Colour variation
Price: $880 £550

YUM-YUM (Style two) HN2899
Designer: W. K. Harper
Height: 10¾in., 27.3cm.
Issued: 1980-1986
Price: $760 £475

YVONNE HN3038
Designer: A. Hughes
Height: 9in., 23cm.
Issued: 1987-1992
Price: $264 £165

YOUNG MISS NIGHTINGALE HN2010

YOUNG MELODY HN3654

YVONNE HN3038

YUM-YUM (Style two) HN2899

TABLE LIGHTERS

BACCHUS D6505
Designer: M. Henk
Height: 3½in., 9cm.
Issued: 1964-1994
Price: $190 £120

BEEFEATER D6233
Designer: H. Fenton
Height: 3½in., 9cm.
Issued: 1958-1973
Price: $190 £120

BUZ FUZ D5838
Designer: H. Fenton
Height: 3½in., 9cm.
Issued: 1958
Price: $240 £150

CAP'N CUTTLE D5842
Designer: L. Harradine
Height: 3½in., 9cm.
Issued: 1958
Price: $240 £150

CAPTAIN AHAB D6506
Designer: G. Sharpe
Height: 3½in., 9cm.
Issued: 1964-1974
Price: $280 £175

FALSTAFF D6385
Designer: H. Fenton
Height: 3½in., 9cm.
Issued: 1958-1973
Price: $240 £150

LAWYER D6504
Designer: M. Henk
Height: 3½in., 9cm.
Issued: 1962-1974
Price: $240 £150

LONG JOHN SILVER D6386
Designer: M. Henk
Height: 3½in., 9cm.
Issued: 1958-1973
Price: $190 £120

MR MICAWBER D5843
Designer: H. Fenton
Height: 3½in., 9cm.
Issued: 1958
Price: $240 £150

MR PICKWICK D5839
Designer: H. Fenton
Height: 3½in., 9cm.
Issued: 1958-1961
Price: $280 £175

OLD CHARLEY D5527
Designer: C. Noke
Height: 3½in., 9cm.
Issued: 1959-1973
Price: $240 £150

POACHER D6464
Designer: M. Henk
Height: 3½in., 9cm.
Issued: 1958-1973
Price: $240 £150

PORTHOS D6453
Designer: M. Henk
Height: 3½in., 9cm.
Issued: 1958
Price: $480 £300

RIP VAN WINKLE D6463
Designer: G. Blower
Height: 3½in., 9cm.
Issued: 1958
Price: $480 £300

MR MICAWBER

LAWYER

CAPTAIN AHAB

BUZ FUZ

BEEFEATER

BACCHUS

LONG JOHN SILVER

POACHER

PORTHOS

LD CHARLEY

CAP'N CUTTLE

RIP VAN WINKLE

FALSTAFF

MR PICKWICK

TINIES

ARTFUL DODGER D6678
Designer: P. Gee
Issued: 1982
Price: $64 £40

BETSY TROTWOOD D6684
Designer: M. Abberley
Issued: 1982
Price: $64 £40

BILL SYKES D6684
Designer: M. Abberley
Issued: 1982
Price: $64 £40

CHARLES DICKENS D6688
Designer: E. Griffiths
Issued: 1982
Price: $80 £50

DAVID COPPERFIELD D6680
Designer: M. Abberley
Issued: 1982
Price: $64 £40

FAGIN D6679
Designer: R. Tabbenor
Issued: 1982
Price: $64 £40

LITTLE NELL D6681
Designer: M. Abberley
Issued: 1982
Price: $64 £40

MR BUMBLE D6686
Designer: R. Tabbenor
Issued: 1982
Price: $64 £40

MRS BARDELL D6687
Designer: R. Tabbenor
Issued: 1982
Price: $64 £40

OLIVER TWIST D6677
Designer: R. Tabbenor
Issued: 1982
Price: $64 £40

SCROOGE D6682
Designer: M. Abberley
Issued: 1982
Price: $64 £40

URIAH HEEP D6682
Designer: R. Tabbenor
Issued: 1982
Price: $64 £40

OLIVER TWIST

BETSY TROTWOOD

DAVID COPPERFIELD

FAGIN

LITTLE NELL

MR BUMBLE

MRS BARDELL

BILL SYKES

URIAH HEEP

ARTFUL DODGER

CHARLES DICKENS

SCROOGE

TEAPOTS

FALSTAFF D6854
Designer: W.K. Harper
Height: 6½in., 16.5cm.
Issued: 1989-1992
Price: $136 £85

LONG JOHN SILVER D6853
Designer: W.K. Harper
Height: 6½in., 16.5cm.
Issued: 1989-1992
Price: $136 £85

OLD BALOON SELLER D6855
Designer: W.K. Harper
Height: 6½in., 16.5cm.
Issued: 1990-1992
Price: $160 £100

OLD CHARLEY D6017
Designer: C. Noke
Height: 7in., 18cm.
Issued: 1939
Price: $1360 £850

OLD SALT D6818
(Collectors' Club)
Designer: W.K. Harper
Height: 6½in., 16.5cm.
Issued: 1988
Price: $224 £140

SAIREY GAMP D6015
Designer: H. Fenton
Height: 7in., 18cm.
Issued: 1939
Price: $1360 £850

TONY WELLER D6016
Designer: H. Fenton
Height: 7in., 18cm.
Issued: 1939
Price: $1360 £850

OLD SALT

OLD CHARLEY

TOBACCO JARS

OLD CHARLEY D5844
Designer: C. Noke
Height: 5½in., 14cm.
Issued: 1938-1941
Price: $1280 £800

PADDY D5854
Designer: H. Fenton
Height: 5½in., 14cm.
Issued: 1938-1941
Price: $1280 £800

PADDY D5854

OLD CHARLEY D5844

TOBY JUGS

The name 'Toby' has long associations with conviviality and it was used by Shakespeare in his Toby Belch and by Laurence Sterne in his character Uncle Toby in 'Tristram Shandy'. Today it has come to signify a jug made like a seated male figure in a tricorn hat with a pipe or a mug of beer on his knee. This is particularly due to the creations of Doulton who took up and developed the long history of the Toby jug and made it beloved by a vast collecting public.

From 1815, when John Doulton first set up his business, the firm made Toby jugs but the earliest examples were only brown salt glazed as they had been for centuries. In 1925 however coloured Toby jugs were added to the range by Harry Simeon and their potential was immediately recognised by Charles J. Noke who made their colours even more vivid and developed them into one of the company's best selling lines.

Charlie Chaplin Toby jug produced in 1918, 11in. high, with detachable bowler hat.

Huntsman, a Royal Doulton Kingsware Toby jug, 7½in. high.

The design of Happy John D6031, introduced in 1939 by Harry Fenton, was clearly inspired by the earlier traditional Staffordshire Toby.

TOBY JUGS

ALBERT SAGGER THE POT-TER
D6745
(Collectors' Club)
Designer: W. Harper
Height: Small 4in., 10cm.
Issued: 1986-1992
Price: $192 £120

CHARLIE CHAPLIN
Designer: Unknown
Height: Large 11in., 28cm.
Issued: c.1918
Price: $3600 £2250

CHARLES DICKENS D6997
In a limited edition of 2500
Designer: S. J. Taylor
Height: 5in., 13cm.
Issued: 1995-1997
Price: $152 £95

CHARRINGTON (TOBY ALE)
D8074
Designer: Unknown
Height: Large 9¼in., 23.5cm
Issued: 1934-1938
Price: $360 £225

CHARRINGTON (ONE TOBY…)
D8074
Designer: Unknown
Height: Large 9¼in., 23.5cm.
Issued: 1937-1938
Price: $520 £325

CHARRINGTON'S D8074
Designer: Unknown
Height: Large 9¼in., 23.5cm.
Issued: 1938-1939
Price: $720 £450

CLIFF CORNELL (Blue Suit)
Designer: Unknown
Height: 9¼in., 23.5cm.
Issued: 1956 in a limited
            edition of 500
Price: $440 £275

CLIFF CORNELL (Brown Suit)
Designer: Unknown
Height: 9¼in., 23.5cm.
Issued: 1956 in a limited
            edition of 500
Price: $392 £245

CLIFF CORNELL (Tan Suit)
Designer: Unknown
Height: 9¼in., 23.5cm.
Issued: 1956 in a limited
            edition of 350
Price: $440 £275

THE CLOWN D6935
Designer: S. Taylor
Height: Medium 5½in., 14cm.
Issued: 1993
Price: $110 £69

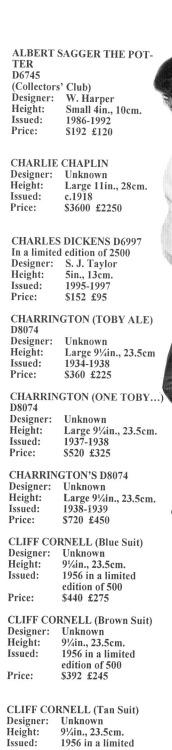

ALBERT SAGGER THE POTTER D6745

CHARLIE CHAPLIN

CLIFF CORNELL (Blue Suit)

CLIFF CORNELL (Brown Suit)

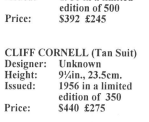

CLIFF CORNELL (Tan Suit)

THE CLOWN D6935

DR. JEKYLL & MR HYDE D7024
Designer: S. Taylor
Height: 5in., 13cm.
Issued: 1996
Price: $128 £80 (R.R.P.)

FALSTAFF D6062
Designer: C. Noke
Height: Large 8½in.., 21.5cm.
Issued: 1939-1991
Price: $152 £95

FALSTAFF D6063
Designer: C. Noke
Height: Small 5¼in., 13.5cm.
Issued: 1939-1991
Price: $104 £65

FATHER CHRISTMAS D6940
Designer: W. K Harper
Height: Medium 5½in.,14cm.
Issued: 1993
Price: $80 £50

GEORGE ROBEY
Designer: Unknown
Height: Large 10½in., 26.5cm.
Issued: c.1925
Price: $4000 £2500

HAPPY JOHN D6031
Designer: H. Fenton
Height: Large 8¾in., 22cm.
Issued: 1939-1991
Price: $152 £95

HAPPY JOHN D6070
Designer: H. Fenton
Height: Small 5½in., 14cm.
Issued: 1939-1991
Price: $120 £75

HONEST MEASURE D6108
Designer: H. Fenton
Height: Small 4½in., 11.5cm.
Issued: 1939-1991
Price: $120 £75

HUNTSMAN D6320
Designer: H. Fenton
Height: Medium 7½in., 19cm.
Issued: 1950-1991
Price: $176 £110

JESTER D6910
Limited edition of 2500
Designer: S. J. Taylor
Height: Medium
Issued: 1992
Price: $216 £135

JOLLY TOBY D6109
Designer: H. Fenton
Height: Medium 6½in., 16.5cm
Issued: 1939-1991
Price: $152 £95

JUDGE & THIEF D6988
Designer: S. Taylor
Height: 5½in., 14cm.
Issued: 1995
Price: $128 £80 (R.R.P.)

JUDGE & THIEF D6988

HONEST MEASURE D6108

FALSTAFF D6063

HUNTSMAN D6320

JOLLY TOBY D6109

GEORGE ROBEY

HAPPY JOHN D6031

DR. JEKYLL & MR HYDE D7024

FATHER CHRISTMAS D6940

KING & QUEEN OF CLUBS
D6999 in a limited edition of 2500
Designer: S. Taylor
Height: 5¾in., 14.5cm.
Issued: 1995
Price: $160 £100

KING & QUEEN OF DIAMONDS
D6969 in a limited edition of 2500
Designer: S. Taylor
Height: 5¼in., 13.5cm.
Issued: 1994
Price: $160 £100 (R.R.P.)

KING & QUEEN OF HEARTS
D7037
Designer: S. J. Taylor
Height: 5in., 13cm.,
Issued: 1996
Price: $160 £100 (R.R.P.)

LEPRECHAUN D6948
Designer: S. Taylor
Height: Medium 5¼in.,
 13.5cm.
Issued: 1994 in a limited
 edition of 2500
Price: $95 £59

OLD CHARLEY D6030
Designer: H. Fenton
Height: Large 8¾in., 22cm.
Issued: 1939-1960
Price: $296 £185

OLD CHARLEY D6069
Designer: H. Fenton
Height: Small 5½in., 14cm.
Issued: 1939-1960
Price: $232 £145

SHERLOCK HOLMES D6661
Designer: R. Tabbenor
Height: Large 8¾in., 22cm.
Issued: 1981-1991
Price: $152 £95

SIR FRANCIS DRAKE D6660
Designer: M. Abberley
Height: Large 9in., 23cm.
Issued: 1981-1991
Price: $152 £95

SQUIRE D6319
Designer: H. Fenton
Height: Medium 6in., 15cm.
Issued: 1950-1969
Price: $392 £245

THE BEST IS NOT TOO GOOD
D6107
Designer: H. Fenton
Height: 4½in., 11.5cm.
Issued: 1939-1960
Price: $392 £245

TOBY XX D6088
Designer: H. Fenton
Height: 6½in., 16.5cm.
Issued: 1939-1969
Price: $312 £195

KING & QUEEN OF CLUBS
D6999

SIR FRANCIS DRAKE D6660

OLD CHARLEY D6030

SQUIRE D6319

KING & QUEEN OF HEARTS
D7037

THE BEST IS NOT TOO GOOD
D6107

KING & QUEEN OF DIAMONDS
D6969

SHERLOCK HOLMES D6661

TOBY JUGS

TOBY XX
Designer: Harry Simeon
Height: Large 7½in., 19cm.
Issued: 1922
Price: $240 £150

TOWN CRIER D6920
In a limited edition of 2500
Designer: S. J. Taylor
Height: Medium
Issued: 1992
Price: $110 £69

WINSTON CHURCHILL D6171
Designer: H. Fenton
Height: Large 9in., 23cm.
Issued: 1941-1991
Price: $152 £95

WINSTON CHURCHILL D6172
Designer: H. Fenton
Height: Medium 5½in., 14cm.
Issued: 1941-1991
Price: $120 £75

WINSTON CHURCHILL D6175
Designer: H. Fenton
Height: Small 4in., 10cm.
Issued: 1941-1991
Price: $104 £65

TOBY XX

WINSTON CHURCHILL

DOULTONVILLE TOBIES

ALDERMAN MACE D6766
Designer: W.Harper
Height: 4in., 10cm.
Issued: 1987-1991
Price: $104 £65

BETTY BITTERS D6716
Designer: W. Harper
Height: 4in., 10cm.
Issued: 1984-1990
Price: $88 £55

CAPTAIN PROP D6812
Designer: W. Harper
Height: 4in., 10cm.
Issued: 1988-1991
Price: $120 £75

CAPTAIN SALT D6721
Designer: W. Harper
Height: 4in., 10cm.
Issued: 1985-1991
Price: $88 £55

CHARLIE CHEER D6768
Designer: W. Harper
Height: 4in., 10cm.
Issued: 1987-1991
Price: $136 £85

DR. PULSE D6723
Designer: W. Harper
Height: 4in., 10cm.
Issued: 1985-1991
Price: $96 £60

FLORA FUCHSIA D6767
Designer: W. Harper
Height: 4in., 10cm.
Issued: 1987-1990
Price: $104 £65

FRED FEARLESS D6809
Designer: W. Harper
Height: 4in., 10cm.
Issued: 1989-1991
Price: $104 £65

FRED FLY D6742
Designer: W. Harper
Height: 4in., 10cm.
Issued: 1986-1991
Price: $96 £60

LEN LIFEBELT D6811
Designer: W. Harper
Height: 4in., 10cm.
Issued: 1988-1991
Price: $104 £65

MADAME CRYSTAL D6714
Designer: W. Harper
Height: 4in., 10cm.
Issued: 1984-1989
Price: $120 £75

MAJOR GREEN D6740
Designer: W. Harper
Height: 4in., 10cm.
Issued: 1986-1991
Price: $88 £55

ALDERMAN MACE D6766

CAPTAIN PROP D6812

BETTY BITTERS D6716

CAPTAIN SALT D6721

CHARLIE CHEER D6768

DR. PULSE D6723

DOULTONVILLE TOBIES

TOBY JUGS

**FRED FEARLESS
D6809**

FLORA FUCHSIA D6767

FRED FLY D6742

**LEN LIFEBELT
D6811**

**MADAME
CRYSTAL D6714**

MIKE MINERAL D6741

**MISS NOSTRUM
D6700**

MAJOR GREEN D6740

MISS STUDIOUS D6722

MONSIEUR CHASSEUR D6769

DOULTONVILLE TOBIES

MIKE MINERAL D6741
Designer: W. Harper
Height: 4in., 10cm.
Issued: 1986-1989
Price: $232 £145

MISS NOSTRUM D6700
Designer: W. Harper
Height: 4in., 10cm.
Issued: 1983-1991
Price: $88 £55

MISS STUDIOUS D6722
Designer: W. Harper
Height: 4in., 10cm.
Issued: 1985-1989
Price: $120 £75

MONSIEUR CHASSEUR D6769
Designer: W. Harper
Height: 4in., 10cm.
Issued: 1987-1991
Price: $104 £65

MR BRISKET D6743
Designer: W. Harper
Height: 4in., 10cm.
Issued: 1986-1991
Price: $120 £75

MR FURROW D6701
Designer: W. Harper
Height: 4in., 10cm.
Issued: 1983-1989
Price: $104 £65

MR LITIGATE D6699
Designer: W. Harper
Height: 4in., 10cm.
Issued: 1983-1991
Price: $104 £65

MRS LOAN D6715
Designer: W. Harper
Height: 4in., 10cm.
Issued: 1984-1989
Price: $88 £55

MR TONSIL D6713
Designer: W. Harper
Height: 4in., 10cm.
Issued: 1984-1991
Price: $88 £55

PAT PARCEL D6813
Designer: W. Harper
Height: 4in., 10cm.
Issued: 1988-1992
Price: $152 £95

REV. CASSOCK D6702
Designer: W. Harper
Height: 4in., 10cm.
Issued: 1983-1990
Price: $104 £65

SERGEANT PEELER D6720
Designer: W. Harper
Height: 4in., 10cm.
Issued: 1985-1991
Price: $104 £65

MR FURROW D6701

MR BRISKET D6743

MRS LOAN D6715

MR LITIGATE D6699

MR TONSIL D6713

PAT PARCEL D6813

REV. CASSOCK D6702

SERGEANT PEELER D6720

SMALL SEATED TOBIES

CAP'N CUTTLE D6266
Designer: H. Fenton
Height: 4½in., 11.5cm.
Issued: 1948-1960
Price: $232 £145

FAT BOY D6264
Designer: H. Fenton
Height: 4½in., 11.5cm.
Issued: 1948-1960
Price: $232 £145

MR MICAWBER D6262
Designer: H. Fenton
Height: 4½in., 11.5cm.
Issued: 1948-1960
Price: $232 £145

MR PICKWICK D6261
Designer: H. Fenton
Height: 4½in., 11.5cm.
Issued: 1948-1960
Price: $232 £145

SAIREY GAMP D6263
Designer: H. Fenton
Height: 4½in., 11.5cm.
Issued: 1948-1960
Price: $240 £150

SAM WELLER D6265
Designer: H. Fenton
Height: 4½in., 11.5cm.
Issued: 1948-1960
Price: $232 £145

MR PICKWICK D6261   SAIREY GAMP D6263   MR MICAWBER D6262

CAP'N CUTTLE D6266   SAM WELLER D6265   FAT BOY D6264

TOOTHPICK HOLDERS

OLD CHARLEY D6152
Designer: C. Noke
Height: 2¼in., 5.5cm.
Issued: 1940-1941
Price: $560 £350

PADDY D6151
Designer: H. Fenton
Height: 2¼in., 5.5cm.
Issued: 1940-1941
Price: $800 £500

SAIREY GAMP D6150
Designer: H. Fenton
Height: 2¼in., 5.5cm.
Issued: 1940-1941
Price: $480 £300

OLD CHARLEY D6152   PADDY D6151   SAIREY GAMP D6150

ANIMAL FIGURES

Before 1912 only a few animal figures were produced by the Doulton potteries but among them were the highly successful Flambé Ware Figures.

However by the time of World War One, Charles J. Noke launched a new line of very realistic figures of animals and birds which proved to be highly popular with the buying public.

In the beginning they were used to decorate ashtrays, bookends and other household objects but later they began to be produced as free-standing figures in their own right. Great care was taken to model and paint them as close to reality as possible.

In 1936 limited numbers of earthenware figures of goats, calves and deer were made by artist Raoh Schorr but one of the first series which was reproduced in large numbers for an eager public was the Championship Dog range, which was launched in 1939. At least 41 models were made and many of them are still in production

The Chatcull Range of animal figures was started in 1940 with figures modelled by artist Joe Ledger, who named the series after his home, Chatcull Hall. Most of these are now out of production.

Character Kitten, HN2584, 1¾in. high, c.m., withdrawn 1995. $105 £65

Bulldog, with the Union Jack draped over his back, c.m.l. & c. Large $640 £400; Med $480 £300; Small $320 £200

Dachshund, HN1128, 3³/₄in. high, c.m., withdrawn 1985. $120 £75

Tiger on Rock, a Royal Doulton Prestige figure, HN2639, 11½ x 14in., c.m.l. & c., withdrawn 1992. $1,040 £650

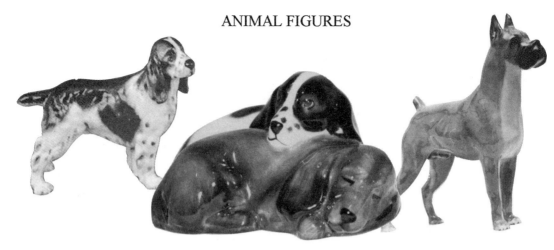

Cocker Spaniel, HN2517, 3½in.
high. $160 £100

Cocker Spaniels, asleep, HN2590,
1¾in. high, c.m.l. & c., withdrawn
1985. $120 £75

Boxer, HN2643, 6½in. high,
withdrawn 1985. $160 £100

Siamese Cat, standing, HN2660,
5¼in. high, c.m., withdrawn 1985.
                    $135 £85

Huntsman Fox, HN6448, 4½in.
high, c.m.l. & c., withdrawn 1985.
                    $190 £120

French Poodle, HN2631, 5½in.
high, c.m.l. & c., withdrawn 1985.
                    $190 £120

Cocker Spaniel carrying a
pheasant, HN1138, 5¼in. high.
                    $360 £200

The Gude Grey Mare, HN2519,
7¾in. high, withdrawn 1960.
                    $560 £350

Scottish Terrier, begging, K10,
3½in. high, withdrawn 1977.
                    $120 £75

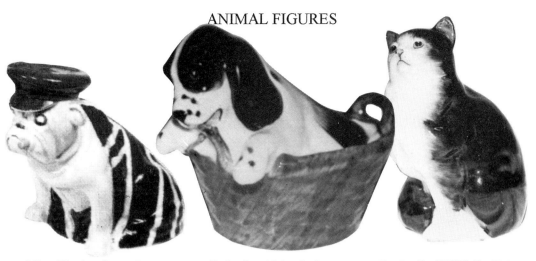

A Royal Doulton figure of a
bulldog draped in the Union Jack,
7in. high, printed marks.
$1120 £700

Cocker Spaniel, in a basket,
HN2586, 2¾in. high, c.m.l. & c.,
withdrawn 1985. $160 £100

Persian Cat, HN999, 5in. high,
c.m.l. & c., withdrawn 1985.
$160 £100

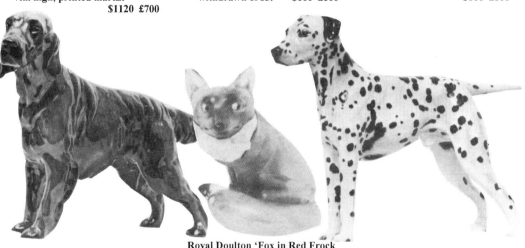

Irish Setter, HN1055, 5½in. high,
withdrawn 1985. $175 £110

Royal Doulton 'Fox in Red Frock
Coat', HN100, 16cm. high, c.m.l. &
c., 1913-1942. $1000 £650

Dalmation, HN1113, 5¼in. high,
withdrawn 1985. $200 £125

Fox Terrier, small, HN1014,
withdrawn 1985. $112 £70

Scottish Terrier, sitting, K18,
2¼in. high, c.m., withdrawn 1977.
$120 £75

Collie, medium, HN1058, 5¼in.
high, withdrawn 1985. $175 £110

Character Dog with plate, Jack Russell HN1158, 3in. high, withdrawn 1985. $135 £85

Character Dog, standing, HN2509, 2½in. high, withdrawn 1959. $225 £140

Puppy in a basket, HN2585, 2in. high, withdrawn 1985. $120 £75

Collie, HN1059, 3½in. high, c.m.l & c., withdrawn 1959. $190 £120

Character dog, sitting, HN1099, 4in. high. $128 £80

Bulldog, white, small, HN1074, 3¼in. high, withdrawn 1985. $360 £200

Model of two loving cats, HN234, impressed date *1920.* $1250 £800

Welsh Corgi, HN2559, 3½in., c.m., withdrawn 1985. $120 £75

A Royal Doulton model, 'Kingfisher', HN131, 10.5cm. high, c.m.l. & c. $160 £100

Cocker Spaniel, K9, 2½in. high,
c.m.l. & c., withdrawn 1977.
$105 £65

Character Dog, bone in mouth,
HN1159, 3¾in. high, withdrawn
1985. $130 £80

Rough Haired Terrier, HN1014,
4in. high, c.m., withdrawn 1985.
$120 £75

Cocker Spaniel & Pheasant,
HN1001, 6½in. high, withdrawn
1985. $400 £250

Labrador, HN2667, 5in. high, c.m.,
withdrawn 1985. $120 £75

A Royal Doulton Cairn, begging,
HN2589, 4in. high, withdrawn
1985. $120 £75

Cairn, sitting, K11, 2¼in. high,
c.m., withdrawn 1977. $120 £75

Three Terrier Puppies, in a basket,
HN2588, 2¾in. high, c.m.l. & c.,
withdrawn 1985. $130 £80

Siamese Cat, sitting, HN2655,
5¼in. high, withdrawn 1985.
$160 £100

Pride of the Shires, HN2528, 9in. high, withdrawn 1960. $560 £350

A figure of a Dachshund, HN1141, 2¾in. high. $120 £75

Royal Doulton model of a rhinoceros, by Leslie Harradine, 6¼in. high. $1200 £750

English Setter and Pheasant, HN2529, 8½in. high, c.m.l. & c., withdrawn 1985. $560 £350

River Hog, HN2663, 3½in. high, c.m.l. & c., withdrawn 1969. $280 £175

Character Kitten, cleaning paw, HN2583, 2in. high, c.m., withdrawn 1985. $112 £70

Cocker Spaniel, HN1036, 5in. high, c.m., withdrawn 1985. $175 £110

Cocker Spaniel, HN1020, 5¼in. high, c.m., withdrawn 1985. $120 £75

English Setter, HN1049, 7¾in. x 12¼in., c.m., withdrawn 1985. $175 £110

ART POTTERY

The most astonishing aspect of Doulton Art Pottery is its range and the variety of styles and techniques introduced by the company.

These were developed in the Lambeth Studios established by Henry Doulton from 1867 onwards. The Studio was financed by the far more prosaic side of the business, sanitary and chemical ceramics.

Henry Doulton provided creative artists with the opportunity of expressing themselves in pottery and it is to his credit that he allowed their talents and eccentricities full flowering . There was never any attempt to impose a 'house style' on them.

"The personal is the true vivifying element in art," he said.

The first big name in Art Pottery was that of George Tinworth, who began making little models of mice and children, mainly for his own amusement. Many of those were never exhibited.

He was followed by over 400 enthusiastic artists who worked at Lambeth over the years. They not only experimented with the sort of sculptures that could be produced in pottery but also in the intricacy of decorative painting and devised a great range of glazing and firing techniques.

CARRARA WARE

Carrara ware got its name because it looks like Italian Carrara marble and is a dense off-white stoneware with a slightly transparent crystalline matt glaze, which is occasionally crackled. The effect was achieved by using more Cornish china clay than usual in the mixture. It was mainly produced between 1887 and 1903 but some examples were still being made in the 1920s when it had a short lived revival.

CHANG WARE

Chang ware was named after a Chinese master potter of the Sung Dynasty and it was an effort by Doulton to produce glazes which old Chinese potters had also tried to create. The first Chang pottery appeared in 1925 and was characterised by thick textured layers of flowing glaze in lustrous colours, which gave a lava like appearance. It was used on vases, some of them festooned with dragons or lizards.

CHINESE JADE

In 1920, after years of experimentation, Charles J. Noke achieved his ambition of reproducing jade in ceramic. His simulated jade was used to make libation cups, figures and bowls and examples of it are now very rare because only a limited number of pieces were successfully made.

CROWN LAMBETH

Crown Lambeth is a fine earthenware remarkable for the richness and transparency of the decorations. It was decorated by hand painting on biscuit ware and, after glazing, was re-fired and re-painted several times. Crown Lambeth was first shown in the Chicago Exhibition of 1893 and was much admired, but production ceased after 1903 because heavy kiln losses meant the line was a loss maker.

CRYSTALLINE WARE

The surface of the Crystalline ware glaze sparkled because zinc oxide was mixed in the glaze compound and it was kept in a high kiln temperature for long periods. It was invented by Cuthbert Bailey who left Doulton in 1907, but examples of crystalline ware were produced till 1914 when production ceased because of the expense by the high number of failures in firing.

CYPRUS WARE

In 1878 Cyprus was annexed to Britain by the Treaty of Berlin and Doulton celebrated the occasion by introducing Cyprus Ware. It is recognisable by the lotus and hatched designs, based on ancient vases excavated on the island of Cyprus about the time of the Annexation.

IMPASTO

The unusual effect of Impasto is achieved by fusing two harmonious pigments and firing with very little gloss. Colour was applied to raw clay and potters used a small amount of relief to add to reality. Impasto colours were browns, yellows, greens and blues and its production in the last quarter of the 19th century coincided with one of the most artistic periods of the Lambeth Pottery.

MARQUETERIE WARE

This is the rarest of the Lambeth wares. Invented in 1886, it was patented in 1887 under the joint names of Doulton and Rix, and was a simulation of the different coloured wood inlays made by cabinetmakers. This was achieved in pottery by cutting thin slices of coloured clay in various patterns. Marqueterie Ware was produced in large quantities until 1906 when it ceased because of heavy production costs.

MORRISIAN WARE

Morrisian ware derives its name from the decorations of Morris dancers with which it was decorated. It was made between 1901 and 1924 at Lambeth and some items were designed by A. Pierce. Other items, not marked as Morrisian but with the same sort of decoration, were painted with figures of golfers in 17th century costume.

PERSIAN WARE

Persian ware was based on Eastern designs with blue, green and orange colouring. Persian ware was produced between 1884 and 1912 and was influenced by the work of William de Morgan. It was used in tiles and panels for wall decoration as well as in pottery. The painting on a white slip coating was done before the glazing and firing.

SUNG

Sung is remarkable for the mottled and veined effect of the glaze produced by high temperatures during firing. The first examples of Sung were exhibited at the British Industry Fair at the Crystal Palace in 1920 and they were of animal and figure models. Two of the best known are the elephant and the lustrous green Buddha. Each piece was signed by Charles J. Noke who developed the glaze.

TITANIAN WARE

Titanian ware derives its name from titanium oxide which gives this ware its characteristic smoky blue colour. It was developed by Charles J. Noke during the early years of World War One and was often decorated with transfer printings of birds of paradise or, during the 1920s when the Tutankhamen fever was at its height, with Egyptian designs. Artists involved were Allen, Raby, Tittensor and Henri.

VELLUMA WARE

Velluma ware was only produced between 1911 and 1914 and as a consequence is extremely rare. The offwhite glaze has a parchment like texture, hence the name. The earthenware shapes were brought from Burslem and painted at Lambeth with transfers from etchings by A.E. Pearce and W. Rowe.

ART POTTERY

An oviform pate-sur-pate vase decorated with birds by Florence Barlow, 15in. high.
$560 £350

Royal Doulton Art Deco period toilet set, the borders painted in green, also decorated with panels of stylised foliage in colours, printed marks and registration number for circa 1910/20.
$320 £200

'Leaping Salmon', a large Chinese jade figure, signed Noke and Nixon, 11½in. high, circa 1930.
$1120 £700

A Doulton Lambeth coffee pot painted with a purple iris, circa 1879.
$352 £220

Doulton Art Pottery jardiniere with a blue ground and applied flowers, 8¾in. high.
$192 £120

Royal Doulton vase painted by Ethel Beard, 13in. high.
$192 £120

Doulton Lambeth Carrara Ware vase with flared neck by Josephine Durtnall, 16in. high.
$525 £350

Pair of Royal Doulton cylindrical vases painted by L. Johnson, 30cm. high.
$640 £400

A Doulton Burslem baluster vase painted with an Edwardian lady, by H.G. Theaker, 10¼in. high.
$400 £250

CHANG

A Royal Doulton 'Chang' jar
and cover, by Harry Nixon, 8in.
high. $1120 £700

A Chang vase by Noke and
Nixon, 7in. high. $1280 £800

Royal Doulton Chang vase by
Nixon and Noke, 5¹/₂in. high,
circa 1920. $800 £500

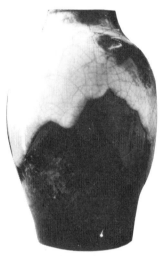

A Chang vase by Noke and
Nixon, 10in. high. $1440 £900

A Chang vase by Noke and
Nixon, 8in. high. $1440 £900

A Chang vase by Noke and
Nixon, 10in. high. $1440 £900

A Chang vase by Noke and
Nixon, 8in. high. $1280 £800

A Chang vase by Noke and
Nixon, 10in. high. $2560 £1600

The Chang Potter lamp base by
Noke and Nixon, 10¹/₂in. high.
                      $3200 £2000

FAIENCE

Doulton Lambeth faience vase with the artist's monogram for Mary Butterton, circa 1880. **$288 £180**

A large Doulton Lambeth faience plaque by Florence E. Lewis, 15½in. diam., circa 1880. **$288 £180**

A Doulton Lambeth faience moonflask, decorated by H. Barlow. **$608 £380**

Doulton Lambeth faience two-handled vase decorated with a band of wild flowers by Margaret M. Challis, 7½in. high, circa 1880. **$176 £110**

A Doulton Lambeth faience coffee service painted with azaleas, dahlias and dog roses, circa 1879. **$352 £220**

A faience vase decorated with panels of flowers, by Alberta L. Green, 9¼in. high, circa 1882. **$240 £150**

Royal Doulton faience vase by John H. McLennan, decorated with panels representing Earth and Water, 13½in. high. **$368 £230**

A pair of Doulton Lambeth faience oil lamp bases decorated by Esther Lewis, 10¼in. high. **$720 £450**

Doulton Lambeth faience vase decorated with daffodils and narcissi, 10½in. high. **$176 £110**

363

HOLBEIN WARE

A Doulton Lambeth Holbein ware charger, by Charles Noke, the centre painted with a bust portrait of a medieval gentleman, 39cm. diameter. $480 £300

A pair of Holbein ware vases with silver rims, 9in. high. $800 £500

A large Royal Doulton Burslem Holbein Ware jardiniere decorated with four cavaliers playing cards, 13¼in. high, signed W. Nunn. $720 £450

IMPASTO

A Doulton Lambeth Impasto jardiniere decorated with wild flowers by Rosa Keen, 10½in. high. $288 £180

A Doulton Lambeth Impasto vase decorated with chrysanthemums, by Rosa Keen, 11in. high. $264 £165

A Doulton Lambeth Impasto wall plaque decorated with chrysanthemums, by Frances Linnell, 14½in. diam., circa 1882. $240 £150

MORRISIAN WARE

An impressive Royal Doulton Morrisian ware flare-mouth vase, decorated 17th-century golfers with Art Nouveau rim and base and gilt edging, 30.5cm. $2720 £1,700

A Doulton Burslem Morrisian Ware teapot decorated with a band of dancing maidens, 7¾in. high, circa 1899 $240 £150

Doulton Burslem Morrisian Ware tobacco jar and cover decorated with a band of dancing girls, 5½in. high. $240 £150

SUNG

A Royal Doulton Sung vase by
Noke, 6³/₄in. high, circa 1928.
$640 £400

Royal Doulton Sung model of a
rabbit, 4in. long, circa 1928.
$480 £300

A Royal Doulton Sung vase by
Charles Noke and Fred Moore,
7in. high, circa 1930.
$880 £550

Royal Doulton Sung vase signed
by A. Eaton, 5³/₄in. high.
$1040 £650

A large Royal Doulton Sung
vase by Arthur Eaton, decorated
with dragons amongst clouds,
13in. high, circa 1930.
$1280 £800

Royal Doulton Sung tobacco jar
and cover of hexagonal form,
6¹/₄in. high, circa 1930.
$525 £350

Royal Doulton Sung vase by
Noke, decorated with flying
birds, 8³/₄in. high. $525 £350

Royal Doulton Sung bowl decorated with a band of geometric
ornament, 8in. diam., circa
1925. $400 £250

Royal Doulton Sung vase by
Noke, decorated with a peacock
painted by A. Eaton, 10¹/₂in.
high. $480 £300

TITANIAN WARE

Royal Doulton Titanian Ware sugar bowl and cover, 4¹/₄in. high, circa 1922. **$120 £75**

A Royal Doulton Titanian Ware teapot, 6¹/₂in. high, circa 1920. **$192 £120**

A Royal Doulton Titanian Ware vase by F. Henri, decorated with a cat seated beneath a crescent moon. **$400 £250**

A Royal Doulton Titanian bowl decorated with a dragon, 14¹/₂in. diam. **$160 £100**

A pair of Royal Doulton Cecil Aldin Titanian glazed Series ware vases, 15.5cm. high, D4525. **$560 £350**

Royal Doulton Titanian figure, 'The Smiling Buddha', by Noke, issued in 1921, withdrawn 1938. **$960 £600**

Royal Doulton Titanian figure of 'Blighty', 11¹/₂in. high, circa 1919. **$1040 £650**

A Royal Doulton Titanian Ware teapot, 6¹/₂in. high, circa 1922. **$192 £120**

Royal Doulton Titanian vase by Harry Allen decorated with a long eared owl, 13in. high. **$560 £350**

KINGSWARE

In 1899 a new method of stoneware production was introduced at Burslem which involved applying colour slips of subdued greens, yellows and reddish browns to the interior of plaster moulds in which a design was impressed. When another brown slip was poured in, the colours fused to give a deep and soft effect to the embossed design.

This came to be known as Kingsware and it was mostly used for the production of pottery flasks to hold whisky.

In 1902 Dewars commissioned Doulton to make a slip glaze whisky flagon for the Christmas trade. The initial run was 1,000 but it is likely that more were eventually delivered. This flagon, 'The Watchman', was the forerunner of the Kingsware flagons and jugs made for the whisky trade between 1902 and 1937. Though Dewar's remained Doulton's most prestigious client, such jugs were were also made for other blenders such as Greenlee's, Bulloch Lade, Glenlivet and Old Smuggler. In 1930 Doulton produced 1,500 Kingsware Highlander character water jugs for D & J. McCallum.

The glaze was most commonly a dark treacle brown but more unusual was a paler yellow called the 'Kingsware yellow glaze'.

Kingsware pieces were further characterised by their subdued colours and the fact that they featured characters from legend and fiction depicted in low relief moulding. Many of these characters, such as Falstaff and the Sporting Squire, also emphasised the pleasures of drinking.

These were often modelled by Arthur Bailey who worked between 1912 and 1932.

Pied Piper, a Royal Doulton Kingsware teapot with silver mounts, circa 1905. $440 £275

Sailor's Story, a Royal Doulton Kingsware flask, circa 1910, 6½in. high. $528 £330

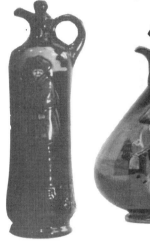

The Watchman, a Royal Doulton Kingsware flask for Dewar's Whisky, 10½in. high, circa 1902. $232 £145

'Nelson', a Royal Doulton Kingsware flask, 7½in. high, circa 1909. $616 £385

Royal Doulton Kingsware tobacco jar decorated in relief, gentleman smoking, 8¼in. high. $350 £220

Beefeater, a Royal Doulton Kingsware flask, Dewar's Whisky, by Noke, 7¼in. high, circa 1908. $616 £385

KINGSWARE

The Macnab, a Kingsware flask, made for Dewar's, 9in. high, circa 1915. $232 £145

Weller, Senior, a miniature Royal Doulton Kingsware vase, with silver hallmarked rim, circa 1909, 2¼in. high. $112 £70

Fagin, a Kingsware water jug, 8¼in. high, circa 1908. $368 £230

'For Thy Sake Tobacco I Would Do Anything But Die', a Royal Doulton Kingsware water jug, hallmarked silver rim, 8¾in. high, circa 1908. $336 £210

The Leather Bottle, a Royal Doulton Kingsware flask, circa 1918, 6¼in. high, 6in. long. $528 £330

Monks in the Cellar, a Royal Doulton Kingsware two-handled vase, 10¼in. high, circa 1912. $304 £190

Mr. Pickwick and Sam Weller on the reverse, a Royal Doulton Kingsware flask, circa 1930, 9½in. high. $440 £275

Uncle Sam, a Kingsware flask made for Dewar's, yellow glaze, 7½in. high, circa 1908. $480 £300

The Connoisseur, a Kingsware pear shaped flask made for Dewar's, 8¾in. high. $480 £300

Stiggins, a Royal Doulton Kingsware whisky flask, issued 1936, 8in. high. $352 £220

Bardolph, a Royal Doulton Kingsware mustard pot with silver hallmarked rim, circa 1904, 3in. high. $136 £85

Artful Dodger and Oliver Twist, a Royal Doulton Kingsware whisky flask, circa 1912, 8in. high. $496 £310

A Hunting Scene (low relief) a Royal Doulton Kingsware water jug, circa 1909, 11in. high. $280 £175

A Royal Doulton Kingsware jardiniere decorated with seagulls, circa 1910, 5½in. high, 9in. wide. $248 £155

Pied Piper, a Royal Doulton Kingsware two-handled vase, signed Noke, circa 1910, 11¾in. high. $304 £190

George The Guard, a Royal Doulton Kingsware whisky flask, Dewar's Scotch Whisky, circa 1908, 8¼in. high. $248 £155

Sporting Squire, a Kingsware flask made for Dewar's, 6¾in. high, circa 1909. $232 £145

Tony Weller, a Royal Doulton Kingsware flask with the inscription, 'Tony Weller Bevare of the Vidders', 8in. high. $232 £145

Sporting Squire, a Royal Doulton Kingsware flask, made for Dewar's Whisky, Royal cypher on reverse, 6³/₄in. high, circa 1909. $280 £175

Peace flagon, a Kingsware flask with brown border, made for Dewar's, No. 181, 7¹/₂in. high, circa 1919. $440 £275

Micawber, a Royal Doulton Kingsware whisky flask made for Dewar's Scotch Whisky, 7in. high, issued 1909. $232 £145

Monks In the Cellar, a Royal Doulton Kingsware flask, Dewar's Scotch Whisky, circa 1905, 8¹/₂in. high. $232 £145

Dickens' Characters, a Royal Doulton Kingsware water jug, 7in. high. $488 £305

Bonnie Prince Charlie, a Royal Doulton Kingsware flask made for Dewar's Whisky, 7in. high, circa 1913. $232 £145

Crusader, a Royal Doulton Kingsware whisky flask, Greenlees Bros. Scotch whisky, circa 1913, 8in. high.
$424 £265

Nightwatchman, a Kingsware water jug, by Noke, 5¹/₂in. high. $128 £80

Don Quixote, a Royal Doulton Kingsware flagon, 10¹/₂in. high, circa 1913. $352 £220

Mr. Pickwick Proposes The Toast, a Royal Doulton Kingsware flask, signed Noke, circa 1912, 8in. high. $392 £245

Mr. Pickwick, a miniature Royal Doulton Kingsware jug with silver hallmarked rim, circa 1907, 2¹/₂in. high. $128 £80

The Jovial Monk, a Kingsware flask made for Dewar's, 8in. high, circa 1908. $248 £155

Oyez, Oyez, ewer shaped Kingsware flask made for Dewar's Scotch Whisky, 10¹/₂in. high, issued 1909. $216 £135

Royal Doulton Kingsware mug with silver rim, 4in. high. $192 £120

Church-Warden, a Kingsware flask made for Dewar's Whisky, 9¹/₂in. high, circa 1907. $496 £310

George The Guard, a Royal Doulton Kingsware whisky flask, Dewar's Scotch Whisky, circa 1908, 10in. high. $232 £145

The Alchemist, a Royal Doulton Kingsware flask, by Noke, circa 1913, 8¹/₄in. high. $352 £220

Pied Piper, a Royal Doulton Kingsware milk jug with silver mounts, circa 1905. $136 £85

Bill Sykes, a miniature Royal Doulton Kingsware loving cup with silver hallmarked rim, circa 1907, 2¹/₂in. high.
$144 £90

Witches, a small pair of Royal Doulton Kingsware two-handled vases, circa 1912, 4¹/₂in. high.
$192 £120

Sam Weller, a miniature Royal Doulton Kingsware loving cup, hallmarked silver rim, circa 1909, 1³/₄in. high. $144 £90

Royal Doulton Kingsware single-handled jug depicting a golfer and his caddie.
$496 £310

Nelson, a Royal Doulton Kingsware triangular flask, 8in. high, 6in. wide, 1914. $392 £245

Pirates, a Royal Doulton whisky flask, by Noke, circa 1909, 6in. high. $396 £310

Ben Jonson, a Kingsware flask made for Dewar's Scotch Whisky, issued 1909, 7in. high.
$216 £135

Sydney Harbour, a Royal Doulton triangular Kingsware flask, Dewar's Scotch Whisky, 6¹/₂in. high, circa 1914.
$568 £355

Double Foxes (one curled), a Royal Doulton Kingsware tobacco jug with silver hallmarked rim, circa 1912, 7¹/₂in. high. $568 £355

Darby and Joan, a Royal Doulton tea cup, circa 1912, 2³/₄in. high. $88 £55

Royal Doulton Kingsware sugar bowl with silver mounts, circa 1905. $152 £95

Mr. Pickwick, a Royal Doulton Kingsware tea cup in low relief, circa 1912, 2¹/₂in. high.
$136 £85

He's A Jolly Good Fellow, Dr. Jonson at The Cheshire Cheese, a Royal Doulton Kingsware whisky flask, circa 1924, 8in. high. $616 £385

Royal Doulton Kingsware Duke of York water jug, 7¹/₄in. high.
$320 £200

Admiral of the Fleet, a Royal Doulton Kingsware flask, Dewar's Scotch Whisky, circa 1916, 7¹/₂in. high. $352 £220

Don Quixote, a Royal Doulton Kingsware mug, 4¹/₂in. high, circa 1912. $128 £80

John Barleycorn, a Royal Doulton Kingsware flask, circa 1931, 7in. high. $392 £245

Squire, a Kingsware Toby jug, hallmarked silver rim, 6¹/₂in. high. $528 £330

A Doulton Kingsware pottery tobacco jar, modelled with numerous golfing figures after Charles Crombie, 6½in. high. $704 £440

Small fox, head down, a Royal Doulton Kingsware tobacco jar with hallmarked silver rim, circa 1912, 7¾in. high. $616 £385

Watchman, a Kingsware globular shaped flask, 8in. high, with modelled head. $248 £155

Royal Doulton Kingsware single handled jug depicting golfers, 9in. high. $616 £385

Huntsman, a Royal Doulton Kingsware loving cup, issued 1932, 8in. high. $248 £155

Pied Piper, a Royal Doulton Kingsware two-handled vase, signed Noke, circa 1910, 11¼in. high. $248 £155

Don Quixote, a Kingsware water jug, 10½in. high, circa 1913. $240 £150

Memories, a Kingsware water jug depicting Dickens' characters. $264 £165

Pied Piper, a Royal Doulton Kingsware water jug with hallmarked silver rim and lid, 8½in. high. $264 £165

374

Bill Sykes, a Royal Doulton Kingsware pear-shaped whisky flask, circa 1905, 7³/₄in. high.
$392 £245

One of the Forty, a Royal Doulton Kingsware ashtray, designed by H. Tittensor, circa 1921, 3³/₄in. high, HN423.
$496 £310

The Crown, a Kingsware George VI commemorative flask, made for Dewar's Whisky, 1,000 issued 1937, 6in. high.
$600 £375

Bardolph, a Royal Doulton Kingsware water jug, 7¹/₄in. high, circa 1902. $160 £100

Pair of Royal Doulton Kingsware candlesticks, a Hunting Scene in low relief, circa 1912, 11in. high. $312 £195

The Alchemist, a Royal Doulton Kingsware clock, 7¹/₂in. high, circa 1913. $704 £440

Parson Jones, a Royal Doulton Kingsware water jug, 7¹/₂in. high, circa 1935. $248 £155

Tony Weller, a Royal Doulton Kingsware whisky flask, circa 1912, 9¹/₂in. high. $792 £495

Pied Piper, a Royal Doulton Kingsware coffee pot with silver mounts, circa 1905. $264 £165

Huntsman, a Royal Doulton Kingsware Toby jug, 7¹/₂in. high. $616 £385

Mr. Pecksniff, a miniature Royal Doulton Kingsware vase with hallmarked silver rim, circa 1909, 2in. high.
$128 £80

Ben Jonson, a Royal Doulton Kingsware flask made for Dewar's Scotch Whisky, 7in. high, issued in 1909.
$216 £135

Falstaff, green hat, a Royal Doulton Kingsware whisky flask, Dewar's Scotch Whisky, 7¹/₂in. high, circa 1907.
$232 £145

Nelson, a Kingsware flat-shaped flask made for Dewar's, circa 1914, 8¹/₂in. high. $440 £275

Tavern Scenes, a Royal Doulton Kingsware two-handled vase, 6in. high, circa 1920.
$352 £220

Chadband (Bleak House), a Royal Doulton Kingsware whisky flask, 8in. high, circa 1912. $616 £385

Nightwatchman, a Royal Doulton Kingsware jug, by Noke, 7in. high. $160 £100

Parson Brown, a Royal Doulton Kingsware water jug, 7¹/₂in. high, circa 1935. $248 £155

Royal Doulton Kingsware whisky flask in the form of Tony Weller, 3¹/₂in. high. $616 £385

Memories, a Kingsware water jug depicting Dickens' characters. $352 £220

Jovial Monk, a Kingsware flask made for Dewar's Scotch Whisky, issued 1908, 7³/₄in. high. $392 £245

Fisherman, a Royal Doulton Kingsware flask, signed Noke, circa 1904, 7in. high. $392 £245

Royal Doulton jug in low relief by Charles Crombie, depicting a golfer, 9¹/₄in. high, circa 1910. $544 £340

A Hunting Scene, Kingsware water jug, 6¹/₂in. high. $176 £110

George V Coronation, a Kingsware jug with silver hallmarked rim, circa 1911, 6³/₄in. high. $392 £245

Mr. Pickwick and Sam Weller, a Royal Doulton Kingsware coffee pot with hallmarked silver rim, signed Noke, circa 1909, 6¹/₂in. high. $392 £245

Drink Wisely But Not Too Well, a Kingsware water jug of a pipe-smoking man, 8in. high. $232 £145

**Wizard, a large Royal Doulton
Kingsware ewer, circa 1905,
16¹/₂in. high.** $616 £385

**Royal Doulton Kingsware coffee
pot, with silver mounts, circa
1905.** $264 £165

**Watchman, a Royal Doulton
Kingsware flask, circa 1930,
10¹/₂in. high.** $232 £145

**A Kingsware two-handled vase
'Here's Health Unto His
Majesty', 13in. high.**
$440 £275

**Coachman, a Doulton Kings-
ware flagon, issued 1932, 10¹/₂in.
high.** $392 £245

**Wizard, a Royal Doulton Kings-
ware flask decorated with a
wizard standing over a cauldron,
designed by Noke, 10in. high,
issued 1904.** $496 £310

LOVING CUPS & JUGS

One of Charles J. Noke's greatest talents was giving the public what it wanted and in 1930 he hit upon the idea of producing a range of limited editions of loving cups and jugs, ornately embossed and decorated to a certain theme.

They were modelled on the slip cast relief jugs which had been made in Staffordshire during Victorian times.

One of their more striking features was the way in which a certain crudeness of design coexisted with elaborate, intricate and highly coloured decoration.

The first one produced was 'The Master of Foxhounds Presentation Jug'. It was modelled in low relief with rich glowing colours painted by William Grace and it set the style of the lip and handle of the jug or cup continuing the theme.

The following year 'The Regency Coach Jug' appeared and it was followed by a new one each year, including the 'Dickens Dream Jug', 'The Shakespeare Jug' and 'Robin Hood and His Merry Men'. The maximum number in each edition was 1,000 and each jug or cup bore a certificate of authenticity.

Some were produced to coincide with significant dates, like the one made in 1932 for George Washington's birth bicentenary, which was designed for the American market.

Loving cups by Cecil Noke were issued for the Coronation of Edward VIII, George VI and Elizabeth II in 1953, and in 1977 another edition of only 250 was produced by Richard Johnson for her Silver Jubilee.

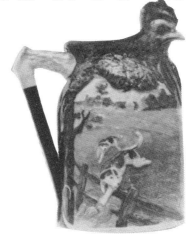

MASTER OF FOXHOUNDS PRESENTATION JUG
Designed by C.J. Noke, 13in. high, Issued 1930
In a limited edition of 500. $720 £450

QUEEN ELIZABETH II CORONATION LOVING CUP
Designed by C.J. Noke & H. Fenton, 10½in. high, Issued
1953 in a limited edition of 1000. $480 £300

GEORGE WASHINGTON BICENTENARY JUG
Designed by C.J. Noke & H. Fenton, 10¾in. high,
Issued 1932 in a limited edition of 1000,
Variation on handle style. $5600 £3500

ADMIRAL LORD NELSON LOVING CUP
Designed by C.J. Noke & H. Fenton, 10¹/₂in.
Issued 1935 in a limited edition of 600.
                                    $800 £500

PIED PIPER JUG
Designed by C.J. Noke & H. Fenton, 10in. high,
Issued 1934 in a limited edition of 600.
                                    $880 £550

KING EDWARD VIII CORONATION LOVING
CUP (Large)
Designed by C.J. Noke & H. Fenton, 10in. high,
Issued 1937 in a limited edition of 2000.
                                    $560 £350

THE THREE MUSKETEERS LOVING CUP
Designed by C.J. Noke & H. Fenton, 10in. high,
Issued 1936 in a limited edition of 600.
                                    $640 £400

WILLIAM SHAKESPEARE JUG
Designed by C.J. Noke, 10³/₄in. high, Issued 1933 in a
limited edition of 1000.   **$560 £350**

REGENCY COACH JUG
Designed by C.J. Noke, 10in. high,
Issued 1931 in a limited edition of 500.
                                    $640 £400

QUEEN ELIZABETH II CORONATION JUG
Designer - Unknown, 6¼in. high,
Issued 1953 unlimited.   **$160 £100**

QUEEN ELIZABETH SILVER JUBILEE LOVING CUP
Designed by R. Johnson, 10½in. high,
Issued 1977 in a limited edition of 250.   **$800 £500**

KING GEORGE VI AND QUEEN ELIZABETH CORONATION LOVING CUP (Large)
Designed by C.J. Noke & H. Fenton, 10½in. high,
Issued 1937 in a limited edition of 2000.
                                  $560 £350

SIR FRANCIS DRAKE JUG
Designed by C.J. Noke & H. Fenton, 10½in. high,
Issued 1933 in a limited edition of 500.
                                  $720 £450

GUY FAWKES JUG
Designed by H. Fenton, 7½in. high, Issued 1934
in a limited edition of 600.   **$720 £450**

JAN VAN RIEBECK LOVING CUP
Designed by C.J. Noke & H. Fenton, 10¼in. high,
Issued circa 1935 in a limited edition of 300.
                                  $2400 £1500

THE APOTHECARY LOVING CUP
Designed by C.J. Noke & H. Fenton, 6in. high,
Issued 1934 in a limited edition of 600.

$640 £400

KING EDWARD VIII CORONATION LOVING CUP (Small)
Designed by C.J. Noke, 6¹/₂in. high,
Issued 1937 in a limited edition of 1000.

$320 £200

MAYFLOWER LOVING CUP
Designed by David Biggs, 10¹/₄in. high,
Issued 1970 in a limited edition of 500.

$240 £150

CAPTAIN COOK LOVING CUP
Designed by C.J. Noke & H. Fenton, 9¹/₂in. high,
Issued 1933 in a limited edition of 350.

$3200 £2000

THE WANDERING MINSTREL LOVING CUP
Designed by C. J. Noke & H. Fenton, 5½in. high,
Issued in a limited edition of 600.   **$480   £300**

TREASURE ISLAND JUG
Designed by C.J. Noke & H. Fenton, 7¹/₂in. high,
Issued in 1934 in a limited edition of 600.
$560 £350

POTTERY IN THE PAST LOVING CUP
Designed by Graham Tongue, 6in. high, Issued 1983.
$232 £145

THE VILLAGE BLACKSMITH JUG
Designed by C.J. Noke, 7¾in. high, Issued 1936
In a limited edition of 600. $720 £450

**KING GEORGE VI AND QUEEN ELIZABETH
CORONATION LOVING CUP (Small)**
Designed by C.J. Noke & H. Fenton, 6½in. high,
Issued 1937 in a limited edition of 2000.
$400 £250

WILLIAM WORDSWORTH LOVING CUP
Designed by C.J. Noke, 6½in. high, Issued 1933
unlimited. $1200 £750

**KING GEORGE V AND QUEEN MARY SILVER
JUBILEE LOVING CUP**
Designed by C.J. Noke & H. Fenton, 10in. high,
Issued 1935 in a limited edition of 1000. $560 £350

DICKENS DREAM JUG
Designed by C.J. Noke, 10½in. high,
Issued 1933 in a limited edition of 1000. $800 £500

JOHN PEEL LOVING CUP
Designer - Unknown, 9in. high,
Issued 1933 in a limited edition of 500.
$720 £450

CAPTAIN PHILLIP JUG
Designed by C.J. Noke & H. Fenton, 9¼in. high,
Issued 1938 in a limited edition of 350.
$4800 £3000

TOWER OF LONDON JUG
Designed by C.J. Noke & H. Fenton, 9½in. high,
Issued 1933 in a limited edition of 500.
$720 £450

GEORGE WASHINGTON BICENTENARY JUG
Designed by C.J. Noke & H. Fenton, 10¾in. high,
Issued 1932 in a limited edition of 1000, colour
variation on handle. $7200 £4500

ROBIN HOOD LOVING CUP
Designed by C.J. Noke & H. Fenton, 8½in. high,
Issued 1938 in a limited edition of 600. $720 £450

CHARLES DICKENS JUG
Designed by C.J. Noke & H. Fenton, 10½in. high,
Issued 1936 in a limited edition of 1000.
$880 £550

SERIES WARE

"Adorn yet serve some useful purpose" was the reasoning behind the very successful introduction of Series Ware which was the brain child of Charles J. Noke, who joined Doulton in 1889.

He realised that standard pottery shapes could be decorated with popular images and sold as 'novelty art wares' to the general public, who were not able to afford the more expensive creations of individual artists.

Designs, many of them by Noke himself, were transfer printed onto plates, jugs, bowls, mugs and tea sets. Refined earthenware or bone china was used and the transfer prints were handcoloured, which gave the technique the name of 'print and tint'.

The first series issued was the 'Isthmian Games' in 1889 and it was followed by a new theme almost every year till World War Two. They include Olde Worlde England, characters from legend, song or story, motoring scenes, characters from Dickens and hunting scenes. Collectors could buy everything from toothbrush holders to dinner plates with their favourite theme and the craze for collecting them continues today.

Noke had a team of skilled artists working with him on Seriesware, but they rarely received a credit on their products. William Edward Grace worked on the range from 1902 until 1959, whilst Walter Nunn is recognised for his work on the Old London Scenes. Some designs come from the artists' own sketchbooks but most designs reflect the influence of contemporary illustrators or cartoonists.

In the 1970s Doulton revived Series Ware when they issued sets of plates for special events and anniversaries called "Collectors' International".

Royal Doulton sampler water jug and teapot, pattern No. D3749, English, early 20th century. $195 £120

The Gleaners, Series ware sandwich tray. $80 £50

Royal Doulton Dickens ware tea service, comprising: sucrier; four cups; six saucers; cream jug; rectangular sandwich plate; six tea plates, all with printed marks. $576 £360

A fine Royal Doulton Crombie series ware bowl, circa 1925, 24cm. diameter. $1,760   £1,100

A Royal Doulton Cecil Aldin Series ware jardiniere, the decoration from the 'Old English Scenes', 18cm. high. $440 £275

A Doulton Burslem wall plaque, painted in blues and whites with a panel of a golfer and his caddy, 14in. diameter. $5,600 £3,500

Willow Pattern Series jar and cover, 6½in. high, circa 1912. $136 £85

A pair of saucer dishes, inscribed *Promise little and do much,* each with different decoration, 14cm. diameter. $225 £140

Nightwatchman Series tobacco jar, 5½in. high circa 1909, by Noke, depicting a watchman carrying a pike. $168 £105

Robert Burns portrait plaque with his cottage in the background, 10¼in. diam. $72 £45

Oliver Twist tankard in low relief, designed by C.J. Noke, issued 1949-1960. $256 £160

A Doulton series ware bowl, with the inscription *Every Dog has his day and every man his hour, give losers leave to speak and winners to laugh,* 3¾in. x 9in. $800 £500

Royal Doulton pottery jardinière, 'The Gallant Fishers', 9in. high.
$400   £250

Hunting Series spirit barrel and stand, 7in. high, circa 1924.
$528   £330

Gallant Fishers large Series art pot, by Izaak Walton, 12in. high, circa 1908.
$496   £310

A Series ware humidor jar, D3395, inscribed *All fools are not knaves but all knaves are fools,* **the cover with pierced recess, 17cm.**
$608   £380

A Royal Doulton 'Reynard the Fox' coffee service, printed marks and pattern number H4927.
$480   £300

Royal Doulton Series ware coffee pot, 7¹/₂in. tall, D5506, 1934.
$168   £105

Royal Doulton 'Aubrey' patterned slop pail and top with bound cane handle, English, early 20ᵗʰ century.
$480   £300

English Cottages Series, two-handled cup, 4in. high, circa 1924, depicting an old English cottage.
$80   £50

Silhouette Series biscuit barrel, silver plated rim and lid, 5¹/₂in. high, depicting Country Scenes.
$168   £105

JUGS

Silhouette Series jug, 4in. high, depicting Country Scenes.
$80 £50

Old Moreton Hall Series water jug, 4½in. high, circa 1915, depicting gentlemen in a mid 16th century scene. $112 £70

Sir Roger de Coverley Series cream jug, 3½in. high, circa 1911, depicting Sir Roger on horseback. $88 £55

Canterbury Pilgrims Series jug, 7½in. high, circa 1909, depicting Pilgrims on Horseback. $112 £70

'Nightwatchman', a Series ware jug by C.J. Noke, 8½in. high, D1198, 1903. $168 £105

Shakespeare Series jug, 12in. high, circa 1912, depicting 'Wolsey'. $168 £105

Huntsman Series water jug, 11in. high, circa 1906, depicting two huntsmen at the inn. $176 £110

Rural England Series Country Gardens jug, 7in. high, circa 1929, depicting a cottage by a pond. $104 £65

Under The Greenwood Tree Series water jug, 8½in. high, circa 1937. $152 £95

JUGS

Water jug in low relief depicting 'Tony Weller', D6397.
$168 £105

'Old London' jug in low relief designed by C.J. Noke, issued 1949-1960, D6291. $312 £195

Famous Sailing Ships Series jug, 4½in. high, circa 1938.
$96 £60

Monks in the Cellar Series water jug, 8in. high, circa 1909.
$104 £65

Under The Greenwood Tree Series, jug, 7in. high, circa 1937, depicting Friar Tuck and Robin Hood. $152 £95

New Cavaliers Series water jug, 12in. high, circa 1907, depicting two cavaliers toasting.
$136 £85

'Sir Toby Belch', Shakespeare Series jug, 8½in. high, circa 1904, quotation 'Maria, I Say a Stoop of Wine'. $152 £95

'Fagin', Dickens' Series jug, 6½in. high, circa 1912.
$152 £95

Wedlock Series water jug, 11in. high, circa 1905, depicting a gentleman and a lady with a fan.
$168 £105

JUGS

'Little Nell', Dickens' Series jug, 7in. high, circa 1908.
$112 £70

A barrel-shaped jug, inscribed *Every dog has its day,* 13cm.
$350 £220

Country Garden Series jug and cover, 7¹/₂in. high, circa 1929.
$136 £85

Rural England Series jug, 7in. high, circa 1933, depicting lambs in a field.
$80 £50

Gleaners and Gypsies Series water jug, 7in. high, circa 1909, depicting a gypsy with bundle of corn.
$136 £85

Egyptian Series jug, 7in. high, circa 1902.
$112 £70

Rural England (Welsh) Series water jug, 12¹/₂in. high, circa 1907, depicting a woman in traditional dress.
$168 £105

Oliver Twist jug designed by C.J. Noke, depicting 'Fagin and Bumble', D5617.
$256 £160

The Bayeux Tapestry Series jug, 6¹/₂in. high, circa 1907, depicting Harold on horseback.
$152 £95

JUGS

'Mr Pickwick', Dickens' Series jug, 7in. high, circa 1912. $136 £85

Desert Scenes Series water jug, 6in. high, circa 1909, depicting a woman on a camel. $104 £65

Gondoliers Series jug, 7in. high, circa 1909, depicting a Venice scene. $152 £95

Gallant Fishers Series jug, by Izaak Walton, 7in. high, circa 1906, depicting a fisherman on the bank. $168 £105

A Jacobean jug 'Ye Old Belle' depicting a serving wench and two cavaliers, 6½in. high. $152 £95

Sunday Smocks Series jug and cover, 8in. high, circa 1936, depicting a man under a tree. $136 £85

'Sam Weller', Dickens' Series jug, 7¼in. high, circa 1912. $136 £85

Under The Greenwood Tree Series jug, 8in. high, circa 1937, depicting Friar Tuck and Robin Hood. $136 £85

Nightwatchman Series water jug, by C.J. Noke, 6¾in. high, circa 1907. $112 £70

Old English Inns Series ware rack plate depicting 'The Bear's Head', 10in. diam. $80 £50

Royal Doulton plate 'An oak is not felled by one blow', ' Take the will for the deed'. $280 £175

'Painted Feelings' rack plate, Behind the Painted Masque Limited Edition Series, 9in. diam., 1982. $168 £105

'Noble Heritage' rack plate, Collectors Series, Limited Edition, 8¼in. diam., 1981. $48 £30

Royal Doulton plate 'Nothing venture nothing win', 'Count not your chickens before they are hatched'. $280 £175

'Marshlands' rack plate, Collectors Limited Edition Series, 10½in. diam., 1981. $64 £40

'Short Headed Salmon', a Royal Doulton rack plate, signed by J. Birbeck, 9½in. diam., circa 1913. $208 £130

Series ware rack plate 'Mother Kangaroo and Joey', 10½in. diam. $48 £30

'Make Me Laugh' rack plate, Behind the Painted Masque Limited Edition Series, 9in. diam., 1982. $152 £95

PLATES

Royal Doulton rack plate 'Short Headed Salmon', signed J. Birbeck, 9½in. diam., circa 1909. $208 £130

Royal Doulton Series Ware plate 'If at first you don't succeed try again', 'A miss is as good as a mile'. $280 £175

Charles Dickens portrait plate with a border of Dickens' characters, 10¼in. diam. $72 £45

'Weathering the Storm' rack plate, Aged in Wood Limited Edition Series, 10¼in. diam., $80 £50

A Royal Doulton Series Ware plate painted with a typical golfing scene inscribed *He hath a good judgement who relieth not wholly on his own*, 10¾in. diameter. $320 £200

'Arabian Nights' rack plate, 'The Arrival of the Unknown Princess', 10¼in. diam. $96 £60

'The Fleur-De-Lys, St. Albans' rack plate, Old English Inns Series, 10¼in. diam., circa 1939. $80 £50

A Royal Doulton Series Ware rack plate inscribed *He hath a good judgement who relieth not wholly on his own,* 10¾in. diameter. $280 £175

'At the Cheshire Cheese', Dr. Jonson Series rack plate, 13in. diam., circa 1909. $104 £65

Series ware rack plate 'The Seasons', 'Winter' $56 £35

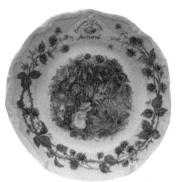

'Edinburgh Castle', rack plate, 10¹/₂in. diam. $64 £40

Rack plate 'Autumn' from 'The Seasons'. $56 £35

'Aero', a Royal Doulton commemorative rack plate, 1909. $352 £220

'Sairey Gamp' rack plate, Dickens' Series, 10¹/₄in. diam., circa 1912. $112 £70

'The Old Balloon Seller' rack plate in low relief, 10¹/₂in. diam. $136 £85

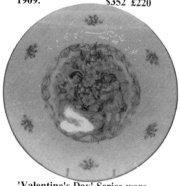

'Valentine's Day' Series ware rack plate, 1985, 6¹/₄in. diam. $48 £30

A square plate with invert corners inscribed *He that always complains is never pitied*, 14.5cm. $175 £110

'Gibson Girl' rack plate designed by Charles Dana Gibson, circa 1901. $168 £105

'Thunder in the Air' rack plate, Aged in Wood Limited Edition Series, 10¹/₂in. diam. $80 £50

Royal Doulton plate 'Fine feathers make fine birds', 'Handsome is that handsome does'. $280 £175

Early Motoring Series titled 'Deaf', 10¹/₂in. diam., circa 1906. $312 £195

'Gallant Fishers' teapot, by Izaak Walton, 6in. high, circa 1906. $264 £165

Under The Greenwood Tree teapot, 4¹/₂in. high, circa 1937, depicting Robin Hood and Friar Tuck. $264 £165

Gondoliers Series teapot, 5¹/₂in. high, circa 1909. $264 £165

Silhouette Series teapot, 5in. high, depicting Country Scenes. $176 £110

A Series ware teapot, 5¹/₂in. high, circa 1930, depicting the Old Woman Who Lived in the Shoe. $280 £175

Old Moreton Hall Series teapot, 4¹/₂in. high, circa 1915, depicting Queen Elizabeth I outside. $256 £160

'Fagin', Dickens' Series teapot, 5¹/₂in. high, circa 1930. $312 £195

Jackdaw of Rheims Series teapot, 6¹/₂in. high, circa 1908, depicting The Cardinal. $264 £165

Sir Roger de Coverley Series teapot, 5in. high, circa 1911, depicting Sir Roger in the garden. $256 £160

Monks in the Cellar Series teapot, 4¹/₂in. high, circa 1909, depicting a monk inspecting the food. $208 £130

Arabian Nights Series teapot, 5in. high, circa 1909, depicting the attendants. $256 £160

'Old Moreton Hall' Series ware teapot, 5¹/₂in. high. $72 £45

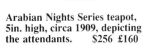

SERIES WARE

Rural England (Welsh) Series, two-handled vase, 12¹/₂in. high, circa 1907, depicting a woman in traditional dress. $192 £120

Rural England Series vase, 4¹/₂in. high, circa 1916, depicting a girl gathering bluebells. $112 £70

'Orlando', Shakespeare Series vase, 8in. high, circa 1912. $168 £105

Old Moreton Hall Series vase, depicting the hall at Moreton, 9in. high, circa 1915. $136 £85

Gleaners and Gypsies Series vase, 7¹/₂in. high, circa 1909, depicting a Gypsy and Child. $136 £85

Feminine Society Series vase, 7¹/₂in. high, circa 1934, depicting a family taking tea. $136 £85

Under The Greenwood Tree Series vase, 7³/₄in. high, circa 1937, depicting 'Robin Hood and Friar Tuck'. $136 £85

Royal Doulton two-handled vase, designed by Charles Crombie, depicting two golfers and a caddie, 8in. high. $616 £385

'Old Houses, All-Saints St. Hastings', Rural England Series vase, 8in. high, circa 1930. $136 £85

STONEWARE

The production of saltglazed stoneware had been carried on at Lambeth for centuries when John Doulton first went into the pottery business there in 1815.

At first his firm continued the prevalent output of cheap, mass produced items like bottles, jugs and barrels, and it was not until John's son Henry joined the business that more complex modelling and detail began to be introduced.

It was Henry who diversified into architectural stoneware and who started to turn his Lambeth Pottery into a centre for the production of decorative stoneware.

In 1866 he took into the company a group of students from the Lambeth School of Art and in the Paris Exhibition of 1867 their work was highly acclaimed.

The people who produced decorative stoneware at this time included the three famous Barlows, Frank Butler, George Tinworth and many others including women like Eliza Simmance. At first designs were based on 16th and 17th century German stonewares and Renaissance styles. Hannah Barlow however preferred incised decorations, which led on to 'pâte sur pâte' work which involved building up a raised outline by delicate brushwork, and to far more sophisticated designs of incised and carved stylised foliage, which were a precursor of the Art Nouveau styles.

Stoneware manufacture ceased entirely at Lambeth in 1956 and had only been on a limited scale there since 1914, but today there is a great resurgence of interest in it among collectors.

ARTHUR BARLOW

One of the first students to be accepted by Henry Doulton from the Lambeth School of Art in 1871, Arthur Barlow's career with the company was short but productive. He used a wide range of subtle colours in his work, and was one of the most successful exponents of the foliate scroll motif. He was constantly dogged by ill health and died at the sadly early age of 34.

FLORENCE BARLOW

Florence followed her brother and sister into Doulton's employ in 1873. At first, her work featured incised decoration of both animals and birds, but the story goes that she came to an arrangement with her sister whereby Hannah would concentrate on animals, leaving the birds to Florence. At first, she also designed pieces with foliate scrolls, but from 1878 onwards all her bird decoration was executed in pâte sur pâte technique. Her style remained fairly constant, and pieces are more readily dated by shape rather than decoration.

HANNAH BARLOW

Sister of Arthur, Hannah Barlow had the distinction of being the first female artist to be employed by Doulton. Like her brother, she studied at the Lambeth School of Art and joined the company in 1871, remaining with them for some 42 years. She was fond of animals and in fact had a small private zoo at her home. This love was translated into her work, and her prolific output is characterised by the frequent use of incised decoration featuring animals and birds, with human figures appearing only occasionally. She must have been a formidable character, losing the use of her right hand early in her career, and retraining herself to work with her left.

FRANK BUTLER

Having joined Doulton in 1872, Frank Butler caught the popular imagination when it became known that he was deaf and dumb and yet a talented sculptor. The company exploited this to a degree by frequently employing him on their stand at exhibitions to model before the public. He was adept at all decorative techniques, but his own speciality was folding soft clay into shapes to produce some of the best foliate designs of the period. Generally considered to be at the height of his powers between 1870-1890, he nevertheless enthusiastically adopted the Art Nouveau style and successfully adapted his style to the new fashion.

EDITH LUPTON

Working at Doulton from around 1875, Edith Lupton produced early pieces which were characterised by their incised, stylised foliate decoration. From around 1880 onwards, she used naturalistically painted designs on pâte sur pâte, and also produced some fine pierced vases. It is uncertain how long she remained with the company, but her death is recorded in 1896.

MARK V. MARSHALL

Mark Marshall worked with Martin Bros. before joining Doulton around 1876. The influence of his previous employers can be seen in his choice of subjects for modelling - dragons, lizards and other grotesque creatures. He was much influenced by the Art Nouveau movement, and translated many of its theories into pottery.

ELIZA SIMMANCE

Eliza Simmance worked at Lambeth between 1873 and 1928 and was at first involved in the production of Barlow vases and silicon pieces. Her own pieces, produced from about 1900, showed some Italian influence and were either incised carved, or modelled then coloured. She also used a technique of building up decoration in coloured slips.

GEORGE TINWORTH

After an unpromising start as the illiterate son of a drunken Walworth wheelwright who did nothing to encourage his son's artistic leanings, George Tinworth gained admittance to the Lambeth School of Art. From there, he moved to Doulton's employ, where he achieved national recognition as a sculptor, his work praised and encouraged by Ruskin, and he produced a number of religious terracotta panels. As a sideline he also modelled humorous little figures and animals, and he also decorated vases and jugs with applied and incised motifs. He remained with Doulton until 1913.

A vase with shaped projections, incised leaves in blue and brown, o.m., 1874, 9½in. high. $400 £250

A salt cellar with incised blue leaves and bead work, c.m 1877, 2¼in. high. $240 £150

A jug with an incised white dog wearing a ruff, DLE, circa 1895, 6½in. high. $600 £375

A vase painted with yellow fruit and dark brown foliage on a brown field, c.m.l & c., circa 1912, 9in. high. $160 £100

A pair of candlesticks with incised geometric patterns in blue and brown on a buff ground, o.u.m., circa 1872, 11in. high. $600 £375

A mounted jug, the mottled brown ground with applied geometric and leaf patterns, c.m., 1878, 9½in. high. $256 £160

A tapered jug, with applied blue and green stylised flower heads, c.m., 1880, 9½in. high. $256 £160

A Punch and Judy clockcase, the buff stoneware with a bright blue glaze, c.m.l. & c., circa 1905, 11½in. high. $3200 £2000

A jug, the light buff body with incised diamonds and applied blue slip flowers, impressed Doulton Lambeth, circa 1868, 9½in. high. $240 £150

Four Doulton Lambeth stoneware decanters in original wicker basket, the shoulder moulded in relief with fruiting vine, 21cm. high. **$800 £500**

An Aesthetic Movement pair of Doulton stoneware oil lamp bases, each ogee body applied with circular panels, 31.5cm. high. **$640 £400**

A good and large Doulton Lambeth stoneware clock case, the whole incised with flowers and moulded with husks, dated *1882*. **$1600 £1000**

Doulton Lambeth stoneware jardinière, ovoid and embossed with classical profile heads and flowers within geometric borders, 8in. high. **$480 £300**

A pair of Doulton Lambeth art stoneware candlesticks, with stiff leaf moulded cicular drip pans issuing from gilt whorl decorated incised stems, 17cm. high. **$480 £300**

Salt glazed stoneware vase designed by Mary Ann Thompson And Jessie Bowditch, circa 1880, 9in, high. **$1600 £1000**

A pepper pot by Hannah Barlow, o.u.m., the silver cover hallmarked 1872, 3in. high. **$240 £150**

Pair of Royal Doulton vases of tapering baluster form with pale green rims, deep blue necks, impressed marks by Florrie Jones, probably circa 1930, 9½in. high. **$288 £180**

A Doulton Lambeth art stoneware ink pot, cover and liner, with incised stiff leaf border over a column moulded body and bead stamped base, dated *1877*, 12cm. high. **$288 £180**

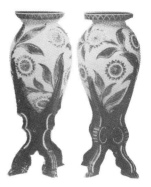

A fine pair of Doulton stoneware candlesticks, each baluster stem and domed foot applied with beads and incised with leaves, 18.8cm. high. $600 £375

An hexagonal salt cellar, the interior glazed blue, o.u.m., circa 1872, 3in. diameter.
$240 £150

Pair of Doulton stoneware vases, England, late 19th century, set in four-prong wood bases, unmarked, 17½in. high overall.
$1200 £750

The 'Lily Maid', a Royal Doulton polychrome glazed stoneware fountain figure, designed by Gilbert Bayes, 61.5cm. high. $24,000 £15000

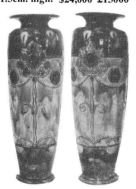

Pair of Royal Doulton decorative large baluster vases, spreading necks, on a central grey/beige washed ground, impressed marks by Bessie Newberry, late 19th century, 13½in. high. $720 £450

A pepper pot by Alice Budden with incised leaves and bead work, c.m., 1880, 2½in. high.
$176 £110

A massive pair of candlesticks by Alice E. Budden, incised overall, r.m., 1881, 11¾in. high. $1040 £650

A jug by Jane S. Hurst with applied green and white geometric patterns in high relief, r.m., 1881, 9½in. high.
$400 £250

A vase by Elizabeth Atkins, the buff ground with an incised scale pattern and four panels, r.m., 1883, 7in. high.
$288 £180

A pair of vases by Margaret Aitken, the white ground with incised flowering foliage painted in green and white pâte-sur-pâte, r.m., 1881, 8in. high.
$320 £200

A vase by Harry Barnard, the cream ground with incised bands of chevrons on which are painted tadpoles, r.m., 1882, 10¼in. high. $512 £320

A vase by Alberta L. Green with incised green leaves growing from a central ochre band, r.m., circa 1882, 8¾in. high.
$145 £90

A pair of vases by Bertha Evans, the mottled blue ground with incised brown scrolls, r.m., 1883, 7in. high. $520 £325

A vase by Ellen Gathercole, the incised brown ground with green plants having white flowers, r.m., 1882, 8½in. high.
$264 £165

A vase possibly by Emily Welch, the grey-green ground with applied blue flowering branches, r.m., circa 1885, 11¾in. high. $256 £160

A pair of vases by Mary Capes painted with green flowers outlined in gilt, r.m., 1884, 7¾in. high. $320 £200

A white stoneware jug with an incised diamond pattern, glazed alternately blue and brown with applied flower heads, o.u.m., the silver cover hallmarked 1872, 7in. high. $440 £275

A jug by Ellen Gathercole decorated in the traditional manner with applied vignettes of sporting scenes, r.m., 1882, 8¾in. high. $616 £385

A pair of candlesticks by Nellie Garbott with incised brown and blue leaves, c.m., 1879, 6¾in. high. $512 £320

A large vase by Harry Barnard, the buff ground with incised foliage, r.m., 1881, 14¼in. high. $1520 £950

A vase by Annie Gentle, with painted white lattice-work and incised green and yellow foliage, c.m., 1879, 9¾in. high.
        $264 £165

A pair of vases by Margaret Aitken, with incised and carved brown and blue leaves, r.m., 1882, 7½in. $448 £280

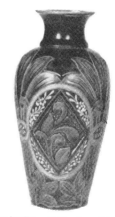

A vase by Eliza S. Banks, with carved panels of blue foliage surrounded by painted white flowers, r.m., 1882, 8½in. high.
        $352 £220

403

An unattributed jug moulded as a uniformed man with peaked hat, r.m., circa 1888, 9¼in. high. $352 £220

A small circular clockcase in buff stoneware with applied rough cast chips, circa 1890, 7¼in. high. $400 £250

An unattributed pair of vases, each with incised pale green and yellow foliage, r.m., circa 1885, 11½in. high. $640 £400

An unattributed beaker, the buff ground with painted white foliage and coloured lines, c.m.l. & c., circa 1902, 5½in. high. $104 £65

A late vase with stylised blue flowers and green leaves edged in white, c.m. & l., circa 1922, 7½in. high. $312 £195

A vase painted with formal purple flowers and green leaves against a white ground, c.m.l. & c., circa 1912, 7¾in. high. $264 £165

An unattributed salt cellar, the bowl with incised brown leaves, c.m., circa 1880, 3½in. high. $416 £260

A monumental clockcase glazed in shades of blue and brown with carved and incised details and applied bead work, c.m., 1879, 15½in. high. $3520 £2200

An unattributed vase with upright blue handles, c.m., 1879, 7½in. high. $176 £110

A vase, the mottled blue ground with incised lines, modelled in high relief with a dragon biting the neck, r.m., 1886, 10in. high. **$544 £340**

An early architectural clockcase glazed ochre and blue, with incised blue, green, and purple leaves, o.m., 1875, 14½in. high. **$2240 £1490**

An unattributed jug, the combed buff ground with incised green fish and plants, DLE, circa 1895, 13¼in. high. **$1088 £680**

A vase with black and purple designs on a white ground, c.m.l. & c., circa 1920, 8¼in. high. **$264 £165**

An architectural clockcase glazed in dark brown, blue and green, r.m., 1884, 10¼in. high. **$2880 £1800**

A cylindrical vase with blue, green and black geometric designs on a lovat ground, c.m.l. & c., circa 1920, 7¾in. high. **$152 £95**

An unattributed jug, the buff ground with white bead work and incised blue and brown leaves, c.m., 1879, 7¾in. high. **$264 £165**

An unattributed hexagonal open-work basket pierced with brown lattice, r.m., 1880, 5¼in. high. **$208 £130**

A horn cup attributed to Mark V. Marshall moulded with a blue and ochre sphinx, c.m., 1876, 9in. high. **$2560 £1600**

A tapered jug with mottled
brown glaze and applied blue
flower heads, o.m., 1875.
10½in. high. $240 £150

A bulbous jug with applied
geometric and floral patterns in
purple and green, c.m., 1879,
7¼in. high. $336 £210

A jug by Harriett E. Hibbut, the
blue ground with an applied
carpet of large flowers predominantly blue, c.m., 1880, 9¼in.
high. $240 £150

A vase by Bessie Youatt, the
white ground with an incised
spiral green leafy branch, c.m.,
1879, 8in. high. $232 £145

A pair of vases by Emily A.
London with a blue hatched
ground, r.m., 1883, 4½in. high.
                            $232 £145

A vase by Bessie Youatt, the
white neck finely combed and
the body painted with brown
leaves, c.m., 1880, 9½in. high.
                            $280 £175

A pâte-sur-pâte jug, the buff
ground with finely incised and
applied green leaves and bead
work, r.m., circa 1882, 8½in.
high. $256 £160

A shaped jug with applied blue
geometric patterns in high
relief, c.m., 1877, 8½in. high.
                            $352 £220

A jug with an overall incised
diamond pattern, glazed
alternately in brown and blue,
r.m., circa 1882, 8¾in. high.
                            $288 £180

A jug, with applied dark green and white shell motifs within various applied borders, c.m., 1880, 9½in. high. $256 £160

A modelled owl with detachable head, the feathers formed by applied motifs in shades of blue, ochre and brown, r.m., circa 1880, 8in. high. $2400 £1500

A vase, the light buff body stencilled overall with impressed concentric circles, r.m., circa 1882, 12¼in. high. $144 £90

A jug by Bessie Youatt, incised and applied with a ring of blue flower heads, c.m., 1879, 8½in. high. $248 £155

A pair of vases by Bessie Youatt, each with four incised shaped panels, r.m., 1883, 10¾in. high. $640 £400

A baluster-shaped jug with incised blue shield-shaped panels on a brown ground, r.m., 1882, 9½in. high. $288 £180

A jug by Emma Shute with applied pale blue and white motifs, c.m., 1880, 9¼in. high. $256 £160

A mug by Constance E. Redford, the buff ground with white dots and incised blue scrolls, r.m., 1882, 5in. high. $216 £135

A jug by Harriett E. Hibbut, the mottled brown body with applied grey and blue leaves, and flower heads, c.m., 1976, 9in. high. $288 £180

A cylindrical jug with a dark brown glaze and applied flower heads, blue triangles and white beads, c.m., 1878, 6¾in. high.
$256 £160

A vase by Mary Aitken of baluster shape, with overall applied bands of graduated beads, r.m., 1880, 14½in. high.
$336 £210

A small bowl by Emily Welch with impressed gilt concentric circles, r.m., circa 1888, 4in. high.
$480 £300

A brown glazed jug with incised acorns, flowers, and leaves, filled with blue slip, o.u.m., circa 1871, 8in. high.
$248 £155

A cruet set by Charlotte Lamb, both bottles with incised flowering plants, c.m., 1879, 4¼in. high.
$480 £300

A blue stoneware jug with carved stylised leaves and a band of applied flower heads, the base incised F.M. and impressed with the letter B, o.u.m., circa 1871, 7¼in. high.
$256 £160

An incised jug, the light buff body with cattle and a goat below leaf bands filled with brown slip, o.u.m., circa 1871, 7in. high.
$1120 £700

A small bowl by Sarah Fisher, the cover pierced with green and blue scrolls, c.m., 1879, 4in. high.
$552 £345

A baluster-shaped jug with a mottled blue glaze, applied blue leaf motifs, and brown bead work, r.m., 1883, 8¼in. high.
$288 £180

A mounted jug with applied geometric patterns and a frieze of multi-coloured applied circles, r.m., 1880, 9½in. high. $288 £180

An egg cup stand by Mary Davies, the ochre stand with incised green foliate scrolls, r.m., 1884, 6in. diameter. $1360 £850

A jug, the cream body with incised and applied blue lily of the valley, o.u.m., circa 1871, 7¼in. high. $320 £200

An inscribed vase by Alice Groom, the buff body with incised green and brown leaves and blue flowers, r.m., 1886, 6½in. high. $256 £160

A large vase attributed to Cund, with two modelled monkeys clinging to the sides, r.m., 1881, 18in. high. $1600 £1000

A jug by Jane S. Hurst with overall applied green and grey motifs, c.m., 1879, 9¼in. high. $256 £160

A pair of vases by Nellie Garbott with incised pale blue flowers on a dark blue ground, r.m., 1881, 6in. high. $352 £220

A jug covered with a pale brown glaze, with applied clusters of green shells. o.m., 1875, 6½in. high. $192 £120

A slip-cast vase by William Rowe with green leaves and a black and white checkered design, s.c.m., circa 1920, 9in. high. $176 £110

Nelson's Centenary, a moulded statuette of the admiral glazed green, c.m.l. & c., circa 1905, 8¼in. high. $640 £400

A vase modelled with shaped panels in relief, on each an applied moulded portrait glazed dark green, r.m., 1888, 9¾in. high. $1280 £800

An unattributed jug with an incised green and brown scale pattern, r.m., 1884, 7in. high. $224 £140

An unattributed vase, the pale blue ground with carved green flowering plants, r.m., 1880, 14¼in. high. $304 £190

A pair of unattributed cylindrical vases, each with applied medallions of fish and a lobster, r.m., circa 1885, 10¼in. high. $384 £240

An unattributed vase decorated with natural coloured foliage, r.m., circa 1885, 11½in. high. $560 £350

A vase painted with plums against buff, purple and pink bands, c.m.l. & c., circa 1912, 7½in. high. $224 £140

A ribbed vase moulded with a cellular pattern and glazed olive-green, s.c.m., circa 1920, 6½in. high. $135 £85

A vase painted with stylised yellow chrysanthemums against a mottled pink ground, c.m.l. & c., circa 1912, 9in. high. $264 £165

CLARA BARKER

A vase by Clara Barker, with incised green scrolls on a hatched blue ground, r.m., 1884, 6in. high. $192 £120

A small tazza by Clara Barker, the stem moulded with eight blue dolphins, c.m., 1878, 3¾in. high. $280 £175

A vase by Clara Barker, the white ground with an incised continuous green foliate band, r.m., 1882, 6½in. high.
$288 £180

ARTHUR BARLOW

A jug with incised green, blue and brown leaves on a white background, o.m., 1875, 10in. high. $304 £190

A pair of vases decorated with incised blue and green stylised leaf designs on a buff ground, o.m., circa 1873, 8¾in. high.
$832 £520

A ewer with deeply incised foliage and geometric patterns, and applied flower heads. o.m., 1874, 10½in. high. $624 £390

A jug with incised green and brown scrolling foliage on a white ground, o.m., 1873, 8¾in. high. $576 £360

A candlestick with lightly incised leaves glazed brown and blue, and applied borders, o.m., 1874, 9½in. high.
$352 £220

A jug with incised blue foliate scrolls on a white ground, o.m., the silver mount hallmarked 1872, 8in. high. $576 £360

ARTHUR BARLOW

A jug with incised pink and blue
foliage on a pale green ground,
o.m., 1874, 10¼in. high.
$400 £250

A flask with incised brown
foliage on a ground impressed
with stars, o.m., 1875, 8¼in.
high. $1088 £680

A pierced vase, the outer wall
with foliage glazed dark brown
on a buff ground, o.u.m., circa
1872, 7¼in. high. $512 £320

A pepper pot by Arthur Barlow,
o.u.m., the silver cover hallmarked 1872, 3¼in. high.
$224 £140

A jug with carved scrolling
foliage and applied flower heads
and beads in brown, green and
blue, o.m., 1874, 6¼in. high.
$512 £320

A large jug with incised brown
foliage, applied bead decoration
and blue flower heads, o.m.,
1876, 12¼in. high. $1104 £690

A ewer, the body with unusual
leaf motifs incised in blue, white
and green, assistants
monogram: Mary A. Thomson,
o.m., 1875, 10in. high.
$944 £590

A jug with incised mottled
brown leaves on a pale buff
ground, o.u.m., circa 1871,
7¼in. high. $608 £380

A vase with incised brown
foliate scrolls and applied white
flowers on a buff ground, o.m.,
1874, 9½in. high. $512 £320

ARTHUR BARLOW

A vase with incised leaves glazed bright blue on a hatched ground, glazed brown, o.u.m., circa 1872, 9in. high. $512 £320

A mug by Arthur Barlow, the light buff body with an incised blue leaf band and applied shell motifs, o.u.m., the silver rim hallmarked, 1871, 4½in. high. $384 £240

A ewer with incised foliate scrolls in blue and green on a buff ground, o.m., 1873, 9¾in. high. $544 £340

A large jug with incised blue and green foliage below various incised and applied borders, o.m., 1874, 14¾in. high. $1520 £950

A dish with incised concave flower heads surrounded by bands of leaves and basketwork in green, brown and blue, o.m., 1874, 10½in. diam. $992 £620

A ewer, the light buff body with incised stiff leaves glazed mottled brown, signed A. B. Barlow, o.u.m., circa 1872, 11in. high. $1104 £690

A jug with incised dark brown foliage on a mottled pink ground, o.m., 1874, 10in. high. $1088 £680

A beaker with applied bead decoration and blue flowerheads, c.m., 1876, 5¼in. high. $352 £220

A vase with finely incised blue and pale green foliage on a brown ground, o.m., 1874, 10in. high. $656 £410

FLORENCE BARLOW

A turkey vase painted in bright green and brown pâte-sur-pâte with a frieze of turkeys, r.m. & e., circa 1895, 14in. high.
$2800 £1750

A biscuit barrel with plate cover and mounts, the sides painted in pâte-sur-pâte with four cockatoos, r.m., 1886, 5½in. high. $1536 £960

A doubled-handled vase with various incised leaf and scroll designs, c.m., 1878, 11¼in. high.
$1520 £950

A vase by Florence Barlow, with three panels of young birds amongst coloured grasses, DSL, 1885, 10½in. high. $1920 £1200

A pair of vases, the alternating panels with incised and cut out stylised flowers and foliage in various shades of blue, c.m., 1878, 10¾in. high. $704 £440

A pair of vases incised on the buff ground with finches amongst grasses, c.m., 1878, 11in. high. $2240 £1400

A vase with incised brown foliate scrolls on a buff ground, the base with incised green and blue leaves, c.m., 1878, 10in. high. $672 £420

A Doulton stoneware jug, decorated by Florence Barlow and Emma Martin, decorated with groups of beaded roundels on a blue ground, 21cm high, dated 1879. $360 £225

A vase decorated in pâte-sur-pâte, the four oval panels each with a garden bird, r.m., 1883, 8in. high. $1120 £700

FLORENCE BARLOW

A jug, the stippled buff ground painted in pâte-sur-pâte with two green and white crested birds, r.m., circa 1885, 5½in. high. $960 £600

A tall vase, decorated with five pâte-sur-pâte tit-mice perched on a branch, r.m. & e., circa 1895, 16in. high. $2000 £1250

A jug with incised scrolling brown foliage and applied white bead work, c.m., 1876, 6¾in. high. $720 £450

A jug painted in pâte-sur-pâte with a hen and her chicks in a shaped panel, r.m., circa 1885, 9in. high, with a beaker en suite, 5½in. high. $1200 £750

A pair of ewers, each with two shaped panels painted in pâte-sur-pâte with a parrot on a branch, r.m. & e., circa 1895, 10¼in. high. $2800 £1750

A tapering jug painted in white, with ducks amongst rushes on a buff ground, c.m., 1879, 9½in. high, with two beakers en suite, 5¼in. high. $1152 £720

A jug with incised horses in blue and brown slip on a buff ground, c.m., 1877, 6¾in. high.
$1040 £650

A massive vase painted in green and white pâte-sur-pâte with garden birds amongst branches and numerous ducks amongst rushes, circa 1880, 26½in. high.
$5440 £3400

A jug decorated with a shaped panel containing two pâte-sur-pâte black swans reserved on a buff ground, r.m., 1884, 7¾in. high. $1216 £760

FLORENCE BARLOW

A vase decorated with brown leaves and blue birds on a buff lace ground, impressed date for 1880 and Doulton Lambeth, 10in. high. **$1200 £750**

A jug with incised squirrels on a buff ground, the base with incised stiff green and blue leaves, c.m., 1877, 7¾in. high, with a beaker en suite, 4½in. high. **$2000 £1250**

An early jug, incised in a white ground with herons standing in water, o.m., 1874, 7½in. high. **$1440 £900**

A pair of vases, each with incised horses and sheep in shaped panels with garden birds in pâte-sur-pâte, the animals by Hannah Barlow; the birds by Florence Barlow, r.m. & e., circa 1895, 16½in. high. **$3120 £1950**

A pair of Doulton Lambeth stoneware vases, circa 1890, decorated by Florence Barlow, in raised slip with panels of birds within a tube-lined stylised floral border, 13½in. high. **$1705 £1100**

A pair of vases, each painted in green and white pâte-sur-pâte with storks standing amongst grasses, c.m.l. & c., date letter for 1906, 14¼in. high. **$3520 £2200**

A doubled-handled vase painted in pâte-sur-pâte with a green and white titmouse perched on a branch, DLE, circa 1895, 9½in. high. **$1568 £980**

A pair of covered vases with upright handles, c.m., 1878, 7¾in. high. **$2320 £1450**

A vase painted on either side with a swallow-tailed butterfly, c.m.l. & c., circa 1906, 11¾in. high. **$1440 £900**

FLORENCE BARLOW

A large vase painted with herons fighting over a fish, the reverse side with herons and a bat against the moon, r.m. & e., circa 1895, 19¾in. high.
$2880 £1800

A large pair of vases, each with three shaped panels painted with garden birds amongst foliage, r.m. & e., circa 1895, 14½in. high. $3520 £2,200

A vase, modelled in high relief, with two budgerigars perched on green leafy branches, r.m., 1886, 12¼in. high. $2000 £1250

A pair of vases, each with three panels decorated in relief with garden birds perched amongst blossom, c.m.l. & c., date letter for 1903, 11½in. high.
$3040 £1900

A lavishly decorated vase commemorating the 1897 Jubilee, the central panel with painted white VR monograms and applied moulded portraits of the Queen, signed in full: F. E. Barlow, r.m. & e., circa 1897, 24¼in. high. $5600 £3500

A small pair of vases painted in green and white pâte-sur-pâte with a frieze of ducks, r.m. & e., circa 1895, 6¾in. high.
$1600 £1000

A large vase with three stippled buff panels painted with garden birds, r.m., circa 1885, 25½in. high. $3120 £1950

A pair of vases with a frieze of ducks and grass, r.m. & e., circa 1895, 9¾in. high.
$2880 £1800

A vase painted in pâte-sur-pâte, with a green bunting perched on a branch, r.m. & e., circa 1895, 13¼in. high. $1920 £1200

HANNAH BARLOW

A large and good Doulton
Lambeth biscuit barrel by
Hannah Barlow, incised with a
band of horses, impressed mark
and dated *1883*, 7¼in. high.
$256 £160

A mug with an incised frieze of
running deer on a buff ground,
c.m., 1878, 3½in. high.
$800 £500

A cream jug with incised
puppies and blue and brown
leaves on a buff ground, o.m.,
1874, 4¾in. high. **$920 £575**

An early jug with incised stiff
leaves filled with blue and
brown slip on a buff ground,
o.m., silver mount hallmarked,
1872, 6¾in. high. **$424 £265**

A large pair of vases, each with
two quatrefoil panels, one of
cats and the other of dogs, the
birds by Florence Barlow, the
background by Eliza
Simmance, r.m. & e., circa
1895, 18in. high. **$5920 £3700**

A cup and saucer with incised
sheep and lambs on a buff
ground, r.m., 1884, the cup 2in.
high. **$928 £580**

A vase with three shaped panels,
each painted with a cat in pâte-
sur-pâte, r.m., 1884. 9in. high.
$2080 £1300

Doulton Lambeth three handled
mug, the silver rim inscribed *To
Joseph McWilliams*, and dated
1880, the three handles moulded
with geometric designs, by
Hannah Barlow, incised marks
1876, 5½in. high. **$720 £450**

A vase with finely incised ponies
and goats in a landscape, c.m.,
1878, 8in. high. **$1248 £780**

HANNAH BARLOW

A small jug with incised goats in pasture on a dark buff ground, o.m., 1874, 5¾in. high.
$760 £475

A tobacco jar and cover, the body with incised brown glazed cows frolicking amongst incised green foliage, r.m. & e., circa 1895, 6½in. high. $760 £475

A small jug with an incised bird on a branch and flowering plants, o.m., circa 1872, 6in. high.
$720 £450

A tall jug with incised deer in a wreath of foliage below incised scrolls, o.m., 1873, 10¾in. high.
$840 £525

A large pair of vases with a boldly incised frieze of goats, borders by Frank Butler, r.m. & e., circa 1895, 21½in. high.
$6560 £4100

A jug with an incised pride of lions on a buff ground, DLE, circa 1895, 8½in. high.
$1760 £1100

A jug, the buff body incised with a dog and plants, titled 'Lost', o.u.m., circa 1871, possibly the work of Hannah Barlow, 6¾in. high.
$1200 £750

A tyg with three incised groups of rabbits in a landscape, the handles with incised flowers, o.m., 1873, 5¾in. high.
$1040 £650

A jug with incised lions in a landscape, filled with a dark blue slip on a light buff ground, o.m., circa 1872, 8in. high.
$1284 £780

HANNAH BARLOW

A small jug with an incised fox stalking a rabbit, filled with a blue slip on a buff ground, o.m., 1875, 6½in. high. $960 £606

A loving cup in buff glazed stoneware, with two boldly incised lions, o.m., silver rim hallmarked 1872, 6½in. high. $1248 £780

A jug with incised cat and rabbits between incised stiff leaves, o.m., circa 1872, 8in. high. $1360 £850

A jug with incised stiff leaves, scrolls, and a frieze of rabbits, o.m., circa 1872, 7½in. high. $992 £620

A terracotta picture, titled 'So near and yet so far', the animals modelled in high-relief in buff terracotta, 1890, 10 x 7in. $2560 £1600

A large vase with an incised frieze of frightened deer being pursued by wolves, o.m., circa 1872, 15¾in. high. $1520 £950

A waisted beaker with an incised frieze of running dogs, o.m., 1873, 6¼in. high. $928 £580

A large tankard with incised water rats stealing eggs from an enraged swan, o.m., circa 1872, 6¾in. high. $928 £580

Doulton Lambeth Hannah Barlow pitcher, England, circa 1895, with incised hounds and pâte-sur-pâte quail on a stippled background, 9in. high. $2000 £1174

HANNAH BARLOW

A waisted beaker with incised sheep and lambs above stiff leaves, o.m., 1873, 6in. high. $928 £580

A salt cellar by Hannah Barlow of hexagonal trencher type, o.u.m., circa 1872, 3in. diameter. $440 £275

A vase with incised herons flying amongst reeds, glazed blue on a white ground, c.m., 1876, 8¼in. high. $928 £580

A tapering jug with incised sheep by a fence, filled with blue slip on a white ground, c.m., 1877, 9¼in. high. $1440 £900

A massive vase, the white ground impressed with blue flower heads and with incised lions in two shaped buff panels, further decorated by Frank Butler, r.m., 1886, 33in. high. $8640 £5400

A jug with an incised band of pheasants above blue and brown leaves, o.m., 1873, 6in. high. $928 £580

A two-handled vase with incised horses between borders of stiff blue leaves on a buff ground, o.m., circa 1872, 10in. high. $1360 £850

A vase, the sides modelled in high relief with wolves chasing deer, o.m., circa 1872, 11¼in. high. $4960 £3100

A jug with incised leaves and flowers glazed dark blue on a pale blue ground, r.m., 1880, 7in. high. $350 £220

HANNAH BARLOW

A vase with incised horses grazing in a field, filled with blue slip on a buff ground, r.m., circa 1882, 13½in. high.
$1520 £950

A double-handled jardinière with an incised frieze of horses, r.m., 1880. 6¾in. high.
$1920 £1200

A vase with two modelled brown glazed dogs, the body with incised blue, green and brown leaves, r.m., 1889, 14in. high.
$3040 £1900

A jug with an incised frieze of cows in pasture on a white ground, c.m., 1878, 9in. high.
$1120 £700

A pair of vases, one with incised children playing with puppies, the companion with a girl watching dogs chase a rabbit, r.m., 1885, 10¾in. high.
$2640 £1650

An amusing jug with an incised dog growling at a bristling cat defending its kittens playing on a tree, r.m., 1883, 9¼in. high.
$1920 £1200

A jug with incised gun dogs sniffing a scent and a fox hiding behind the handle in long grass, c.m., 1880, 9½in. high.
$1600 £1000

A tankard with incised farm horses in a landscape, one ploughing, o.m., silver rim hallmarked 1872, 6¾in. high.
$1120 £700

A jug with incised herons amongst reeds, in a bright blue slip on a buff ground, c.m., 1877, 9in. high. **$1440 £900**

HANNAH BARLOW

A two-handled vase with an incised frieze of kangaroos, filled with blue slip on a white ground, r.m., 1886, 14¼in. high. $2560 £1600

A jardinière with an incised frieze of deer in a landscape on a light buff ground, c.m., 1877. 6½in. high. $1920 £1200

An unusual vase, with an incised frieze of sheep in pasture, c.m.l. & c., circa 1905, 7¾in. high. $960 £600

A mounted jug with incised horses in a landscape on a white ground, c.m., 1878, 9¼in. high. $1120 £700

A large pair of vases, each with an incised frieze of wolves and their cubs amongst foliage, r.m., 1885, 16½in. high. $4480 £2800

A large vase painted in green and white pate-sur-pâte with a frieze of cattle, r.m. & e., circa 1895, 18½in. high. $2560 £1600

A jug with the incised figure of a young girl behind a tree watching pigs, r.m., 1883, 8¾in. high. $1520 £950

A jardinière with a frieze of incised lions, and borders with incised foliage, r.m., 1882, 9¾in. high. $2480 £1550

A vase with an incised frieze of horses, and foliate borders in green, blue and brown, r.m., 1883, 9in. high. $1200 £750

HANNAH BARLOW

A vase decorated with incised goats grazing, with blue and brown slip designs on a brown ground, r.m., 13³/₄in. high.
$1520 £950

A pair of Royal Doulton stoneware ewers, by Hannah Barlow and Emily Stormer, each incised and painted with a group of ponies in a moorland setting, 31.4cm. high. $1040 £650

A vase decorated with incised goats, beads and foliage designs on a blue brown ground, r.m., impressed date for 1881, 9³/₄in. high. $1120 £700

A tea-set, comprising a teapot, cream jug and sugar bowl, each piece with an incised frieze of goats on a buff ground, o.m., 1875, the teapot 4¹/₄in. high.
$2560 £1600

A vase decorated with incised lions, stiff leaves and beads on a blue ground, r.m. & e., 1891-1902, 10¹/₂in. high. $1520 £950

A tea-set, comprising a teapot, cream jug and sugar bowl, each with an incised frieze of rabbits above green and blue leaves, c.m., 1880, 1886, 4¹/₂in. high.
$2560 £1600

A vase decorated with an incised frieze of goats and donkeys with slip design scroll borders on a brown and green ground, r.m. & e., 12in. high. $1152 £720

A large pair of vases with an incised frieze of white deer in a mountainous landscape, borders by Florence Barlow, DLE, circa 1895, 17¹/₄in. high.
$5440 £3400

A jug with an incised farm worker and a donkey pulling a cart loaded with tree branches, r.m., 1887, 9¹/₄in. high.
$1120 £700

HANNAH BARLOW

A vase with three incised donkeys in a landscape on a buff ground, r.m. & e., circa 1892, 9in. high. $1200 £750

A pair of ewers, each with incised lions in a landscape on a white ground, r.m., 1883, 11¾in. high. $2400 £1500

A vase with incised horses in a landscape, borders by Bessie Youatt, c.m., 1879, 10¼in. high. $1200 £750

A tea-set, comprising a teapot, cream jug and sugar bowl, each piece with incised kangaroos and emus, c.m., 1878, the teapot 4½in. high. $3120 £1950

A vase decorated with incised moorland ponies, a band of stiff leaves and flowers on a blue green ground, impressed date 1880 and Doulton Lambeth, 9½in. high. $1200 £750

A tea-set, comprising a teapot, cream jug and sugar bowl, each piece with an incised frieze of rabbits, borders by Lucy Barlow, r.m., 1883, the teapot 4½in. high. $2560 £1600

A jug with an incised frieze of goats in a rocky landscape, c.m., 1879, 10½in. high. $1120 £700

A good pair of Doulton Lambeth vases and covers by Hannah Barlow, incised with a band of lions, 13in. high. $2560 £1600

A tapering jug with incised stags and does in a landscape, c.m., 1878, 9½in. high. $1120 £700

JOHN BROAD

"The Boer War Soldier", a buff glazed figure of an infantry man, r.m. & e., circa 1900, 12½in. high. **$2080 £1300**

A modelled group, on a circular base with a buff glazed donkey, c.m., 1879 6½in. high. **$3120 £1950**

A terracotta statuette of King Edward VII standing against a column, the base inscribed ERI, c.m.l. & c., circa 1901, 16¾in. high. **$1600 £1000**

A slip-cast figure of "The Bather", the white glazed nude seated on a purple sphere, s.c.m., circa 1912, 13in. high. **$2880 £1800**

Queen Victoria, a buff salt-glaze figure commemorating her life, incised Doulton Co. Ltd. Lambeth, circa 1901, 11¾in. high. **$2000 £1250**

Pitt's Centenary, a grey terracotta portrait-bust of the statesman, the shaped base inscribed "William Pitt 1759-1806", Sc., c.m.l. & c., circa 1906, 13¾in. high. **$912 £570**

ROSINA BROWN

A large vase with running green glaze by Rosina Brown, c.m.l. & c., 14½in. high. **$152 £95**

A jug by Rosina Brown, the shaded green ground with incised scrolls, r.m. & e., circa 1892, 7¼in. high. **$512 £320**

A pierced vase by Rosina Brown cut with geometric patterns, r.m., circa 1885, 7in. high. **$448 £280**

FRANK BUTLER

A small early jug, the buff body with deeply incised foliate scrolls, o.u.m., silver mount hallmarked 1873, 5in. high.
$784 £490

A candlestick with incised geometric and leaf designs, o.m., 1874, 5in. high. $464 £290

A flask of flattened circular shape incised in green, brown and purple, c.m., 1878, 8in. high. $1120 £700

A jug with incised stiff leaves and scrolls in green, blue and brown, o.m., 1873, 7in. high.
$672 £420

A jardinière decorated with a frieze of applied moulded bust-portraits representing Queen Victoria, Victor Emmanuel of Italy, Napoleon III, Empress Eugenie and Kaiser Wilhelm of Germany, o.m., 1874, 8¼in. high. $2400 £1500

A jug with incised blue leaves on a brown ground, o.m., 1874, 5¼in. high. $480 £300

A jug with deeply incised brown and blue foliage, o.m., 1873, 9 in. high. $448 £280

Doulton Lambeth stoneware pilgrim vase, England, circa 1885, serpent handles, impressed marks and *Frank A. Butler* signature, 12¾in. high.
$1088 £680

A vase with incised blue leaves, applied white beads on a sepia ground, c.m., 1876, 7½in. high.
$448 £280

FRANK BUTLER

A vase modelled in relief with a
stylised plant, r.m., circa 1890,
12in. high. $1248 £780

A shaped bowl richly decorated
on the inside and outside with
incised leaves and foliate scrolls,
c.m., 1880, 10¼in. diameter.
$1600 £1000

An egg cup by Frank Butler
with incised blue leaves on a
buff ground, circa 1872, 3½in.
high. $192 £120

A jug with carved and incised
blue leaf patterns on a stippled
buff ground, r.m., 1881, 13½in.
high. $1360 £850

A large pair of vases, the three
panels with incised foliate
scrolls in lovat, blue and ochre,
r.m., 1882, 17½in. high.
$2080 £1300

A portrait jug, the dark blue
ground with impressed flower
motifs, c.m., 1877, 10½in. high.
$1040 £650

A vase with incised green and
blue foliage and brown cross-
hatched panels, r.m., 1884,
7¾in. high. $928 £580

An inscribed bowl with incised
blue flowers and scrolls on an
olive-green ground, 1894, 8¼in.
diameter. $1088 £680

A large vase, the central panel
with carved brown scrolls on a
hatched blue ground between
incised leaf and scroll borders,
r.m., 1884, 14¼in. high.
$1568 £980

FRANK BUTLER

A goblet-shaped vase, with applied stylised blue flowers on a brown panel, c.m.l. & c., circa 1905, 8½in. high.
$672 £420

A shallow dish with incised scrolls and the name K. B. Smallfield, 1897, on a green ground, r.m., 6½in. diameter.
$784 £490

A tall vase with incised dark green plants on a brown ground, c.m.l. & c., date letter for 1909, 17½in. high.
$1088 £680

A large jug, ornately decorated with incised, applied and impressed work. o.m., 1874, 17in. high. $2240 £1400

A pair of vases, each with incised scrolls and leaves, c.m., 1876, 14¼in. high. $2080 £1300

A jug with a profusion of incised leaves in blue, green, pink and brown, o.m., 1875, 14½in. high. $1840 £1150

A jug with incised green and purple leaves on a brown ground, c.m., 1878, 10in. high.
$1088 £680

A shell-shaped bowl painted with white flowers on a green panel, r.m. & e., circa 1895, 4¾in. high. $1120 £700

A jug, modelled in relief with depressed fan-shaped motifs, c.m., 1879, 8¼in. high.
$1200 £750

FRANK BUTLER

A vase with flowering plants against a brown background, r.m. & e., circa 1895, 13in. high. $1920 £1200

A pair of vases, modelled with stylised plants having green bulbs, brown stems and leaves, and blue flowers, DLE, circa 1895, 9¾in. high. $2160 £1350

A vase with stylised flowering plants in blue and brown, r.m. & e., circa 1895, 13¼in. high. $2000 £1250

A covered sprinkler, the squashed body with incised blue and green flowers, FAB., 1894, 10¼in. high. $792 £495

A pair of vases, modelled with projecting brown forms growing from a green ground, c.m.l. & c., date letter for 1906, 7in. high. $864 £540

An Art Nouveau vase with dark blue flowers and seed pods on a pale blue ground, DLE, circa 1900, 13in. high. $1040 £650

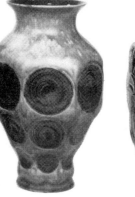

A shaped flask, each side decorated with pierced and carved green foliate scrolls, r.m. & e., circa 1895, 9½in. high. $1568 £980

A pair of vases, the mottled green ground modelled with projections divided by graduated brown and blue circles, r.m. & e., circa 1895, 9¾in. high $1120 £700

A vase modelled with projecting flowers, with green leaves and brown stems, c.m.l. & c., date letter for 1909, 14¾in. $2000 £1250

LOUISA DAVIS

A mounted jug, the incised buff ground with impressed flowers, c.m., 1880, 9½in. high.
$784 £490

A jug, the brown ground with impressed flower motifs, c.m., 1876, 6in. high. $225 £150
$632 £395

A vase, the white ground with an incised spiral band of foliage with blue flowers, c.m., 1877, 11¾in. high. $384 £240

A vase, the buff ground with incised long lovat leaves, brown foliage, and blue flowers, c.m., 1877, 9³/₄in. high. $384 £240

A bowl, the brown ground with incised blue flowers and scrolling, c.m., 1878, 7½in. high. $1920 £1200

A vase decorated with incised blue leaves and flowers with bands of applied beads and florets, on a blue ground, impressed dated for 1878 and Doulton Lambeth, 9¹/₄in. high. $672 £420

W. EDWARD DUNN

A small vase by W. Edward Dunn, painted in green and white pâte-sur-pâte with a dog's head, r.m., 1883, 5¼in. high. $1040 £650

A pilgrim bottle by W. Edward Dunn, one side with incised sheep in a landscape glazed green, the other with women gleaning, r.m., 1883, 9in. high. $1360 £850

A vase by W. Edward Dunn, each side with an incised blue bird on a buff panel, r.m., 1882, 12in. high. $1200 £750

STONEWARE

EMILY EDWARDS

A jug by Emily J. Edwards with a mottled brown glaze and applied flower heads within incised borders, o.u.m., circa 1872, 7in. high. $512 £320

A flower-shaped dish, the brown ground with incised lines and green and purple leaves, impressed Doulton Lambeth, 1876, 10½in. diameter.
$512 £320

A jug with incised green scrolls and blue leaves on a scored brown ground, o.m., 1873, 7¼in. high. $384 £240

LOUISA EDWARDS

A jug with incised dark brown leaf scrolls on a buff ground, c.m., 1878, 10¾in. high.
$464 £290

A jug with incised green and yellow plants with blue flowers, c.m., 1878, 7¼in. high.
$248 £155

A vase, the pale blue ground with finely incised foliage, r.m., 1881, 10in. high. $400 £250

A jug, the buff ground with fine incised lines and impressed flower heads, c.m., 1879, 9½in. high. $464 £290

A vase with incised blue flowering foliage on a pale blue ground, c.m., 1879, 11in. high.
$448 £280

A jug, the body with incised bands of stylised leaves in green and purple, c.m., 1879, 9½in. high. $464 £290

HERBERT ELLIS

A cream coloured terracotta figure of a partly draped woman holding a plaque, impressed Doulton & Co., Lambeth, incised H. Ellis Sc., circa 1910, 13¹/₂in. high. $880 £550

An unglazed cream coloured terracotta figure of a nude woman kneeling on a net, incised H. Ellis Sc., circa 1910, 9¹/₂in. high. $800 £500

An unglazed moulded terracotta figure, the partly draped woman holding a branch of foliage. Impressed Doulton & Co., Lambeth, circa 1910, 11in. high. $720 £450

ELIZABETH FISHER

A jug, the brown ground with incised panels in green, purple and brown, c.m., 1876. 9in. high. $576 £360

A pair of vases with incised foliate scrolls in two shades of blue, r.m., 1883, 11in. high. $672 £420

A jug, the blue ground with incised leaves, buff panels with impressed flower heads, c.m., 1878, 8½in. high. $352 £220

A beaker, the brown ground with impressed flower heads, c.m., 1876, 5¼in. high. $160 £100

A pair of candlesticks with incised blue leaves and applied flower heads and bead work, c.m., 1877, 8½in. high. $672 £420

A jug, incised in blue and brown on a buff ground, r.m., 1881, 9¼in. high. $352 £220

LESLIE HARRADINE

A brown salt-glaze spirit flask modelled as John Burns, the Labour leader, DLE, circa 1912, 7¼in. high. $400 £250

A cast figure of Sairey Gamp, the light buff glaze, s.c.m., circa 1913, 8in. high. $560 £350

A brown salt-glaze spirit flask modelled as David Lloyd George, DLE, circa 1912, 7¾in. high. $400 £250

A vase by Leslie Harradine cast into a square section and moulded with laburnum, s.c.m., circa 1912, 8¾in. high. $240 £150

A brown terracotta bust of George V, the reverse stamped Doulton Lambeth, L. Harradine Sc., circa 1910, 7½in. high. $496 £310

A vase after a design by Leslie Harradine with moulded yellow flowers, s.c.m., circa 1910, 9¾in. high. $256 £160

A slip-cast figure of Mr. Pickwick in a light buff glaze, s.c.m., circa 1913, 8½in. high. $616 £385

A white glazed figure of a peasant woman wearing a blue checkered dress, RDE, circa 1905, 8½in. high. $616 £385

A moulded figure of a farm labourer holding a scythe, wearing a blue shirt, circa 1905, 7½in. high. $616 £385

LESLIE HARRADINE

A brown salt-glaze spirit flask modelled as President Roosevelt, DLE, circa 1912, 7½in. high.
$320 £200

"Motherhood", a white glazed figure of a mother cradling her baby, the dress with blue flowers, RDE, circa 1912, 6in. high.
$616 £385

A brown salt-glaze spirit flask modelled in the traditional style with Austen Chamberlain, DLE, circa 1912, 7¾in. high.
$280 £175

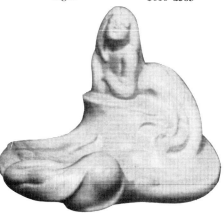

A brown salt-glaze figure of Mr. Pecksniff, s.c.m., circa 1913, 9¼in. high
$616 £385

A white slip-cast group modelled with two mermaids, s.c.m., circa 1910, length 7in.
$624 £390

Dickens, a moulded white glazed stoneware figure of Mr. Squeers, s.c.m., circa 1913, 9¼in. high.
$616 £385

VERA HUGGINS

A large vase with incised green flowering foliage on a mottled blue ground, c.m. & l., circa 1925, 12¾in. high. $672 £420

A bowl painted with pink and blue flowers against a brown field, c.m. & l., 1926, 5in. high.
$608 £380

A vase glazed in green, blue and brown with incised and raised borders, c.m. & l., circa 1925, 11¼in. high. $624 £390

FRANCES LEE

A vase, the buff ground with impressed concentric circles, heightened with gold, c.m., 1886, 10in. high. $352 £220

A pair of vases, the panels with incised green leaves and bordered by purple leaves, c.m., 1877, 9¾in. high.
$608 £380

A vase, the royal blue ground with four stippled buff panels painted with dolphins, c.m., 1883, 9¾in. high. **$512 £320**

A jug with four oval panels with incised green foliage, c.m., 1878, 5¼in. high. $480 £300

A shallow bowl with incised green and blue panels supported by three columns, c.m., 1884, 8¼in. high.
$1920 £1200

A jug, the neck with incised blue flowers on a brown ground, c.m., 1879, 6¾in. high.
$448 £280

A jug, the incised brown leaves with applied bead work and flower heads, c.m., 1877, 9¼in. high. **$352 £220**

A pair of vases, with finely incised foliage, painted overall in pâte-sur-pâte with blossom, c.m., 1882, 9in. high.
$496 £310

A jug carved with green flower heads on a blue ground, c.m., 1881, 9½in. high. **$512 £320**

EDITH LUPTON

A jug with incised green, blue
and brown leaves, o.m., 1875,
6½in. high. $288 £180

A large pierced vase with three
shaped panels painted in pâte-
sur-pâte with wild flowers,
r.m., 1882, 14in. high.
$1920 £1200

A jug with incised stiff blue
leaves and carved seed pods,
c.m., 1876, 8¼in. high.
$232 £145

A small jug with incised green
foliage on a brown ground,
c.m., 1876, 7½in. high.
$264 £165

A pair of salt cellars with incised
leaves, o.m., 1875, 3¼in. high.
$616 £385

A candlestick modelled with
three buff cranes between
incised green and blue columns,
c.m., 1875, 8in. high. $608 £380

A mounted jug with incised blue
and green leaves, o.m., 1875,
6¾in. high. $232 £145

A vase by Edith Lupton with
chocolate panels painted with
blue flowers, DSL, 1884, 9½in.
high. $608 £380

A large vase by Edith Lupton,
pierced overall with flowering
plants and foliage, DSL, 1884,
15¼in. high. $608 £380

EDITH LUPTON

A large vase with incised mottled foliage and seed pods, r.m., 1886, 14in. high.
$768 £480

A vase with incised green leaves and painted blossom and berries, r.m., 1886, 6¾in. high.
$352 £220

A jug with incised blue and white leaves on a brown ground, c.m., 1876, 7½in. high.
$280 £175

An ecclesiastical vase modelled in the form of a tower, and on each corner the letters IHS in brown shields, r.m., 1881, 13¾in. high $560 £350

A small pair of church vases, the quatrefoil necks with incised blue scrolls, r.m. & e., circa 1892, 6in. high. $456 £285

A jug with incised dark brown scrolls on a royal blue ground, c.m., 1880, 9in. high.
$560 £350

A tapering jug with incised green, brown and blue scrolls, 9½in. high, with two beakers en suite, 5½in. high, c.m., 1879. $832 $520

A globular vase, the stippled buff ground with incised fruiting vine, r.m., 1886, 10in. high. $672 £420

A mounted jug with incised foliate scrolls in shades of blue and green, r.m., 1880, 9½in. high. $480 £300

MARK V. MARSHALL

A large vase, one side modelled with a profile female portrait, the other with a bird amongst flowers, r.m. & e., circa 1895, 15in. high. $2400 £1500

A paperweight modelled as a smiling creature glazed brown, RDE, circa 1902, 2½in. high. $496 £310

A vase after a design by Mark V. Marshall with purple foliage and sepia fruit, c.m. & l., circa 1922, 8¼in. high. $464 £290

A vase with pink swirling panels painted with blue flowers and green leaves, c.m.l. & c., date letter for 1905, 12in. high. $768 £480

A pair of vases pressed from the inside with pink fruits against green foliage on a pale pink ground, c.m.l. & c., date letter for 1903, 10¾in. high. $1312 £820

A vase painted with pink flowers and brown veined white leaves, c.m.l. & c., date letter for 1906, 11½in. high. $704 £440

A buff coloured vase with two modelled monkeys grasping the neck of the vase, r.m. & e., circa 1895, 6¾in. high. $800 £500

An unusual bowl of flattened disc shape painted with purple foliage in shaped sepia panels, c.m., circa 1890, 4in. height, 14½in. diameter. $1200 £750

An elaborate jug with incised lip and blue neck, the base of the handle modelled with the head of a dark-skinned Arab wearing a kefiya, r.m. & e., circa 1895, 11¼in. high. $1920 £1200

MARK V. MARSHALL

A tankard, the grey-green ground indented with purple foliate scrolls and a grotesque mask, DLE, circa 1895, 6½in. high. **$232 £145**

A jug modelled as a fabulous fish with legs and cloven feet, c.m., circa 1885, 9in. high. **$2400 £1500**

A vase pressed from the inside with russet and lovat foliate scrolls, r.m. & e., circa 1895, 10¾in. high. **$2400 £1500**

A paperweight modelled as a duck with mottled blue and green glaze, c.m.l & c., circa 1902, 2³/₄in. high. **$736 £460**

An inkwell modelled as a stylised bird glazed blue and green, RDE, circa 1902, 2¼in. high. **$736 £460**

A paperweight modelled as a green glazed cat with grinning features, RDE, circa 1902, 3¼in. long. **$736 £460**

A dark blue glazed vase, the body modelled in high relief with a sinuous dragon rising from blue waves, c.m., 1880, 10in. high. **$4320 £2700**

An Art Nouveau jug, the base of the handle modelled with a hare's head, c.m.l & c., date letter for 1909, 10³/₄in. high. **$1360 £850**

A standing bowl attributed to Mark V. Marshall, supported by three moulded and modelled heraldic beasts, c.m.l. & c., circa 1902, 9in. high. **$1040 £650**

MARK V. MARSHALL

A gourd-shaped vase, incised and modelled in relief with fruiting foliage in brown and white, c.m.l. & c., date letter for 1904, 10½in. high.
$1520 £950

An early grotesque bowl modelled as a fish, 8½in. high.
$6720 £4200

A vase, the glaze shading from white through purple to blue at the base, around which climbs a fabulous buff scaly creature, c.m.l. & c., date letter for 1904, 10½in. high. $2560 £1600

A salt cellar modelled as a frog glazed brown, DLE, circa 1900, 1¾in. high. $704 £440

A 'Borogove' vase modelled as a hedgehog-like creature, r.m., circa 1890, 8in. high. $2720 £1700

An unattributed model of a rabbit glazed light brown, c.m. & l., circa 1922, 2¾in. long.
$400 £250

A vase painted on either side with a stylised plant in shades of green, r.m. & e., circa 1895, 8¼in. high. $1120 £700

An inkwell modelled with two fabulous beasts glazed ochre, blue and brown, r.m., 1884, 5¼in. high. $2240 £1400

A jug modelled in low relief with brown leaves against a royal blue ground, DLE, circa 1895, 8½in. high. $1520 £950

MARK V. MARSHALL

A trumpet-shaped vase, incised overall and glazed blue, circa 1879, 10¼in. high. $1568 £980

A paperweight modelled as a bird glazed brown, c.m.l. & c., circa 1902, 3in. high. $720 £450

A vase modelled in low relief, with purple and pink sea-weed on a claret ground, r.m. & e., circa 1895, 9in. high. $928 £580

A tall jug, decorated with rambling blue and pink roses on which perch garden birds, c.m., circa 1880, 19¼in. high. $5120 £3200

Pair of Doulton Lambeth Art pottery vases, circa 1900, in squat globular form with floral banded design, by Mark Marshall, 5¾in. high. $640 £400

A large covered vase, each side modelled in relief, one with a music conductor with human head and the body of a bird, the other with a lizard and flowering plants, c.m., circa 1885, 26¾in. high. $24000 £15000

A slender vase painted in outline with three long-tailed birds perched amongst foliage, c.m.l. & c., circa 1902, 10in. high. $1520 £950

A pot-pourri bowl with pierced blue cover overlaid with green foliate scrolls in high relief, r.m. & e., circa 1895, 5½in. high. $720 £450

A shaped vase, the mottled blue ground with incised green markings and white neck, c.m., circa 1890, 8½in. high. $672 £420

ISABELLA MILLER

A vase by Isabella Miller, the mottled purple ground with incised green and blue scrolls, c.m., 1880, 7¼in. high.
$352 £220

A vase by Isabella Miller, the green and ochre ground with incised dark green scrolls and plants, r.m., 1884, 10¼in. high.
$400 £250

A ewer by Isabella Miller with incised green and blue leaves and flowers, c.m., 1880, 6½in. high.
$352 £220

MARY MITCHELL

A vase by Mary Mitchell, with the incised figures of two girls playing with a ball, r.m., 1881, 10¾in. high.
$1520 £950

A jug by Mary Mitchell, with two oval panels, with incised children in a landscape, c.m., 1879, 9¼in. high. $2560 £1600

A vase by Mary Mitchell, the white ground with incised green foliage and purple flowers, c.m., 1879, 7in. high.
$720 £450

WILLIAM PARKER

A massive jug carved in high relief with green and brown flowers, c.m., 1879, 15¼in. high.
$1760 £1100

A vase with incised flowers on a pale buff ground, r.m., 1883, 7½in. high.
$960 £600

An inscribed jug with carved and incised pale green leaves, the neck with incised patterns and blue borders, c.m., 1881, 13¼in. high.
$1280 £800

WILLIAM PARKER

A vase with incised foliate scrolls in shades of blue, c.m., 1879, 11¾in. high. **$480 £300**

A vase incised through the celadon ground with blue and white flowering plants, r.m., 1883, 7in. high. **$768 £480**

A vase with finely incised flowering plants in mottled blue and green, r.m., 1884, 8¼in. high. **$448 £280**

A vase with finely incised blue convolvulus, sweet-peas, and clover, r.m., 1883, 9½in. high. **$560 £350**

A pair of vases, with an incised continuous blue branch bearing yellow fruits, r.m., 1884, 9½in. high. **$560 £350**

A vase carved with a frieze of green foliage scrolls within blue and green incised borders, c.m., 1881, 13¼in. high. **$992 £620**

FRANCIS POPE

A bottle with applied handle, and incised blue and green foliage, c.m.l. & c., silver rim hallmarked 1913, 8¼in. nigh. **$352 £220**

A slip-cast vase of gourd-shape with projecting ribs and a mottled blue glaze, circa 1920, 5¾in. high. **$240 £150**

A vase painted with green flowers growing from black stems, c.m.l. & c., circa 1905, 10in. high. **$352 £220**

FRANCIS POPE

An unusual vase, modelled in relief with a mermaid riding on a fish amongst underwater plants, c.m.l. & c., circa 1905, 11¾in. high. $392 £245

A pair of tall vases, each with incised mottled blue, pink and green leaves, c.m.l. & c., date letter for 1904, 15¼in. high. $832 £520

A handled bottle or spirit decanter with incised green leaves, c.m.l. & c., silver hall-marked 1913, 7½in. high. $320 £200

A slip-cast vase, the mottled blue body with brown ribs and pale blue scrolls in relief, s.c.m., circa 1920, 6¼in. high. $304 £190

A slip-cast vase moulded with arched panels covered in a mottled ochre and pale blue glaze, s.c.m., circa 1920, 6¼in. high. $192 £120

A vase with deeply incised black and brown scrolls on a green ground, c.m.l. & c., 5½in. high. $192 £120

A vase modelled in relief with a white bird amongst white foliage, c.m.l. & c., circa 1905, 9¾in. high. $672 £420

A pair of slip-cast vases of hexagonal section with a mottled green glaze, s.c., circa 1910, 11in. high. $896 £560

A slip-cast vase of square section, moulded on each side with a blue bird, s.c.m.. circa 1920, 8¾in. high. $304 £190

FLORENCE ROBERTS

A mug by Florence C. Roberts, the combed buff ground with impressed flowers, r.m., 1884, 5¼in. high. $192 £120

A pair of vases by Florence C. Roberts, the buff ground modelled in relief with green, blue and brown stylised flowers and leaves, r.m., 1884, 10¼in. high. $640 £400

A vase, the buff ground stippled and modelled in relief with blue flowers and mottled green foliage, r.m., 1885, 12in. high. $544 £340

EDITH ROGERS

A vase with incised blue flowers heightened with white, r.m., 1883, 7¾in. high. $304 £190

A jug, the silicon body painted in rust and blue, DSL, 1884, 7¼in. high. $248 £155

A vase, with finely incised blue flowering plants, the ground over-glazed in brown, r.m., 1883, 8in. high. $280 £175

A vase painted in green and white pâte-sur-pâte with foliate scrolls on an orange ground, r.m., 1881, 10½in. high. $264 £165

A pair of vases with overall incised white and buff scrolls, one with three plaques inscribed 'Burns, Scott and Keats', r.m., 1882, 11½in. high. $600 £375

A vase, the white ground with a thick dark olive-green glaze, r.m., 1882, 10¼in. high. $384 £240

MARTHA ROGERS

A vase, the buff ground with finely incised foliage, r.m., 1881, 7¾in. high. $264 £165

A vase, the buff ground with painted white foliage, r.m., 1881, 12¾in. high. $440 £275

A vase, the dark blue ground with incised pale blue foliage edged with gilt piping, r.m., 1884, 11in. high. $384 £240

A vase, the pale ground with incised brown foliate scrolls bordered by incised blue leaves, r.m., 1883, 12¼in. high. $352 £220

A pair of vases, the orange ground with painted white motifs, r.m., 1882, 8¾in. high. $528 £330

A vase by Martha M. Rogers, the stippled frieze glazed blue, with pale blue scrolls, DSL, 1883, 10½in. high. $264 £165

ELIZA SAYERS

A flask of flattened shape, each side with incised green berried foliage, c.m., 1880, 8½in. high. $1440 £900

A jug with incised dark brown and blue stylised foliage enriched with white bead work, c.m., 1877, 9in. high. $544 £340

A jug with incised green foliage and applied beads on a brown ground, c.m., 1877, 7in. high. $400 £250

STONEWARE

HARRY SIMEON

A vase painted with ears of corn in brown, green and purple against a mottled blue ground, c.m. & l., circa 1922, 9in. high. $720 £450

A vase painted with a parrot amongst green tropical foliage, c.m. & l., circa 1922, 10½in. high. $1120 £700

A vase painted in polychrome colours with a cockerel and a blue pheasant, c.m. & l., circa 1922, 9¾in. high. $992 £620

ELIZA SIMMANCE

A jug painted with vine leaves and purple grapes against a pink ground, c.m.l. & c., date letter for 1910, 8½in. high. $1248 £780

A Doulton silicon biscuit barrel with plated mount, the engraved cover with a sphinx knop, decorated by Eliza Simmance, 18.3cm. high. $400 £250

A jug with incised yellow leaves and impressed brown berries against a mottled blue ground, c.m.l. & c., date letter for 1909, 9in. high. $1248 £780

A vase with incised pale blue flowers and brown foliage edged in white, DLE, circa 1895, 14in. high. $1920 £1200

A waisted jar and cover painted with rings of white flowers, c.m.l. & c., date letter for 1907, 6½in. high. $768 £480

A large ribbed vase painted with blue leaves and pale blue flowers, c.m.l. & c., date letter for 1906, 15in. high. $2080 £1300

ELIZA SIMMANCE

A vase modelled with orange trees against a blue sky with birds, c.m.l. & c., date letter for 1905, 13in. high. $1568 £980

A pair of vases with incised and painted pale blue cornflowers, r.m. & e., circa 1895, 11¼in. high. $2400 £1500

A vase painted with purple and green flowering plants, c.m.l. & c., date letter for 1915, 12¾in. high. $1520 £950

A vase painted with purple berried trees against a pale blue background, c.m.l. & c., date letter for 1907, 13¾in. high. $1520 £950

A pair of ribbed vases with incised green leaves, c.m.l. & c., date letter for 1910, 10in. high. $1520 £950

A vase with a frieze of green trees edged in white, c.m.l. & c., circa 1907, 13½in. high. $1520 £950

A vase painted with pink roses, the stems brown against a pale pink ground, c.m.l. & c., date letter for 1910, 11in. high. $1520 £950

A pair of vases after Charles Rennie Mackintosh, with incised green roses, c.m.l. & c., date letter for 1910, 9in. high. $1520 £950

A tall vase painted with pink pomegranates growing against a green ground, c.m.l. & c., date letter for 1910, 19¼in. high. $2240 £1400

ELIZA SIMMANCE

A vase with incised blue flowers against a buff panel of white scrolls, r.m. & e., circa 1895, 14in. high. $1920 £1200

A pair of vases by Eliza Simmance, the smooth cream ground with incised and painted flowering plants, r.m., circa 1890, 7¾in. high. $1520 £950

A vase painted with green and white pâte-sur-pâte blossom on a stippled buff ground, r.m. & e., circa 1892, 8¼in. high. $1088 £680

A vase painted with pale green foliate scrolls on a darker green ground, r.m., 1884, 8¼in. high. $704 £440

A stoneware bracket clockcase by Eliza Simmance, inspired by 18th century models, r.m. & e., circa 1895, 14½in. high. $6720 £4200

A vase with shaped panels painted in pâte-sur-pâte natural colours with blackberries, r.m., 1881, 10¾in. high. $720 £450

A vase with shaped panels of incised stylised flowers in blue and green, r.m., 1884, 11in. high. $672 £420

A pair of vases with incised blue foliage and modelled green chrysanthemums, r.m. & e., circa 1895, 9¾in. high. $1520 £950

A vase painted with pale green and blue leaf sprays, r.m., 1883, 9¼in. high. $672 £420

450

ELIZA SIMMANCE

A vase painted with blue dolphins and green sea-weed on a pale pink ground, c.m.l. & c., date letter for 1910, 10½in. high. $1920 £1200

A bowl painted with alternate floral panels in pale green and blue on a dark green ground, r.m., 1883, 7in. high. $1920 £1200

A vase with incised green and brown sea-weed on an undulating green ground, c.m.l. & c., circa 1905, 9in. high. $1184 £740

A jug with incised green and blue leaves on a buff ground, silver mount hallmarked 1875, 8in. high. $560 £350

A pair of vases by Eliza Simmance, the light grey ground with incised and painted brown plants, DSL, 1884, 7¼in. high. $992 £620

A pepper pot attributed to Eliza Simmance with pottery sprinkler and pierced base, r.m., 1884, 3¼in. high. $160 £100

A vase by Eliza Simmance, the brown ground with three shaped panels, DSL, 1884, 8in. high. $384 £240

An octagonal plate painted with white pâte-sur-pâte flowers on a brown ground, c.m., 1878, 10in. diameter. $1152 £720

An Art Union vase and cover painted with green and white pâte-sur-pâte blossom on a buff stippled ground, r.m. & e., circa 1895, 11½in. high. $2240 £1400

ELIZA SIMMANCE

A cachepot with a broad pâte-sur-pâte band of Renaissance scrollwork and grotesques on an olive-green ground, dated 1882, 26cm. high. $2000 £1250

A vase by Eliza Simmance, the glazed buff ground with incised scrolls, r.m., 1881, 3¾in. high. $240 £150

A vase modelled with yellow apples growing from green branches, r.m., 1887, 9½in. high. $1216 £760

A vase with incised royal blue flowers and leaves. r.m., circa 1887, 10in. high. $672 £420

A pair of cylindrical vases incised through the pale blue glaze onto the white body, c.m., 1879, 6¾in. high. $1152 £720

One of a pair of vases with incised and modelled blue flowers, c.m.l. & c., date letter for 1909, 9¾in. high. (Pair) $1344 £840

A vase painted with green and white pâte-sur-pâte blossom on a Doulton and Slater buff lace ground, r.m., circa 1889, 6½in. high. $464 £290

A tazza, the surface with an incised blue and brown leaf pattern, c.m., 1877, 6½in. high. $1536 £960

A vase with an incised foliate design in pale green and dark blue, c.m., 1876, 7¼in. high. $464 £290

ELIZA SIMMANCE

A small vase by Eliza
Simmance, the brown ground
painted with white blossom and
dark brown leaves, DSL, 1884,
4in. high. $192 £120

A pair of Doulton stoneware
bottle vases with everted rims,
decorated by Eliza Simmance,
25cm. high. $760 £480

A three-handled loving cup with
green and white pâte-sur-pâte
flowering scrolls, r.m., 1881,
6in. high. $1216 £760

A pair of vases painted with
long-tailed blue birds, c.m.l. &
c., date letter for 1916?, 15¾in.
high. $1440 £900

A mustard pot by Eliza
Simmance, the handle and body
with incised blue leaves, o.m.,
1875, 2¼in. high. $208 £130

A pair of vases by Eliza
Simmance, with incised and
painted brown garden birds and
white daisies, DSL, 1885,
10¼in. high. $1264 £790

ELIZABETH SMALL

A vase, the mottled blue ground
with incised bright blue
flowering foliage, r.m., 1884,
12½in. high. $672 £420

A pair of vases with incised blue
and brown berried foliage on a
mottled pale blue ground, r.m.,
1884, 10¼in. high. $1312 £820

A beaker, the buff ground with
incised blue foliage, the
entwined panels painted with
white flowers, r.m., 1882,
4¾in. high. $160 £100

EMILY STORMER

A pair of vases, each with incised brown foliage above stiff green leaves, c.m., 1877. 10¾in. high $944 £590

A pair of flasks, with white bead work and an incised green, blue, and brown flower, c.m., 1878, 8¼in. high. $1760 £1100

A vase, the handles modelled as brown peacocks, the body with incised blue and yellow foliate scrolls, r.m. & e., circa 1892, 12½in. high. $1280 £800

A candlestick, the base with carved green stylised leaves, r.m., 1886, 7in. high, $560 £350

A mounted jug with incised green flowers on a blue ground with incised brown scrolls, r.m., 1884, 6¾in. high. $400 £250

A jug, the buff body with impressed white circles and incised blue foliage and leaves, c.m., 1879, 9¼in. high. $384 £240

GEORGE H. TABOR

A vase by G. H. Tabor with carved blue oak branches and acorns, r.m., 1883, 9¼in. high. $232 £145

A pair of vases by G. H. Tabor, the green ground with overall incised blue masks, r.m., 1884, 9½in. high. $1920 £1200

A vase by G. H. Tabor, the buff stippled ground with incised brown masks, urns and foliate scrolls, r.m., 1881, 10¾in. high. $624 £390

GEORGE TINWORTH

A baluster vase, the mottled brown ground with incised blue foliate scrolls, r.m. & e., circa 1892, 12½in. high. $640 £400

A frog and mouse group with frogs riding mice over a water jump, o.m., circa 1875, 4½in. high. $4480 £2800

A large jug, the hatched pale green ground with incised green and brown scrolls, o.m., 1874, 11¼in. high. $1312 £820

A brightly glazed jug, the green ground with an incised shaped blue panel, c.m., 1876, 9¾in. high. $1088 £680

A pair of Doulton Lambeth vases by George Tinworth, with incised and applied decoration of a central band of scrolling foliage set with floral medallions, dated 1875, 25cm. high. $960 £600

A mounted jug, with an incised green foliate meander, c.m., 1877, 9½in. high. $1088 £680

An early pair of candlesticks glazed blue, with incised leaves each supported by two buff winged putti, o.m., 1875, 7in. high. $2880 £1800

A monkey group inscribed A United Family, sitting on a bench and sheltering under an ochre umbrella, r.m. & e., circa 1892, 5in. high. $2880 £1800

An early vase, the burnt sienna ground with incised blue and pale green scrolls, o.u.m., circa 1871, 9¾in. high. $1200 £750

GEORGE TINWORTH

A carpenter's bag attributed to George Tinworth, glazed in shades of brown, c.m., circa 1880, length 5in. $800 £500

The young carpenter, a brown salt-glaze model of a young boy planing at a bench, DLE, circa 1892, 5¼in. high. $1200 £750

A salt cellar, the bowl and stand glazed blue and brown, the moulded drummer boy glazed buff, r.m., circa 1885, 3½in. high. $1200 £750

A jug, the lovat ground with an incised blue and buff fence decorated with pale blue bead work, c.m., 1879, 9½in. high. $1040 £650

A blue glazed frog playing cricket with a brown bat, r.m., circa 1880, 4¾in. high. $3520 £2200

A tapering jug, the dark brown ground with an incised spiral band, c.m., 1878, 9¾in. high. $1040 £650

A jug, the light buff ground with incised scrolling blue foliage, o.u.m., circa 1872, 10½in. high. $1040 £650

A blue glazed group of two frogs riding on the backs of two mice, o.m., circa 1875, 3¾in. high. $1920 £1200

One of a pair of vases, the buff ground with a painted white cellular pattern, c.m.l. & c., date letter for 1903, 10¾in. high. (Pair) $920 £575

GEORGE TINWORTH

A candlestick with incised blue leaves on a brown ground, c.m., 1876, 8¼in. high. $1312 £820

A quatrefoil inkwell with cover and liner, the body with incised blue leaves, c.m., 1879, 4in. high. $1920 £1200

Mr Pickwick, the modelled figure glazed green and standing on a brown chair inscribed Pickwick Bachelor, DLE, circa 1895, 5in. high. $960 £600

A vase with a mottled blue ground with incised dark brown scrolls and applied flower heads, o.u.m., circa 1872, 9½in. high. $1248 £780

A model of a green frog riding a yellow and brown penny farthing, r.m., circa 1880, 4½in. high. $2880 £1800

A vase, the brilliant royal blue ground with incised mottled brown scroll-work, r.m. & e., circa 1892, 8in. high. $1040 £650

A standing salt cellar, supported by moulded blue and brown dolphins, incised Doulton & Co., Lambeth, with the monogram GT, 4in. high. $1040 £650

A double vase, the moulded buff putto with a blue garland standing on a brown sphere, r.m., circa 1885, 5¼in. high. $1760 £1100

The eagle and the fox, a fable group with a brown trumpet-shaped vase, incised Doulton & Co., Lambeth, circa 1882, 7in. high. $2880 £1800

GEORGE TINWORTH

A letter rack, the stoneware compartments with incised leaves and flowers in brown, blue and green, r.m., circa 1885, length 14in. $4160 £2600

The Drunken Husband, a modelled fable group with an old man wearing a blue night-gown, sitting on the detachable lid of a coffin, r.m., 1881, length 7¾in.　　$5120 £3200

A brown salt-glazed group modelled with a frog painting and a country mouse holding an upturned basket of fruit, circa 1885, length 7in. $4000 £2500

A pair of mantle ornaments, each moulded with a kneeling figure of a young Egyptian boy, r.m., circa 1885, 9in. high.
(Pair) $2880 £1800

An umbrella stand modelled naturalistically with a brown glazed kangaroo holding a dark brown ring, incised Doulton Lambeth, circa 1885, 38¾in. high.　　$25600 £16000

A pair of salt cellars attributed to George Tinworth, supported by three buff winged putti, o.m., 1875, 3½in. high.
$1600 £1000

A brown glazed stoneware mirror frame carved in low relief with a head and shoulders portrait of a young girl, c.m., circa 1880, 18in. high.
$968 £605

The Fables Clock, the stone-ware case modelled with the interior of a house and numerous figures and animals, the base inscribed: H. Doulton & Co., Lambeth, and G. Tinworth, circa 1882, 11¼in. high.　　$13760 £8600

The Vain Jackdaw, a fable group with the peacock's display forming a fan-shaped vase, incised H. Doulton, Lambeth, circa 1882, 6in. high.
$2000 £1250

458

GEORGE TINWORTH, MERRY MUSICIANS

A boy kicking a tambourine, DLE, incised Doulton Lambeth, circa 1895, 5in. high.
$1200 £750

A kneeling boy playing a harp, RDE, circa 1902, 3³/₄in. high. $1200 £750

A moulded and modelled figure of a seated boy with a cittern, DLE, circa 1895, 4³/₄in. high.
$1200 £750

A cello played by a seated boy, DLE, circa 1895, 4¹/₂in. high. $1200 £750

A boy with a white face playing a cello, RDE, circa 1902, 4³/₄in. high.
$1200 £750

An upright piano played by a boy seated on a stool, printed circle mark: Doulton Lambeth England, circa 1895, 4in. high. $1200 £750

A brown glazed figure of a boy playing a rebec, DLE, circa 1895, 5¹/₄in. high. $1200 £750

A seated boy playing a harp, DLE, circa 1895, 4in. high. $1200 £750

A cornet played by a seated cross-legged boy, RDE, circa 1902, 4¹/₂in. high. $1200 £750

A boy leaning against a cylinder playing a concertina, DLE, circa 1895, 4¹/₂in. high.
$1200 £750

A boy playing a fiddle supported on his foot, DLE, circa 1895, 4¹/₄in. high. $1200 £750

A seated figure with a light buff face playing a French horn, RDE, circa 1902, 4³/₄in. high.
$1200 £750

GEORGE TINWORTH, MOUSE FIGURES

A mouse group with a white mouse playing a tuba and a little mouse playing the cornet, o.m., circa 1875, 3³/₄in. high.
$1920 £1200

A knight from a chess set glazed white, r.m., 1884, 3¼in. high.
$880 £550

Play Goers, the group glazed pale brown with a blue and brown shaped base, r.m., 1886, 5¼in. high. $3520 £2200

A mouse group with a green vase and pale green mice playing ochre double-basses, r.m., circa 1885, 5¼in. high.
$1600 £1000

A tea party with pale green mice seated on brown chairs, the hollow oval base inscribed Tea-Time Scandal, r.m., circa 1885, 3½in. high. $3040 £1900

A green vase on an oval base modelled with a pale green mouse playing a brown harp, and a little mouse playing a cornet, r.m., circa 1885, 5¼in. high. $1760 £1100

A blue spill vase, with a mouse sleeping on the ground with a broom, r.m., circa 1885, 4in. high. $1280 £800

A menu holder with a white mouse playing a harp and a little mouse playing a double bass, r.m., 1885, 3³/₄in. high.
$1920 £1200

A bishop from a chess set, glazed white with a blue mitre, r.m., 1884, 3in. high. $880 £550

GEORGE TINWORTH, MOUSE FIGURES

A menu holder with two white mice playing a double-base and a cornet, inscribed Doulton Lambeth, circa 1880, 3¾in. high. $1920 £1200

A brown glazed mouse-pawn holding an axe, r.m., 1884, 2½in. high. $880 £550

A tobacco jar, the lid with a green mouse sitting on a blue cushion smoking a brown pipe, r.m., circa 1885, 7in. high. $960 £600

A musical group with a blue vase and pale green mice, one playing an organ and the other a triangle, r.m., circa 1885, 5½in. high. $1760 £1100

A mouse group moulded with three minstrels on a green mound, r.m., circa 1885, 3¾in. high. $2560 £1600

A mouse-pawn glazed white, inscribed Pawn, r.m., 1884, 2½in. high. $880 £550

A model of a blue mouse eating a currant taken from the brown bun on which he sits, circa 1880, 2¾in. high. $928 £580

A blue spill vase modelled with a pale green mouse sitting comfortably in a brown chair, r.m. & e., circa 1895, 4½in. high. $1280 £800

A menu holder with a little mouse about to steal an apple from a stall, r.m., circa 1885, 3¾in. high. $2080 £1300

GEORGE TINWORTH, PLAQUES

A Guard's Chapel maquette glazed green, blue and brown, and modelled with the parable of the lost piece of silver, inscribed H. Doulton & Co., Lambeth, G. Tinworth, circa 1877, 12in. x 9in. **$2880 £1800**

A cream coloured terracotta self-portrait plaque inscribed G. Tinworth, circa 1913, 5³/₄in. x 4³/₄in. **$800 £500**

Tinworth's boyhood, a terracotta plaque modelled in high relief with George Tinworth as a young boy carving a small wooden bust in his father's wheelwright's workshop while his mother looks on, and a small boy watches for the possible arrival of his father, circa 1877, 8in. x 8in. **$2720 £1700**

A terracotta tile picture moulded and carved in low relief with Samson, DLE, circa 1880, 8¹/₂in. x 8¹/₂in. **$1040 £650**

A terracotta tile picture moulded and carved in low relief with the Saviour and woman at the well, DLE, circa 1880, 8¹/₂in. x 8¹/₂in. **$1040 £650**

A stoneware maquette with blue and brown glaze of David and Goliath, inscribed: H. Doulton & Co., Lambeth, G. Tinworth, with impressed oval stamps Doulton & Co., Lambeth London, circa 1877, 12in. x 9in. **$2880 £1800**

GEORGE TINWORTH, PLAQUES

A Station of the Cross, a terracotta plaque modelled in high relief with some free-standing figures, incised: H. Doulton & Co., Lambeth, G. Tinworth, circa 1878, 6in. x 13in. $2880 £1800

The Four Seasons, a set of four plaques in salt-glaze stoneware carved in high relief and glazed in shades of brown and blue, circa 1875, 8½in.×4in. $10880 £6800

Zacchaeus, a terracotta plaque modelled in high relief and inscribed Make Haste and Come Down for Today I Must Abide at Thy House and He Made Haste and Come Down, and Received Him Joyfully, in ebonised frame, circa 1878, 6in.×13in. $2880 £1800

GEORGE TINWORTH,
PLAQUES

A religious plaque glazed in brown and blue and carved in high relief with the Resurrection, circa 1880, 12¼in.×4½in. $3200 £2000

A religious terracotta plaque modelled in high relief and inscribed When She Had Heard of Jesus Came in the Press Behind and Touched His Garment, inscribed: H. Doulton & Co., Lambeth, G. Tinworth, circa 1878, 6in.×13in. $2880 £1800

John the Baptist, a terracotta plaque modelled in high relief with Salome demanding the head of John the Baptist, circa 1878, 6in×13in. $2880 £1800

GEORGE TINWORTH,
PLAQUES

The Nativity, a terracotta plaque modelled in high relief and inscribed And They
Came with Haste and Found Mary, and Joseph, and the Babe Lying in a Manger, the
Poor of this World Rich in Faith, circa 1878, 5½in. x 12in. $2880 £1800

A small plaque, the stoneware glazed blue and brown on a white ground and carved in
high relief, circa 1875, 8½in. ×4in. $2880 £1800

A Parable, a terracotta plaque modelled in high relief and incised And Jesus Called
a Little Child Unto Him and Set Him in the Midst of Them, Humble Yourselves
Therefore Under the Mighty Hand of God, circa 1878, 5½in. x 12in. $2880 £1800

BIBELOTS

A match striker advertising
Dewar's Whisky, c.m.l. & c.,
2½in. high. $136 £85

A tray glazed green and brown,
with a central blue horse's
head, c.m.l. & c., circa 1910,
4¼in. diameter. $576 £360

A match striker with Art
Nouveau designs, DLE, 4in.
high. $104 £65

A moulded tray centred by a
brown mouse and a tree stump,
s.c.m., circa 1925, 4in. high.
          $608 £380

The Suffragette Movement, an
inkwell modelled as a baby with
hinged head, R.D.E., circa
1905, 3¼in. high. $1520 £950

A circular ring tray, slip-cast
with a glazed brown rabbit,
s.c.m., circa 1925, 3¼in. high.
          $624 £390

An inkwell moulded with a
grumpy old lady, the green
apron inscribed 'Votes for
Women', c.m.l. & c., circa
1905, 3½in. high. $1520 £950

A book-end glazed dark brown
and modelled with a monkey
clutching its young, DLE, circa
1900, 6½in. high. $560 £350

A moulded ring tray edged with
green leaves on which sits a
bird, DLE, Made in England,
circa 1925, 4in. high. $464 £290

A group of two white ducklings squatting on a blue rockwork base, c.m.l. & c., circa 1920, 4¼in. high. $576 £360

An ashtray match holder, 'Queen Anne's Mansion', DLE. $176 £110

A ring tray attributed to Vera Huggins with a brown and buff owl. s.c.m., circa 1925. 4in. high. $624 £390

A trump indicator attributed to Leslie Harradine, RDE, circa 1910, 4in. high. $736 £460

A slip-cast ring tray modelled with a nymph seated on a ring of flowers, s.c.m., circa 1925, 4¼in. high. $784 £490

A match striker attributed to Harry Simeon, modelled with an old soldier seated next to a hollow drum, DLE, 4¾in. high. $672 £420

A shaped blue and brown ring tray on which perches a large billed bird, s.c.m., circa 1925, 4¼in. high. $624 £390

A match striker attributed to Harry Simeon with a toper wearing a blue coat, s.c.m., circa 1925, 3¾in. high. $672 £420

A whist booby attributed to Leslie Harradine, moulded with a skeleton, RDE, circa 1910, 4¼in. high. $624 £390

COMMEMORATIVE WARE

A jug with white relief lettering 'Christopher Columbus sighted America Oct 12 1491', flanking a buff portrait of the explorer, r.m. & e., 6¼in. high. $432 £270

A shallow bowl, with applied moulded celadon portraits of Queen Victoria, Disraeli and Lord Salisbury r.m., circa 1885, 6in. diameter. $704 £440

A jug commemorating Benjamin Disraeli, the buff portrait in high relief flanked by a quotation, r.m., 6½in. high $496 £310

A tankard designed by John Broad commemorating the 1897 Jubilee, DLE, circa 1897, 6½in. high. $304 £190

A bellarmine jug commemorating Queen Victoria's Golden Jubilee, r.m., 9in. high. $480 £300

A coronation jug commemorating the accession of Edward VII and Queen Alexandra, DLE, circa 1902, 7½in. high. $624 £390

A jug with a portrait of H. M. Stanley below the inscription 'Emin Pasha Relief Expedition 1887-1889', r.m. & e., 7½in. high. $464 £290

A Doulton Lambeth stoneware jug commemorating Victoria's Diamond Jubilee, inscribed 'She Brought her people lasting good', 24cm. $400 £250

General Gordon, a jug commemorating his death at Khartoum in 1884, the buff ground with applied motifs and inscriptions, r.m., dated 1884, 7½in. high. $496 £310

COMMEMORATIVE WARE

A three-handled mug commemorating the coronation of King George V in 1911, moulded with relief portraits in pale green and blue, c.m.l. & c., 6¼in. high.
$400 £250

A jug commemorating the Golden Jubilee of Queen Victoria, with green glazed portraits of the Young and Old Queen on a blue ground, DLE, 9in. high. $512 £320

A three-handled mug commemorating the hoisting of the flag at Pretoria, DLE, 6½in. high.
$1104 £690

A jug commemorating the hoisting of the flag at Pretoria, DLE, circa 1900, 8¼in. high.
$1280 £800

A double-handled tankard commemorating War in the Sudan, r.m., 1883, 6in. high.
$576 £360

An oviform vase made to commemorate the Coronation of Edward VII and Queen Alexandra in 1902, c.m.l. & c., 27.5cm. high. $672 £420

William Ewart Gladstone, the jug printed with quotations below the title, 'England's Great Commoner', DLE, 7½in. high.
$384 £240

A small jug designed by John Broad commemorating the 1887 Jubilee, DL, 4½in. high.
$400 £250

A Nelson jug, moulded with a portrait of the famous admiral flanked by naval battle scenes, c.m.l. & c., 8in. high.
$864 £540

DOULTON & SLATER'S PATENT

A jug, overlaid with a grey and brown lace pattern on which mistletoe is applied, r.m. & DSP, circa 1888, 7¾in. high. $160 £100

A pair of ewers with rough brown lace ground decorated with floral sprays, Slater's Patent 'Chine', DLE, 8in. high. $192 £120

A dated vase with brown lion's head handles and applied green foliage on a brilliant blue ground, r.m. & DSP, 1886, 11in. high. $440 £275

A jug, the dark green elaborate lace ground overlaid with two celadon classical portraits, r.m. & DSP, circa 1888, 7½in. high. $160 £100

A jug, the blue lace ground with the impressions of large ferns and overlaid with bouquets of ochre flowers, r.m. & DSP, circa 1890, 7in. high. $144 £90

A jug, with a grey lace panel overlaid with moulded white and brown foliage enclosing six oval medallions, r.m. & DSP, circa 1888, 6in. high. $232 £145

A vase decorated with bands of applied stiff leaves on a blue ground, Slater's Patent 'Chine', DLE, 11³/₄in. high. $152 £95

A pair of vases, each with three panels of white flowering foliage, r.m. & e. & DSP, circa 1895, 10in. high. $392 £245

One of a pair of vases with rough brown lace ground decorated with floral sprays, Slater's Patent 'Chine', c.m.l. & c., 14¹/₄in. high. $232 £145

DOULTON & SLATER'S PATENT

A vase with four moulded blue-glazed cupids and numerous stars superimposed on a plain dark green lace ground, r.m. & DSP, circa 1888, 10¼in. high.
$248 £155

A pair of vases moulded with celadon fish and dragon medallions, r.m. & DSP, 1885, 9¼in. high. $232 £145

A vase with rough brown lace ground decorated with floral sprays, Slater's Patent 'Chine', r.m. & e., 10¾in. high.
$216 £135

A jug with applied pale blossom in high relief and two moulded medallions, one of a snake and a mouse, r.m. & DSP, circa 1888. 7½in. high. $290 £180

A teapot with rough brown lace ground decorated with floral sprays, Slater's Patent 'Chine', r.m., 4¾in. high. $120 £75

A jug, with two impressed lace patterns and decorated round the centre with three white medallions, r.m. & DSP, circa 1888, 6¾in. high. $232 £145

A vase with blue handles and neck, the rough brown lace ground with incised brown and blue foliage, r.m. & e. & DSP, circa 1895, 12in. high.
$280 £175

A pair of oriental vases, applied flower head and brown dragons supporting beige lace impressed medallions, r.m. & DSP, circa 1888, 8in. high. $528 £330

A small vase with a blue lace frieze in which are the impressions of dark green ferns, r.m. & DSP, circa 1890, 5½in. high. $144 £90

MINIATURES

Miniature Doulton Lambeth
stoneware mug with silver
hallmarked rim and decorated
with applied toping scenes.
$144 £90

A narrow vase with incised blue
leaves and bead work, c.m.,
1877, 5in. high. $192 £120

Miniature Doulton Lambeth
stoneware jug with applied
toping scenes. $80 £50

A bowl by Alberta Green, the
buff ground with white bead
work, r.m., 1887, 3¼in. high.
$120 £75

A double-handled vase with
incised blue and green flowers,
r.m. & e., circa 1892, 5in. high.
$136 £85

Doulton Lambeth miniature
stoneware mustard pot with
'Colman's' in relief and applied
moulding. $72 £45

A handled bottle with overall
applied pink, brown, and white
fan-shaped patterns, r.m.,
1882, 3¼in. high. $96 £60

A miniature Doulton Lambeth
stoneware caster with plated lid
and applied moulding.
$88 £55

A jug by Edith Lupton with
green panels painted in pâte-
sur-pâte, c.m., 1878, 4¾in.
high. $120 £75

NATURAL FOLIAGE WARE

A 'natural foliage-ware' vase with the impression of veined leaves glazed olive-green, c.m.l. & c., circa 1905, 8¾in. high. $384 £240

A pair of 'natural foliage-ware' vases with the impression of veined leaves, r.m. & e., 16¼in. high. $784 £490

A 'natural foliage-ware' vase, the rough ochre ground impressed with two types of reddish-brown leaves, DLE, circa 1895, 12½in. high $464 £290

SIMULATED WARE

Cast iron, a covered box in silicon ware, simulating an iron 14 lb. weight, DSL & e., the silver handle hallmarked 1898. 5in. high. $136 £85

A silicon jug, the dark brown body simulating leather with stitched joints, 9¾in. high, with two beakers en suite, hallmarked 1899, 4¼in. high, DSL & e. $320 £200

Doulton Lambeth silicon ware brown ground simulated leather tankard, incised *Here's Luck*, hallmarked silver band, London 1910, 6in. $120 £75

A Doulton & Slater's patent mug, simulating brown leather with stitched panels, r.m. & e. & DSL, the silver rim hallmarked 1893, 6¼in high. $160 £100

A Doulton Lambeth silicon stoneware match holder with silver rim, simulating a leather cricket ball, 3in. diam. $320 £200

A stoneware jug simulating a black jack, the dark brown leather with stitched joints, DLE, the silver rim hallmarked 1897, 9in. high. $200 £125

STONEWARE

SILICON WARE

A small vase of hexagonal section inscribed on either side 'The Waning of the Honey-Moon', supported on an oval base with two hares sitting defiantly at either end, r.m., 1880, 4³/₄in. high. $1920 £1200

A pair of ewers decorated with applied slip flower, leaf and bead designs, DSL, circa 1891, 7¹/₄in. high. $176 £110

A jug with impressed flower and leaf motifs, and applied blue flower heads, DSL, 1884, 5½in. high. $168 £105

A jardiniere decorated with applied and incised flower and leaf designs on a blue ground, DSL, 7¹/₂in. high. $192 £120

A modelled owl with brown wings and feet, the detachable head and the body decorated with applied blue, green and white motifs, DSL, circa 1880, 7½in. high. $2240 £1400

A jardiniere decorated with blue floret and incised designs on a buff ground, DLE, impressed date for 1884, 6³/₄in. high. $192 £120

A water filter with incised, carved and applied decoration on a buff ground, DSL, 14¹/₂in. high. $616 £385

A tobacco jar decorated with applied blue and white beads, r.m., impressed date for 1888, 4¹/₄in. high. $88 £55

A tapering jug with overall incised diamond patterns, DSL, circa 1880, 8in. high. $136 £85

474

SPORTING SUBJECTS

A cricketing jug printed in dark brown, with portraits of George Griffin, W.G. Grace and K.S. Ranjitsinhji on the buff ground, DLE, 7in. high $960 £600

A silver mounted cycling jug and two beakers, DLE, circa 1900, the jug 8in. high, the beakers 4³/₄in. high.
$1280 £800

A sporting jug commemorating the untimely death of F.J. Archer, the champion jockey in 1886, r.m., 6¹/₂in. high.
$456 £285

A golfing jug, sprigged in white, with the panels of the 'Last Ball', 'Putting' and 'Driving', impressed Lambeth mark, circa 1880, 20cm. high. $2000 £1250

A waisted mug applied with moulded white figures of a bowler, wicket keeper, and a batsman, DLE, circa 1900, 6in. high. $616 £385

A cricketing jug, the moulded relief figures against the buff salt glaze ground within stylised floral borders outlined in white slip and coloured in blue and green, DLE, circa 1900, 9¹/₄in. high. $1920 £1200

A silver mounted sporting tyg, DLE, circa 1900, 6in. high, the silver rim maker's mark H.W., Sheffield. $832 £520

A cricketer's mug applied with moulded white figures of a bowler, wicket keeper and a batsman, circa 1880, 15.5cm. high. $784 £490

A cricketing tyg, impressed Registration mark, r.m., and dated 1884, 6¹/₄in. high.
$1120 £700

SPORTING SUBJECTS

A mug with applied moulded golfing vignettes of 'the drive', and 'the lost ball', DLE, circa 1900, 5in. high. $1440 £900

A beaker with relief white figures of a shot putter, a runner, and a long-jumper, DLE, the silver rim hallmarked 1900, 5in. high. $352 £220

A cycling mug with three applied white figures inscribed Military, Road, and Path, DLE, circa 1900, 4¾in. high. $784 £490

A cycling jug with three white vignettes, inscribed Military, Road and Path, DLE, circa 1900, 7¼in. high. $832 £520

A sporting jug with three moulded white vignettes, a man running, men playing football, and a man putting the shot, DLE, circa 1900, 8in. high.
$784 £490

A cricket jug with applied vignettes of a bowler, wicket keeper and a batsman, DLE, circa 1900, 7in. high. $1520 £950

A rugby football jug with vignettes of two men kicking a ball, a scrummage and two of the men running with a ball, r.m., 1883, 7½in. high. $1088 £680

A cricket mug with three applied figures of batsmen in high relief, registration mark of 1880, r.m., 1882, 5¼in. high.
$1120 £700

A golfing jug with three applied white vignettes of 'the lost ball', 'putting', and 'driving', DLE, circa 1900, 7¾in. high.
$1760 £1100

DOULTON ARTISTS & ASSISTANTS MARKS

Adelaide AARON	aO	Florence E. BARLOW	FEB
Christine ABBOT	CA	Hannah B. BARLOW	HB
Elizabeth J. ADAMS	LA	Lucy A. BARLOW	AL
Ella H. ADAMS	aa A	Harry BARNARD	B
Matilda S. ADAMS	MsA	V. BARNES	V
Margaret AITKEN	(monogram)	W. BARON	WB
Mary AITKEN	MA	Mary A. BARRETT	bbO MAB
Emily ALLEN	EEA	Ethel BEARD	EB
Fannie J. ALLEN	Æ	George W. BEARNE	B
E. ARCHER	(symbol)	Acidalia E. C. BECK	AB
Helen A. ARDING	A	N. BEEDEN	(symbol)
Mary M. ARDING	M.M.A	Arthur BEERE	AB
Margaret M. ARMSTRONG	(monogram)	G. BENSON	(symbol)
A. ASKEW	:: a	A. BENTLEY	(symbol)
Elizabeth ATKINS	EA	Augusta M. BIRNIE	b̄ AB
N. ATKINS	(symbol)	Florence M. BIRT	qb
Lizzie AXFORD	a:	Ernest R. BISHOP	B
Louisa AYLING	a	Eborah BISSMIRE	bOO
Agnes E. M. BAIGENT	ÆB	F. BLACKSTAFFE	)(
Clara BAKER	bbb	H. BLAKE	[b]
Emily BAKER	b:b	O. BOUCHER	br
Edith H. BALL	B̄ bq	Maud BOWDEN	MB
E. BANFIELD	bd	Florence BOWDITCH	:b:
Eliza S. BANKS	EfB	Jessie BOWDITCH	B
Alice M. E. BARKER	b: B AMB	Eliza BOWEN	bb:
Clara S. BARKER	CSB	L. F. BOWEN	LfB
G. BARKER	-//-	Winnie BOWSTEAD	W.B
Arthur B. BARLOW	(monogram)	Jessie BOYCE	J·B

Name	Mark
N. BRAKE	∧
Daisy BRIANT	D.B
John BROAD	ℬ
D. BROND	F
F. BROOKE	F
Rosina BROWN	R B
Alice E. BUDDEN	AEB. b
Mary BUDDEN	obo
C. BUNN	tʊ
Alice L. BURLTON	ALB. B
Georgina BURR	b+ G.D.B
Eleanor BURRELL	ⓑ
Emma A. BURROWS	o b
Frank A. BUTLER	ℱℬ
Mary BUTTER	bb M.B
Mary BUTTERTON	ℬ
Alice CAFFIN	Ⱥ
Alice CAMPBELL	A.C.
Bertha M. CAPES	ℬ
Mary CAPES	ℳ
Annie M. CASTLE	A6.
Kate J. CASTLE	c
M. CAUTY	cᶜc m.ℓ.
Margaret M. CHALLIS	MM
Emily M. CHANDLER	ℰ ℐ
J. CHANDLER	Ƈ
Clara CHURCHER	▪c▪
Emily CLARK	E.C.
Fanny CLARK	FC
L. CLARK	C
E. CLARKE	S
Frances CLEMENTS	Ⱦ
Miss COCKS	CO
Edith M. COLEMAN	EG.
F.M. COLLINS	ℂℳ
Rose COLLINS	RC
Miss CONGDON	c ▪▪
Alice COOKE	ccO
D. CORDERO	ℨ
Joan COWPER	Joan Cowper
Minna L. CRAWLEY	ℂ ℂℳ
D. CROFTS	ℱ
Ellen CROSBY	ⱸ
Emily CROSBY	cOO
James R. CRUICKSHANK	ȼ
Annie CUPIT	cc
Lilian CURTIS	L.C. c c▪
Lizzie M. DAINTREE	dO
Olive DALE	d▪
A. DANIELS	Ⱡ
Kate M. DAVIS	K.D.
Louisa J. DAVIS	₥
Mary A. DAVIS	ℳƉ d+
W. DAVISON	Ɖ
Elizabeth DAYTON	ⓓ
Mary DENLEY	Ⓜ
Ada DENNIS	AƉ AƉ d▪
Florence DENNIS	⊧ dd▪
Miss DOUTHWAITE	ddd
Amelia A. DRAKE	A.D.
M. DRIVER	⊕
A. DUNCAN	ⱴ
Edward DUNN	Ɖ Ɖ
W. Edward DUNN	wƉ

M.	DUNTON	
Beatrice M.	DURTNALL	D
Josephine A.	DURTNALL	J.D
L. Imogen	DURTNALL	ID dd
Alice K.	EARL	
Florence	EARL	
Alice	ECKENSTEIN	e A.E.
Lottie	ECKENSTEIN	eeO
M.	EDERMANIGER	
Emily J.	EDWARDS	
Louisa E.	EDWARDS	
Edward E.	EGGLETON	
Fanny	ELLIOTT	
Herbert	ELLIS	HE
Sarah	ELLIS	SE
C.	EMERTON	E
Bertha	EVANS	e
Kate	EVERETT	e e
John	EYRE	JEyre
Miss	FELTON	f
Ada E.	FIMISTER	
Elizabeth	FISHER	
Sarah	FISHER	SF f
Emily A.	FORSEY	fO E.A.F.
Minnie	FORSTER	ff
E.	FORSYTH	
Constance	FOSTER	ff
M.	FOX	M.F.
D.	FRAMPTON	
Catherine	FRANCIS	F
L.	FRANCIS	f
May	FREAKES	fr

Lizzie	FRENCH	ff
A. E.	FRENCH	ÆF
M.	FRICKER	f
Elizabeth A.	GADSDON	ga
Jessie	GANDY	JG. go
Walter	GANDY	W G
Nellie	GARBETT	g EG
Ellen	GATHERCOLE	NGg g
Sarah P.	GATHERCOLE	g
Annie	GENTLE	AG.
Kate R.	GIBLIN	G go
Elizabeth M.	GILLMAN	g
Emily J.	GILLMAN	
L.	GOLDSACK	LY
Mary A.	GOODE	g g
Laura	GOODERHAM	g gO
M.	GOODING	g
E.	GRAVER	H
M.	GRAY	
Alberta L.	GREEN	AG
Edith	GREEN	G
Laura	GREEN	g
Lydia	GREIG	OgO
A.	GRIGGS	g
Alice E.	GROOM	G .G.
Jessie	GUEST	gOO
Alice	HALL	
Elizabeth	HAMILTON	E.H.
J. B.	HARDING	BH
B.	HARMAN	h
A. Leslie	HARRADINE	H
Edith	HARRINGTON	hOO

Name	Surname	Monogram
Rosina	HARRIS	RH
Emma C.	HARRISON	H
Nellie	HARRISON	hn
W.	HASTINGS	W
Lizzie	HAUGHTON	Hl
Ethel	HAWKINS	h k
Emily M.	HAWKSBY	hh▪ E.M.H.
Emily	HAYNES	hh
A.	HAYS	AH
E. Violet	HAYWARD	hd
L.	HAYWARD	◁
Rosetta	HAZELDINE	▪h▪
O.	HEATH	hOh
Alice G.	HELLIS	h̅
E.	HENDERSON	(·)
Alice M.	HERAPATH	H h▪ A.M.H
Edith	HERAPATH	hh
F.	HEWITT	hhh
K.	HEYWOOD	ɔ
E.	HIBBERD	⊏⊐
Harriett E.	HIBBUT	HEH
Jessie	HINCHLIFF	(h)
Marion	HOLBROOK	MH
Eliza J.	HOLLIS	hhO E.H.
Joan	HONEY	JH
Agnes S.	HORNE	ho H̅
Annie	HORTON	ho▪
Agnete	HOY	AH
Eliza L.	HUBERT	ELH
Vera	HUGGINS	v.H ᴴ YH
Kate	HUGHES	h:: K.H
Annie M.	HULFORD	H.x.
Florence L.	HUNT	J.H.
Jane S.	HURST	H
John	HUSKINSON	H
Ernest	JARRETT	Ĵ
E.	JESSETT	⊖
Doris	JOHNSON	DJ
Florrie	JONES	FJ
Gladys	JOYCE	J̇
Ivy	JOYCE	ʝ
Rosa	KEEN	RK
Edith	KELSEY	J
Edith L.	KEMP	K EK
Harriette E. E.	KNIGHT	k
Alice	LACY	ll O
Charlotte	LAMB	CL
Ulrique	LARCHER	UL
J.	LASHAM	(ll)
Marion	LAYZELL	ll
Francis E.	LEE	FEL
Harriette E.	LEE	L ll
Nellie	LEGGE	⇶1
Esther	LEWIS	£
Florence E.	LEWIS	£
Isabel	LEWIS	⊥
Ada C.	LILLEY	ll▪
Mary M. S.	LILLEY	1▪
Frances M.	LINNELL	FL
Ada	LONDON	l
Emily A.	LONDON	L EA
Alice	LONGHURST	1::
Jessie	LORD	1d
Edith D.	LUPTON	EDL

Annie	LYONS	*A.L.*
W. W.	MACKAY	M
B.	MACNAE	(X
Matilda	MARLYN	m▬m
Emma	MARRIOTT	⊞
L.	MARRIOTT	÷
Alice	MARSHALL	A.M.
Mark V.	MARSHALL	M·Y·M
Susan	MARSHALL	m
Eliza	MARTIN	m m
Emma	MARTIN	EM.
M.	MARTIN	m▪m
Matilda	MARTYN	m m m
F.	MASKELL	⋇
Louisa	MATTERSON	mO
Ada	MAYCOCK	m▬
Emily	MAYES	m
Emily W.	MAYNE	EM.
John H.	McLENNAN	J.H.Mc
L.	MEAR	HC
Miss	MEDLICOTT	mt
Miss	MIDDLEMISS	mi
Alice	MILBORROW	▬▬m
Isabella	MILLER	M M
A.	MILLS	Y
Annie	MILNE	ⓜ
Mary	MITCHELL	MM
Ada	MORGAN	mOO
Joseph H.	MOTT	JHM
Iza M.	MUNDAY	EM
E.	NAISH	↗
H.	NAISH	ⓝ

Annie	NEAL		n
Minnie	NEAL		Z
William J.	NEATBY		WJN
Bessie	NEWBERY		BN
Josephine E.	NEWNHAM		N
Mary	NEWSON		m n
E.	NOBLE		•n•
Lilla	NOTTINGHAM		N
E.	NORRIS		x↗
F.	NORRISH		↗↙
W. J. W.	NUNN		⋙
Gertrude	NYE		Ж
A.	ORCHIN		Ⓐ
Lizzie	PADBURY	P	LP
D.	PAINTER		P
Ellen	PALMER		Op
L.	PARKER		◇
William	PARKER		ωp
Emily J.	PARTINGTON		EP
Lily	PARTINGTON		LP
Annie	PARTRIDGE		P▪
Arthur E.	PEARCE	AEP	R
Georgina	PEARSON		P▪P
S.	PEARSON		P.
Helena M.	PENNETT		PP
F.	PERRIN		↗x
E.	PHEBY		▪P▪
E.	PICKERSGILL		Pₐ
F.	POMEROY		FP
Francis C.	POPE	.P.	F·C·P
A.	POTTERTON		⅄
R.	PRITCHARD		R

481

M.	PRYCE	⚹	Agnes D.	SANDES	A.S.	
Jane	RABBIT	rrO	F.	SAWYER	2	
Emily	RANDALL	E.R.	A.	SAYERS	sO A.S.	
L.	RAWLINGS	rg	Elizabeth A.	SAYERS	EAS	
Frank W.	READER	R FR	Fanny	SAYERS	sOO	
Constance E.	REDFORD	R r:	Rosalie	SCOTT	ssO	
George W.	RHEAD	GMR	G.	SHARPE	X	
S.	RICKARDS	r:	G.	SHEARS	sr	
Alice M.	RITCHIN	AR	Elizabeth	SHELLEY	E.S	
Emma	ROBERTS	ER	Annie	SHELTON	ss:	
Florence C.	ROBERTS	FER	Lizzie	SHETTLEWORTH	£	
Emily L.	ROBINSON	R	F.	SHIPMAN	ү	
Alice	ROBJENT	ⓡ	A.	SHUTE	ss:	
Edith	ROGERS	EER	Emma	SHUTE	E.S.	
Isabel	ROGERS	JR	Harry	SIMEON	HS	
Kate	ROGERS	R	Eliza	SIMMANCE	S ES	
L.	ROGERS	Ⓜ	Alice M. M.	SKIDMORE	OsO	
Martha M.	ROGERS	MMR	Mary	SLATTER	M.S.	
A.	ROHSS	F	Elizabeth M.	SMALL	ƎMS	
Letitia	ROSEVEAR	r	Katherine B.	SMALLFIELD	KBS R	
William	ROWE	WR	Mildred B.	SMALLFIELD	MBS	
M.	RUCKSTUHL	mr	Alice G.	SMITH	A.S.	
E.	RUDDOCK	E.R	Ellen B.	SMITH	E.B.S S. ss	
Agnes M.	RUFF	ᗰ	E.	SMITH	ᒐ	
Ellen	RUMBOL	ER RO	Frances	SMITH	F.S.	
Jane	RUMBOL	rOO	Georgie	SMITH	GS	
Alice	RUSSELL	:r:	Gertrude	SMITH	S S	
F.	RUSSELL	⅄	Catherine A.	SPARKES	CAS	
Kate E.	RUSSELL	rɹ	E.	SPONG	Ⓢ	
Louisa	RUSSELL	┐└ R LR	A.	SPURRELL	↓	
Clara	RYMER	rO	Fanny	STABLE	F.S.	
Susanna M.	SANDERSON	S.S	Mary	STAREY	SMS s:	

Name	Mark		Name	Mark
Eliza STOCK	s		Bessie M. VARNEY	v
Emily E. STORMER	EES		C. VIGOR	C.V.
N. STRAKER	[monogram]		Emily M. VINER	E.Y.
Emilie M. STRATFORD	s:s		E. WAKELY	w:
E. STRATTON	st		Louisa WAKELY	w LW
Katherine STURGEON	[monogram]		K. WALKER	[monogram]
George Hugo TABOR	GTH		Helen WALTERS	X
Winifred TALBOT	tl		L. WATERS	L.W.
N. TAYLOR	[monogram]		Linnie WATT	Watt
Florence TEGETMEIER	to		Minnie WEBB	MW
A. Euphemia THATCHER	[monogram]		Jenny F. WEEKES	wO
Elsie S. THOMAS	tt		Emily M. R. WELCH	EW
Margaret E. THOMPSON	TM [monogram]		M. WELSBY	[monogram]
Marie E. THOMPSON	tx		Georgina WHITE	G.W.
Minnie G. THOMPSON	MGT		Onslow E. WHITING	O.W.
Mary Ann THOMSON	[monogram]		K. WHITTON	[monogram]
Walter THORNEMAN	[monogram]		H. WILKINSON	[monogram]
M. THORNTON	%		Arthur WILLCOCK	W
George TINWORTH	[monogram]		A. WILSON	[monogram]
H. TOLAND	[monogram]		Edgar W. WILSON	[monogram]
Louisa E. TOMKINS	[monogram]		Louie WILSON	[monogram]
F. TOMLYN	[monogram]		R. WILSON	[monogram]
Ada TOSEN	AT		Ada M. WOOD	wOO
A. TOSEN	[monogram]		Christina WOOD	C.W
Eleanor TOSEN	ttt		Emily WOOD	ww
Ellen C. TOWNSEND	t••		Edith H. WOODINGTON	W
A. TRANTER	[monogram]		Rosetta S. WOODS	RW
Ethel TRANTER	tOO		Ada L. WORTHEY	AW.
A. TURNER	[monogram]		C. M. WRAY	[monogram]
M. UNWIN	U:		Bessie J. YOUATT	[monogram]
C. VARGAS	[monogram]		L. YOUNG	y
R. VARGAS	[monogram]		A. ZURCHER	Z

DOULTON MARKS

DOULTON & WATTS   Impressed or incised mark used on stoneware, 1827–1858.

 Circular mark impressed with date, used on Doulton Ware and Lambeth Faience, 1876–1880.

DOULTON & WATTS
LAMBETH POTTERY
LONDON   Impressed or incised mark used on stoneware, 1827–1858.

 Impressed or printed mark used on stoneware, with England added after 1891, 1879–1902.

 Impressed or incised mark used on stoneware, 1827–1858.

 Rosette Mark impressed or printed on Doulton Ware and Lambeth Faience, 1880-1891.

(r.m. – rosette mark)

DOULTON
LAMBETH   Impressed or printed mark used on stoneware, with England added after 1891, 1858–1910.

H. DOULTON & CO.   Incised on panels and plaques by George Tinworth.

 Oval undated mark impressed on early Doulton Ware, 1869–1872.

(o.u.m. – oval undated mark)

DOULTON & SLATERS
PATENT   Doulton and Slater's Patent, 1885–1939.

(DSP – Doulton & Slater's Patent)

 Oval mark impressed and dated used on Doulton Ware, 1872–1876.

(o.m. – oval mark)

 Doulton Silicon Lambeth, with England added after 1891, 1880–1932.

(DSL – Doulton Silicon Lambeth)

 Circular mark, impressed or printed, and sometimes dated in the centre, used on Lambeth Faience, 1873–1914.

(c.m. – circular mark)

 Rosette mark with England added, used on Doulton Ware and Lambeth Faience, 1891–1902.

(r.m. & e. – rosette mark and England)

Impressed or printed mark, with England added after 1891, used on Lambeth Faience, 1873–1914.

DOULTON
LAMBETH
ENGLAND   Impressed or printed on small objects of Doulton Ware, 1891–1956.

Doulton Lambeth England, used on Doulton Ware and Lambeth Faience, 1891–1956.

(DLE – Doulton Lambeth England)

 Impressed or printed mark used on Crown Lambeth Ware, 1891–1905.

 Impressed or printed mark used on Impasto Ware, often dated in the centre and with England added after 1891, 1879–1914.

 Used on objects with a metallic coating, circa 1900.

 Printed mark used on Faience, with England added after 1891, 1880–1914.

 Printed on Morrisian Ware, 1901–1924.

 Impressed or printed on Marqueterie Ware, with England added after 1891, 1887–1906.

 Printed mark used on Brangwyn Ware.

 Impressed or printed on Marqueterie Ware, with England added after 1891, 1887–1906.

 Circle mark, lion and crown used on Doulton Lambeth and Burslem Ware, 1902–1956.

(c.m.l. & c. – circle mark, lion and crown)

 Impressed or printed on Marqueterie Ware, with England added after 1891, 1887–1906.

 Circle mark used on small objects of Doulton Lambeth and Burslem Ware, 1902–1956.

(RDE – Royal Doulton England)

 Impressed or printed on Marqueterie Ware, with England added after 1891, 1887–1906.

 Printed mark used on Royal Doulton Flambe, with 'Made in England' added from 1930, 1902–1930.

 Impressed or printed mark used on Carrara Ware, 1891–1924.

 Royal Doulton Flambe mark used on small pieces, 1904–1930.

 Printed on Velluma Ware, 1911–1914.

 Impressed or printed mark used on Persian Ware, 1920–1936.

 Impressed or printed mark used on Doulton Ware, 1912–1956.

(s.c.m. – slip cast mark)

 Printed mark used on Burslem stoneware, 1922–1927.

 Printed mark used on Royal Doulton Titanian Ware, 1916–1929.

 Circle mark and lion, impressed or printed on Doulton Ware, 1922–1956.

(c.m. & l. – circle mark and lion)

 Printed mark used on Royal Doulton Titanian Ware, 1916–1929.

  Printed mark used on Chang Ware with the monogram of H. Nixon, 1925–1940.

 Printed mark used on hard-paste figures, 1918–1933.

 Printed mark used on Chinese Jade, 1920–1940.

 Mark used mainly on wall plaques, 1925–1939.

 Printed mark used on Burslem earthenware, 1932 –present day.

 Printed Flambe mark with Sung in script, 1920–1940.

Mark in current use, 1959–present day.

INDEX CHARACTER JUGS

JOHN SHORTER D6880
JOHNNERS D7018
JOHNNY APPLESEED D6372
JUGGLER D6835

K

KING ARTHUR D7055
KING ARTHUR/GUINEVERE D6836
KING CHARLES D6917
KING EDWARD VII D6923
KING PHILIP II of SPAIN D6822

L

LAWYER D6498
LAWYER D6504
LAWYER D6524
LEPRECHAUN D6847
LEPRECHAUN D6899
LEWIS CARROLL D7096
LITTLE MESTER D6819
LOBSTER MAN D6617
LOBSTER MAN D6620
LOBSTER MAN D6652
LOBSTER MAN D6783
LONDON BOBBY D6744
LONDON BOBBY D6762
LONDON BOBBY D6763
LONG JOHN SILVER D6335
LONG JOHN SILVER D6386
LONG JOHN SILVER D6512
LORD MAYOR OF LONDON D6864
LORD NELSON D6336
LOUIS ARMSTRONG D6707
LUMBERJACK D6610
LUMBERJACK D6613

M

MACBETH D6667
MCCALLUM
MAD HATTER D6598
MAD HATTER D6602
MAD HATTER D6606
MAE WEST D6688
MAORI
MARCH HARE D6776
MARK TWAIN D6654
MARK TWAIN D6694
MARK TWAIN D6758
MASTER (THE) D6898
MEPHISTOPHELES D5757
MEPHISTOPHELES D5758
MERLIN D6529
MERLIN D6536
MERLIN D6543
MICHAEL DOULTON D6808
MIKADO D6501

MIKADO D6507
MIKADO D6525
MINE HOST D6468
MINE HOST D6470
MINE HOST D6513
MINNIE THE MINX D7036
MONTGOMERY D6908
MONTY D6202
MOZART D7031
MR MICAWBER D5843
MR MICAWBER D5843
MR MICAWBER D6138
MR MICAWBER D6143
MR PICKWICK D6060
MR PICKWICK D5839
MR PICKWICK D5839
MR PICKWICK D6245
MR PICKWICK D6260
MR PICKWICK D7025
MR QUAKER D6738
MRS CLAUS D6922
MUTINY ON THE BOUNTY CAPTAIN BLIGH AND FLETCHER CHRISTIAN D7074, D7075

N

NAPOLEON D6941
NAPOLEON AND JOSEPHINE D6750
NEPTUNE D6548
NEPTUNE D6552
NEPTUNE D6555
NIGHT WATCHMAN D6569
NIGHT WATCHMAN D6576
NIGHT WATCHMAN D6583
NORTH AMERICAN INDIAN D6611
NORTH AMERICAN INDIAN D6611
NORTH AMERICAN INDIAN D6614
NORTH AMERICAN INDIAN D6665
NORTH AMERICAN INDIAN D6786

O

OLD CHARLEY D5420
OLD CHARLEY D5527
OLD CHARLEY D6046
OLD CHARLEY D6144
OLD KING COLE D6036
OLD KING COLE D6037
OLD KING COLE (Yellow Crown) D6036
OLD KING COLE (Yellow Crown) D6037
OLD SALT D6551

OLD SALT D6554
OLD SALT D6557
OLD SALT D6782
OLIVER CROMWELL D6968
OLIVER HARDY
OTHELLO D6673

P

PADDY D5753
PADDY D5768
PADDY D6042
PADDY D6145
PARSON BROWN D5486
PARSON BROWN (White) D5486
PARSON BROWN D5529
PARSON BROWN D6955
PAUL McCARTNEY D6724
PEARLY BOY (Blue)
PEARLY BOY (Blue)
PEARLY BOY (Blue)
PEARLY BOY (Brown buttons)
PEARLY GIRL (Blue)
PEARLY KING D6760
PEARLY KING D6844
PEARLY QUEEN D6759
PEARLY QUEEN D6843
PENDLE WITCH D6826
PHANTOM OF THE OPERA D7017
PHARAOH D7028
PIED PIPER D6403
PIED PIPER D6462
PIED PIPER D6514
PIPER, THE D6918
PLUG D7035
POACHER D6429
POACHER D6464
POACHER D6515
POACHER D6781
POLICEMAN D6852
PORTHOS D6440
PORTHOS D6453
PORTHOS D6516
PORTHOS D6828
POSTMAN D6801
PUNCH AND JUDY MAN D6590
PUNCH AND JUDY MAN D6593
PUNCH AND JUDY MAN D6596
PUNCH AND JUDY MAN D6946

Q

QUEEN ELIZABETH 1st of ENGLAND D6821
QUEEN VICTORIA D6816
QUEEN VICTORIA D6788

INDEX OF FIGURES

G

INDEX OF FIGURES

N

INDEX OF FIGURES

U

V

W

Y

INDEX

INDEX

INDEX

509

INDEX